Progressive Problems for Higher Physics

by

W. Kennedy

ISBN 0 7169 3245 8

ROBERT GIBSON · Publisher
17 Fitzroy Place, Glasgow, G3 7SF

PREFACE

Progressive Problems for Higher Grade Physics covers the topics studied for the SQA Higher Grade Physics syllabus. It contains **a planned sequence of questions** constructed to guide the pupil systematically from the simplest to the most difficult problems, thereby laying a firm foundation to build upon.

This method of problem solving helps to overcome the difficulties associated with mixed ability classes by encouraging the slow learner while stretching the more able pupils.

In addition to the progressive nature of the problems, the book has been subject-categorised to give a breakdown of every aspect of the course. [This enables the teacher to pick his / her own area and, where appropriate, alter the order of teaching to suit individual needs.]

The material has been used extensively. It has been closely monitored as to its value and relevance to the learning process. Consequently it has been developed and refined to its present level.

W. Kennedy, 2000.

ACKNOWLEDGEMENTS

I would like to thank the physics department, staff and pupils of St. Mungo's High School, Falkirk, who trialled the materials and helped to refine them.

CONTENTS

DATA SHEET

COMMON PHYSICAL QUANTITIES

Quantity	*Symbol*	*Value*	*Quantity*	*Symbol*	*Value*
Speed of light in vacuum	c	$3{\cdot}00 \times 10^{8}$ m s^{-1}	Mass of electron	m_e	$9{\cdot}11 \times 10^{-31}$ kg
Charge on electron	e	$-1{\cdot}60 \times 10^{-19}$ C	Mass of neutron	m_n	$1{\cdot}675 \times 10^{-27}$ kg
Gravitational acceleration	g	$9{\cdot}8$ m s^{-2}	Mass of proton	m_p	$1{\cdot}673 \times 10^{-27}$ kg
Planck's constant	h	$6{\cdot}63 \times 10^{-34}$ J s			

REFRACTIVE INDICES

The refractive indices refer to sodium light of wavelength 589 nm and to substances at a temperature of 273 K.

Substance	*Refractive index*	*Substance*	*Refractive index*
Diamond	2·42	Water	1·33
Crown Glass	1·50	Air	1·00

SPECTRAL LINES

Element	*Wavelength / nm*	*Colour*
Hydrogen	656	Red
	486	Blue-green
	434	Blue-violet
	410	Violet
	397	Ultraviolet
	389	Ultraviolet
Sodium	589	Yellow
Cadmium	644	Red
	509	Green
	480	Blue

Lasers

Element	*Wavelength / nm*	*Colour*
Carbon dioxide	9550 10590	Infrared
Helium-neon	633	Red

PROPERTIES OF SELECTED MATERIALS

Substance	*Density / kg m^{-3}*	*Melting Point / K*	*Boiling Point / K*
Aluminium	$2{\cdot}70 \times 10^{3}$	933	2623
Copper	$8{\cdot}96 \times 10^{3}$	1357	2853
Ice	$9{\cdot}20 \times 10^{2}$	273	....
Sea Water	$1{\cdot}02 \times 10^{3}$	264	377
Water	$1{\cdot}00 \times 10^{3}$	273	373
Air	1·29	....	....
Hydrogen	$9{\cdot}0 \times 10^{-2}$	14	20

The gas densities refer to a temperature of 273 K and a pressure of $1{\cdot}01 \times 10^{5}$ Pa.

Acknowledgement is hereby given to the SQA to reproduce this data sheet.

FORMULAE LIST

UNIT 1

Average speed $= \dfrac{\text{total distance travelled}}{\text{total time taken}}$

Average velocity $= \dfrac{\text{displacement}}{\text{total time taken}}$

$a = \dfrac{v-u}{t}$

average speed $= \dfrac{u+v}{2}$

$v = u + at$

$s = ut + \frac{1}{2}at^2$

$v^2 = u^2 + 2as$

$W = mg$

$F = ma$

$W.D. = Fd$

$E_p = mgh$

$E_k = \frac{1}{2}mv^2$

$P = \dfrac{E}{t}$

$p = mv$

$Ft = mv - mu$

Density $= \dfrac{m}{V}$

Pressure $= \dfrac{\text{Force}}{\text{Area}}$

$p = h\rho g$

$p \propto \dfrac{1}{V}$

$V \propto T_K$

$p \propto T_K$

$T_K = T_{°C} + 273$

$\dfrac{p_1V_1}{T_1} = \dfrac{p_2V_2}{T_2}$

UNIT 2

$Q = It$

$W = QV$

$R_T = R_1 + R_2 + R_3$ (series)

$\dfrac{1}{R_T} = \dfrac{1}{R_1} + \dfrac{1}{R_2} + \dfrac{1}{R_3}$ (parallel)

$V = IR$

$V_1 = \dfrac{R_1}{R_T} \times V_{supply}$ (voltage division)

$P = VI = I^2R = \dfrac{V^2}{R}$

$E = Ir + V_{\text{t.p.d.}}$

$\dfrac{R_1}{R_2} = \dfrac{R_3}{R_4}$

$Q = CV$

$E = \frac{1}{2}QV = \frac{1}{2}CV^2 = \frac{1}{2}\dfrac{Q^2}{C}$

$V_{peak} = \sqrt{2} \times V_{rms}$

$V_0 = -\dfrac{R_f}{R_1}V_1$

$V_0 = (V_2 - V_1)\dfrac{R_f}{R_1}$

Voltage gain $= \dfrac{\text{output voltage}}{\text{input voltage}}$

Power gain $= \dfrac{\text{output power}}{\text{input power}}$

UNIT 3

$v = f\lambda$

$f = \dfrac{1}{T}$

$S_2P - S_1P = n\lambda$

$S_2Q - S_1Q = \left(n + \frac{1}{2}\right)\lambda$

$d \sin\theta = n\lambda$

$n = \dfrac{\sin\theta_1}{\sin\theta_2} = \dfrac{v_1}{v_2} = \dfrac{\lambda_1}{\lambda_2}$

$n = \dfrac{1}{\sin\theta_C}$

Intensity $= \dfrac{\text{Power}}{\text{Area}}$

$I \propto \dfrac{1}{d^2}$

$E = hf \qquad I = Nhf$

$W_2 - W_1 = hf$

$hf = hf_0 + \frac{1}{2}mv^2$

$A = \dfrac{N}{t}$

$D = \dfrac{E}{m}$

$H = DQ$

$\dot{H} = \dfrac{H}{t}$

$E = mc^2$

UNIT 1

MECHANICS AND PROPERTIES OF MATTER

CHAPTER 1

VECTORS

1. What is a scalar quantity?
What is a vector quantity?
Give three examples of each.

2. A man walks 8 km east and then 6 km north. Using a scale diagram (or otherwise) find out how far he finishes from his starting point, give magnitude and direction.

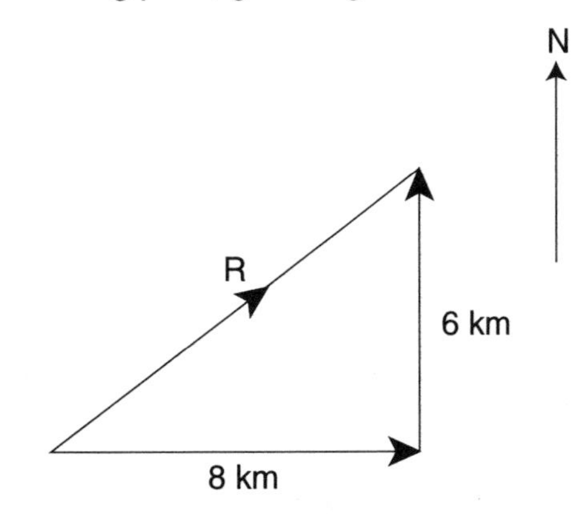

In problems 3 to 8, a number of displacements are combined. Find the resultant displacement (magnitude and direction) in each case. Assume NORTH is at the top of the page.

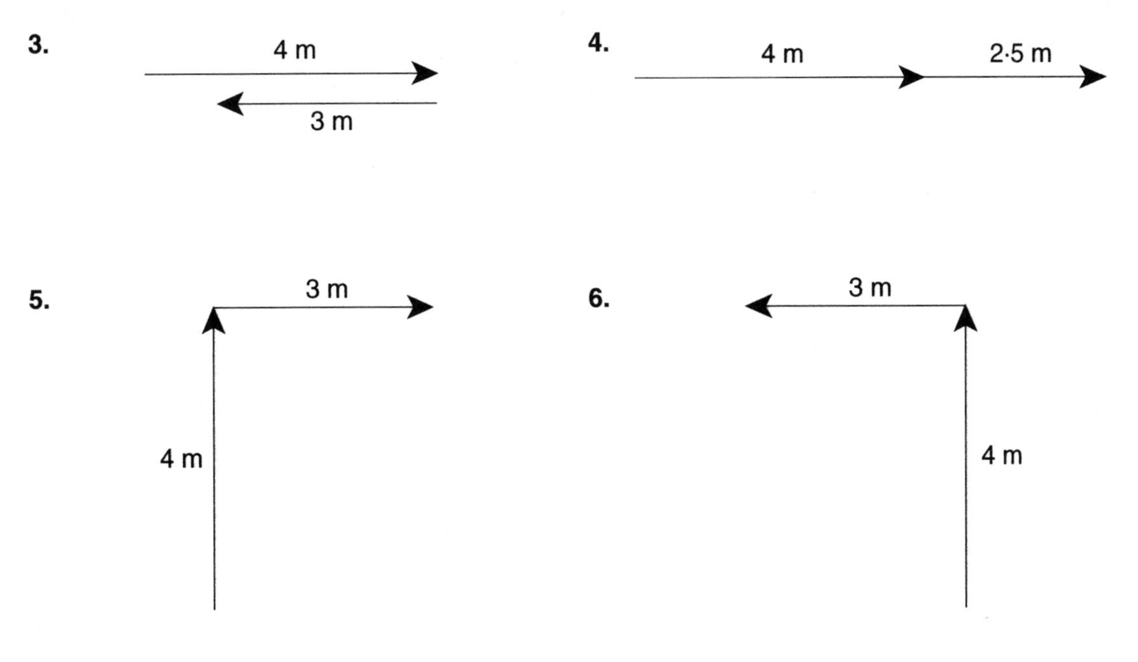

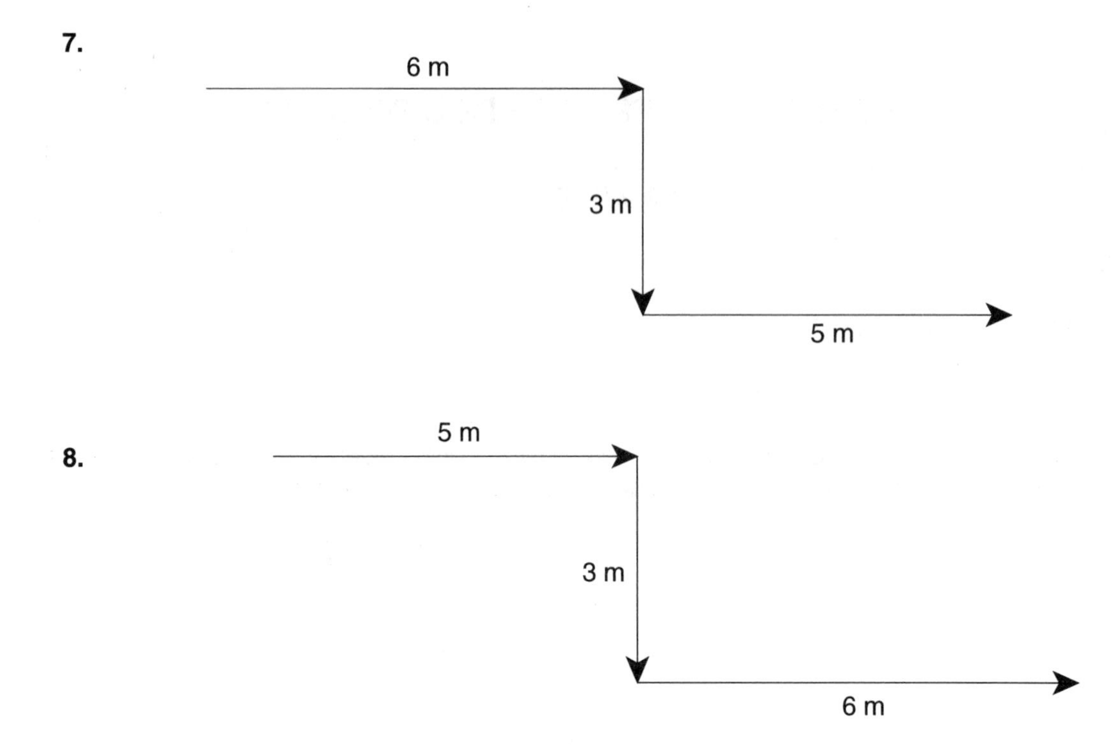

9. A man walks 4 km north, then turns east and walks another 3 km.
It takes the man 1 hour to walk the 4 km and another hour to walk the 3 km.

(a) What is the total distance gone by the man?

(b) What is his average speed?

(c) What is his displacement from his starting point (magnitude and direction)?

(d) What is his average velocity (magnitude and direction)?

10. A car travels east for 1 hour at a speed of 60 km h^{-1}. The driver turns south and travels for another hour at a speed of 40 km h^{-1}.

(a) What is the total distance gone by the car?

(b) Calculate the average speed.

(c) What is the car's displacement from its starting point (magnitude and direction)?

(d) What is the average velocity (magnitude and direction)?

11. An orienteer runs 5 km east, 4 km south and 1 km west. If she completed the course in exactly 1 hour, calculate:

(a) the total distance gone;

(b) her average speed;

(c) her displacement from the start (magnitude and direction);

(d) her average velocity (magnitude and direction).

12. A man is trying to swim at 3 m s^{-1} from A to B across a river.

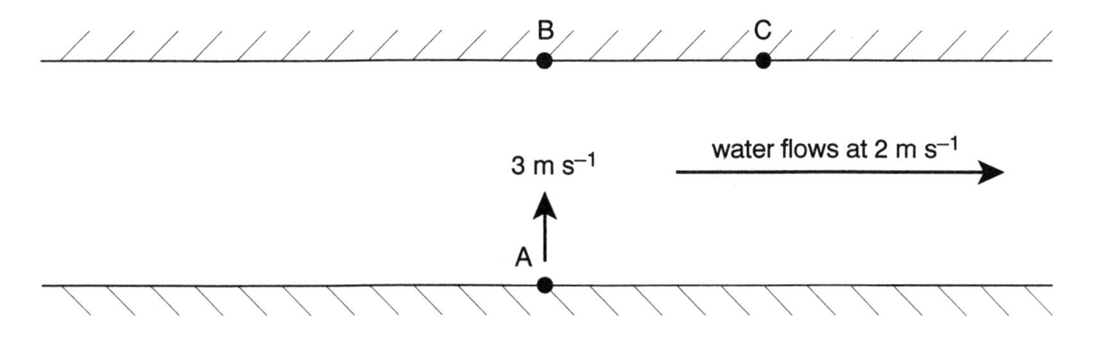

The current in the river is flowing at 2 m s^{-1} at 90° to the swimmer.

(a) What is the resultant velocity of the swimmer (magnitude and direction)?

(b) The distance between A and B is 30 m. The swimmer lands on the opposite bank at point C. Calculate the distance between B and C.

In problems 13 to 18, a number of forces are acting on a mass. Assume NORTH is at the top of the page.

(a) Find the resultant force (magnitude and direction) in each case.

(b) Hence, find the acceleration of the mass (magnitude only) in each case.

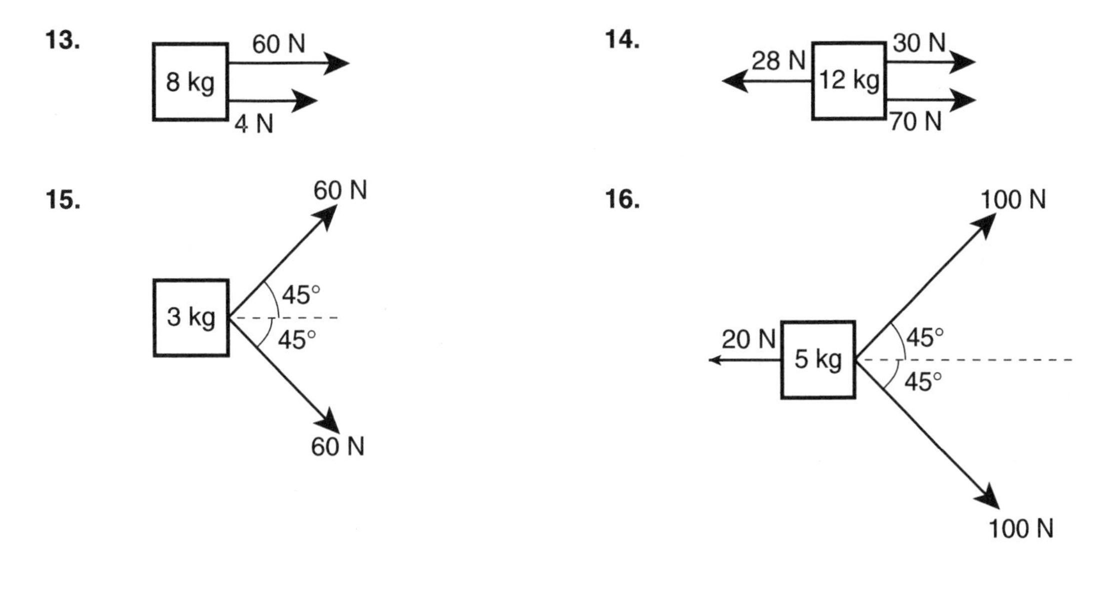

17.

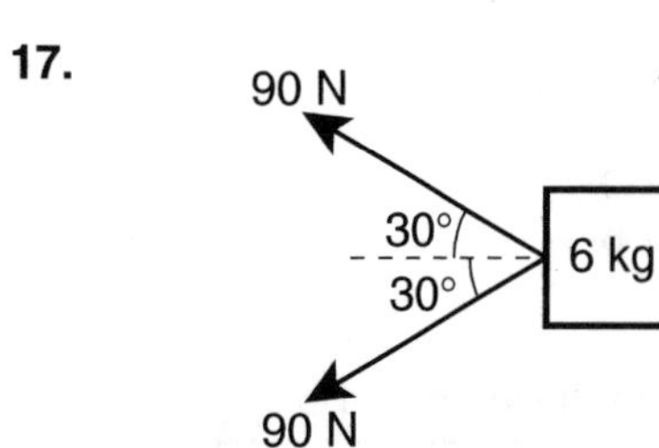

18.

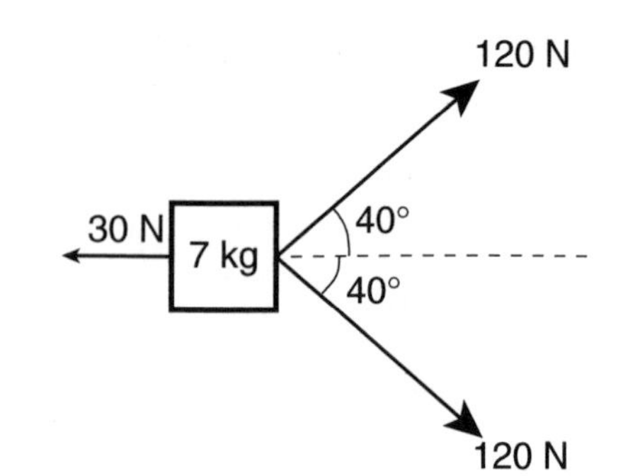

19. Niall uses a spring balance to pull a 2 kg trolley along a horizontal bench. The spring balance reads 10 N.

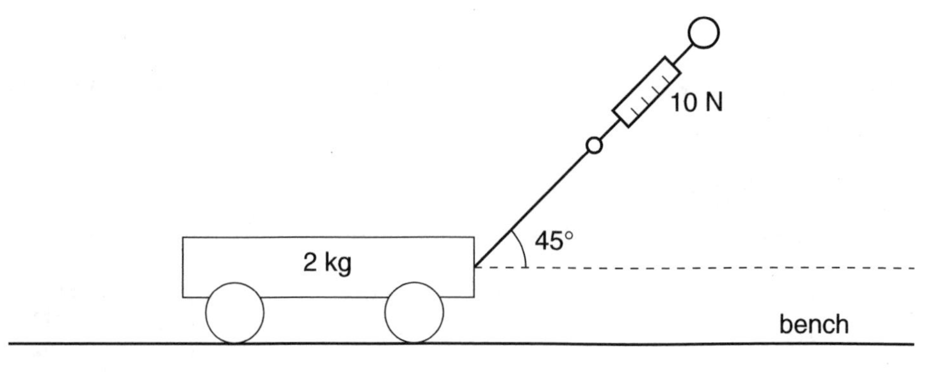

Niall thinks that the acceleration is 5 m s^{-2}.

(a) Calculate the component of force parallel to the bench.

(b) Calculate the true acceleration of the trolley.

20. A shell is fired at 100 m s^{-1} at 45° to the horizontal.

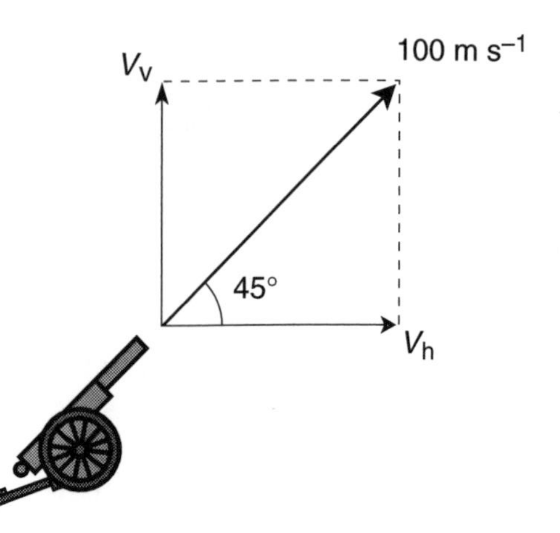

(a) Calculate the horizontal component of the velocity.

(b) Calculate the vertical component of the velocity.

21. An arrow is fired from a bow. The vertical component of velocity is 6 m s^{-1} and the horizontal component of velocity is 10 m s^{-1}.

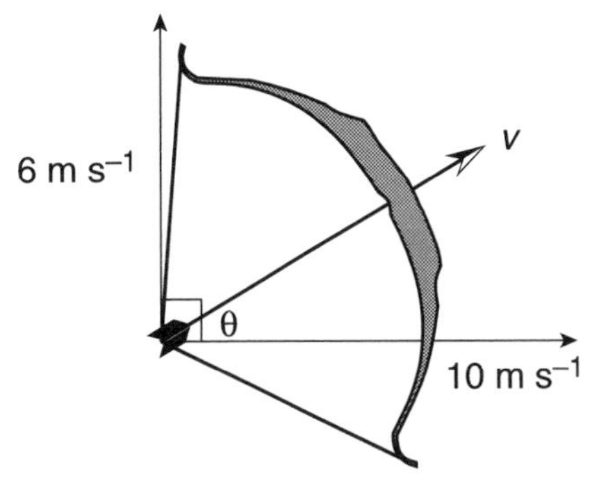

(a) What is the resultant velocity, *v*?

(b) What angle is the arrow to the horizontal θ?

22. A ball is kicked at 6 m s^{-1} horizontally from the top of a cliff. It strikes the ground 2 seconds later.

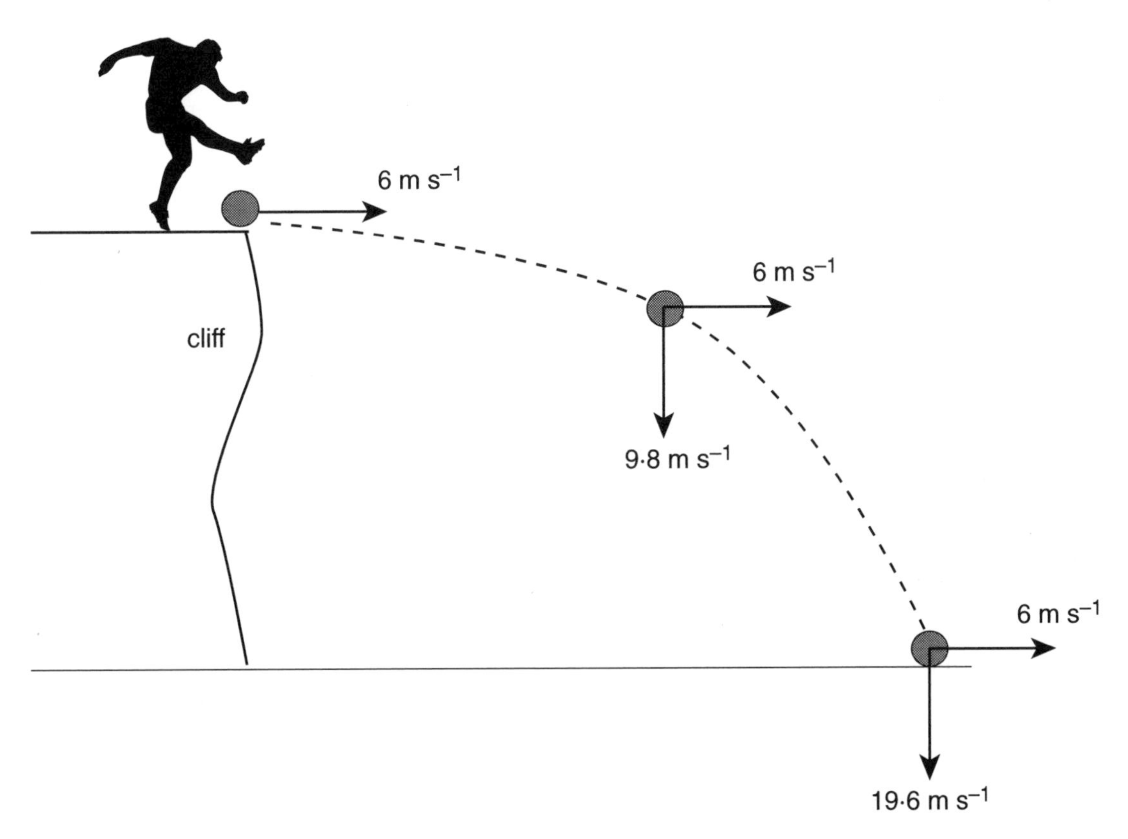

(a) Find the resultant velocity after 1 s (magnitude and direction).

(b) Find the resultant velocity after 2 s (magnitude and direction).

CHAPTER 2

EQUATIONS OF MOTION

GRAPHS OF MOTION

1. A car accelerates constantly from rest to 15 m s^{-1} in 3 s, travels at constant speed for another 3 s, and decelerates to rest in 4 s.

Draw a speed-time graph of the journey and find:

(a) the acceleration;

(b) the deceleration;

(c) the total distance travelled;

(d) the average speed.

2. A lorry decelerates constantly from 20 m s^{-1} to 10 m s^{-1} in 4 s and travels at this steady speed for a further 6 s.

Draw a speed-time graph of the motion and find:

(a) the deceleration;

(b) the average speed.

3. A car, initially at rest, accelerates at 4 m s^{-2} for 5 s, travels at this steady speed for another 5 s and accelerates again to 30 m s^{-1} in 10 s.

Draw a speed-time graph of the motion and find the average speed over the 20 s.

4. A ball is thrown vertically upwards at 9·8 m s^{-1}. One second later it has reached its highest point.

The motion of the ball is described by a velocity-time graph.

(a) What feature distinguishes it from a speed-time graph?

(b) Calculate the acceleration during the first second.

(c) Calculate the acceleration during the second second.

(d) How high did the ball go?

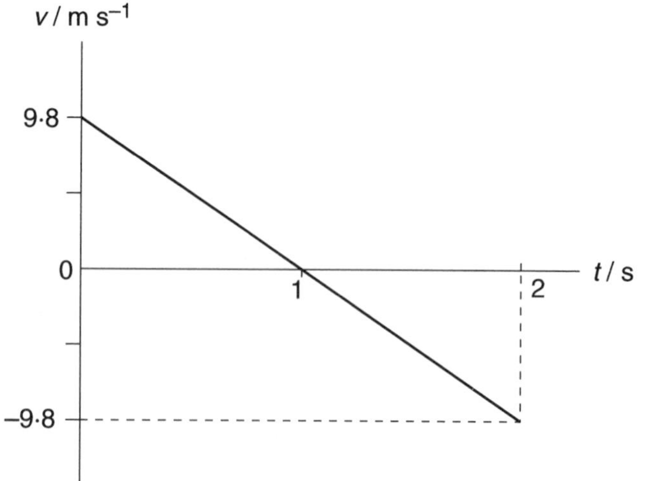

5. A vehicle accelerates as shown in the graph.

(a) Calculate the acceleration.

(b) Draw an acceleration-time graph of the motion.

6. The velocity-time graph shows the motion of a remote control car during the first 6 s of its journey.

(a) Calculate the acceleration during the first 3 s.

(b) What is the acceleration during the next 3 s.

(c) Draw an acceleration-time graph for the 6 s.

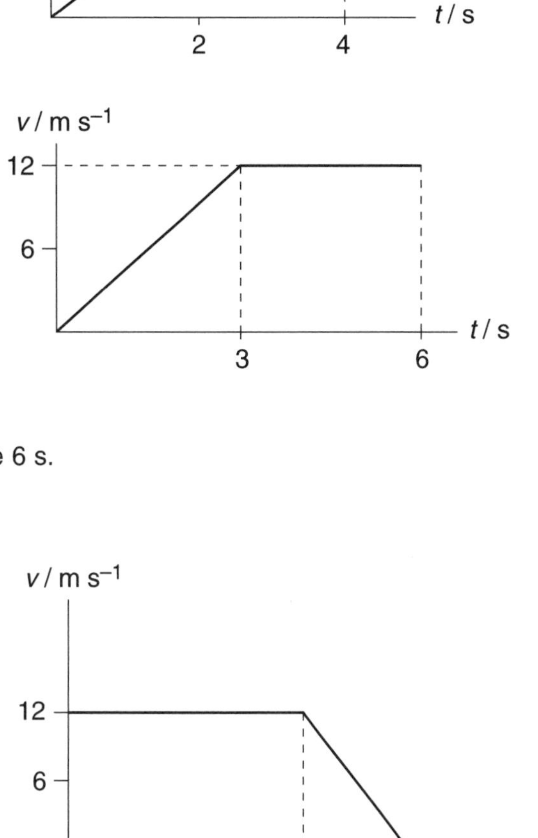

7. The velocity-time graph shows the motion of a car during a 6 s period of its journey.

Draw the equivalent acceleration-time graph for the same 6 s.

8. A car accelerates for 4 s, travels at a constant velocity for 4 s and decelerates to rest in 2 s as shown in the graph.

(a) Find the acceleration for the first 4 s.

(b) Find the acceleration for the next 4 s.

(c) Find the acceleration for the last 2 s.

(d) Draw an acceleration-time graph of the motion.

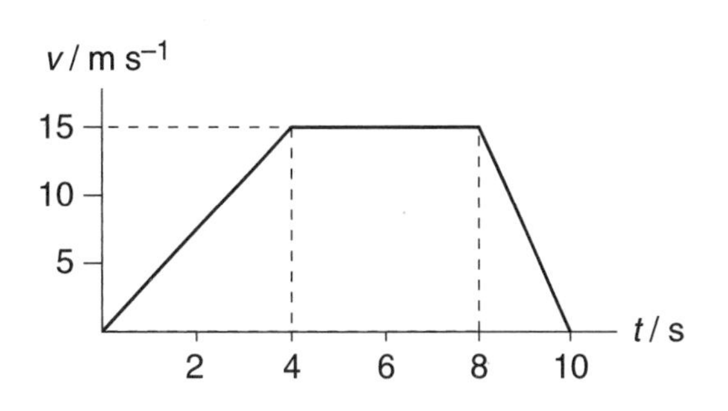

9. A lift accelerates from rest to 3 m s^{-1} in 2 s, travels at this constant velocity for 6 s and decelerates to rest in a further 2 s.

(a) Draw a velocity-time graph of the motion.

(b) Draw an acceleration-time graph of the motion.

(c) Draw a displacement-time graph for the first 8 s.

10. The velocity-time graph of a bouncing ball is shown below.

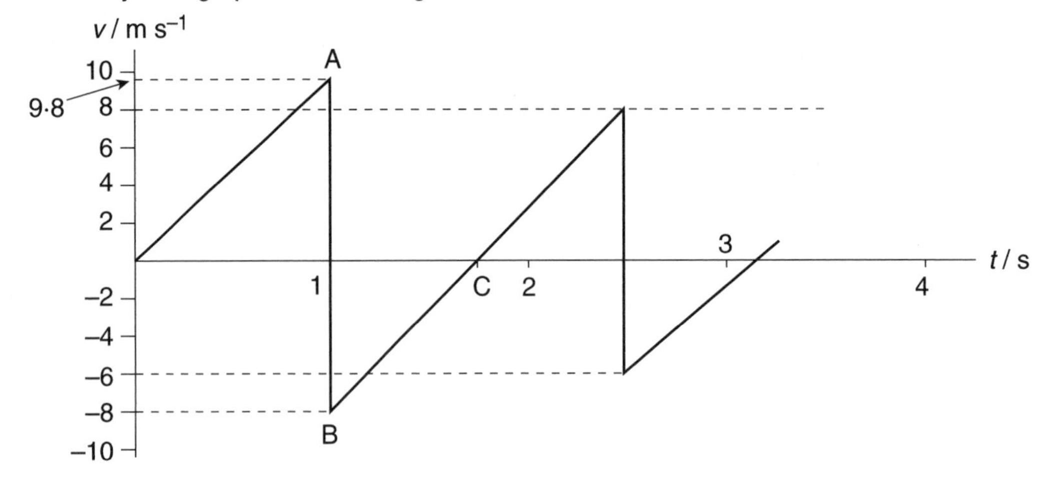

(a) What is the velocity at point A?

(b) What is the velocity at point B?

(c) Where is the ball at point C?

11. Refer to the graph of the bouncing ball in question 10.

(a) How often does the ball strike the ground in 3 s?

(b) From what height was the ball originally dropped?

(c) How high did the ball go before its second bounce (given that point C is approximately 1·82 s)?

12. A trolley accelerates constantly from u m s^{-1} to v m s^{-1} in t seconds as shown in the velocity-time graph.

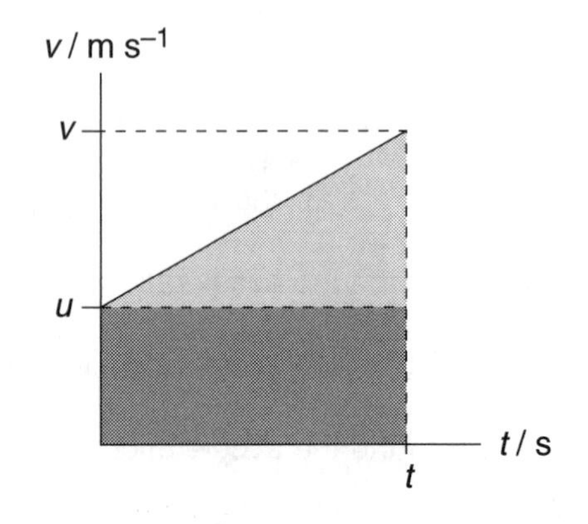

From the graph:

(a) What is the area of the shaded rectangle?

(b) What is the area of the shaded triangle?

(c) Use the acceleration equation to prove the formula

$$s = ut + \frac{1}{2}at^2$$

THE EQUATIONS OF MOTION (A)

Solve numbers 1–4 using the equation $v = u + at$.

1. A car initially at rest accelerates constantly at a rate of 4 m s^{-2} for 3 s. Calculate the final velocity of the car.

2. A bus accelerates constantly at 3 m s^{-2} for 4 s. If the velocity of the bus at the end of 4 s is 15 m s^{-1}, calculate the initial velocity of the bus.

3. A trolley is accelerating at a constant rate of 3 m s^{-2}. How long would it take to speed up from 2 m s^{-1} to 11 m s^{-1}?

4. An air pellet is fired vertically upwards with a velocity of 29·4 m s^{-1} and 3 s later it comes to its highest point. Calculate the constant acceleration of the pellet during the 3 s.

Solve numbers 5–8 using the equation $s = ut + \frac{1}{2}at^2$

5. A car initially at rest accelerates constantly at 4 m s^{-2} for 2 s. How far is the car from where it started?

6. A car accelerates constantly from 5 m s^{-1} for 5 s. If the car travelled 100 m, calculate the acceleration.

7. A lorry accelerates constantly at 3 m s^{-2} for 2 s. If the lorry covered 20 m in the 2 s, calculate the initial velocity of the lorry.

8. A stone is dropped from a height of 78·4 m and accelerates under the influence of gravity at 9·8 m s^{-2}. If the initial velocity of the stone is 0 m s^{-1}, calculate how long it takes to strike the ground.

Solve numbers 9–12 using the equation $v^2 = u^2 + 2as$.

9. A stone is dropped from a height of 122·5 m and accelerates at 9·8 m s^{-2}. If the initial velocity of the stone is 0 m s^{-1}, calculate the velocity with which it strikes the ground.

10. A motorcycle covers 240 m when it accelerates constantly from 10 m s^{-1} to 40 m s^{-1}. Calculate the acceleration.

11. A trolley accelerates constantly at 0·2 m s^{-2} down an inclined plane cutting two light beams at A and B

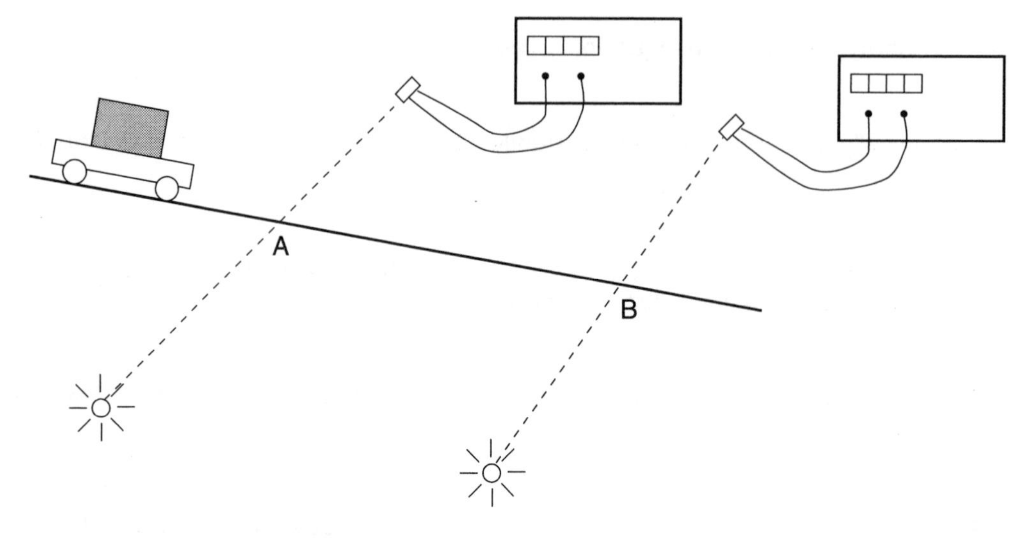

The velocity at point A is 0·3 m s^{-1}.
The velocity at point B is 0·6 m s^{-1}.

What is the distance between A and B?

12. A car travelling at a constant velocity suddenly accelerates uniformly at 3 m s^{-2} to achieve a velocity of 11 m s^{-1}. If the car travelled 16 m during this period of acceleration, calculate the original constant velocity.

THE EQUATIONS OF MOTION (B)

Choose the correct equation of motion to solve the following problems.

1. A stone, initially at rest, is dropped from the edge of a cliff and 3·5 s later it hits the ground.

How high is the cliff?

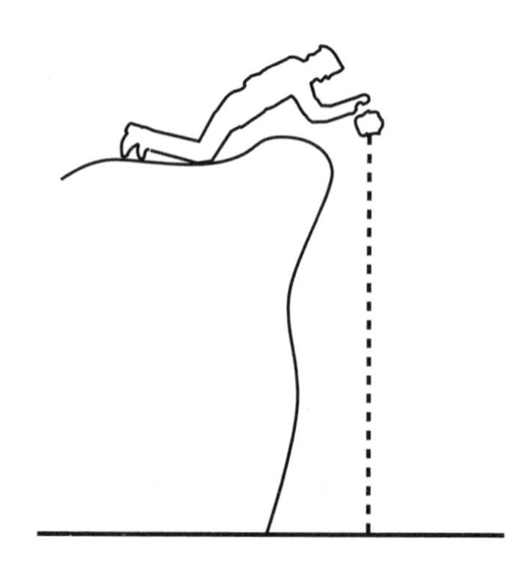

2. A trolley covers 1·0 m when it accelerates from 0·3 m s^{-1} to 0·6 m s^{-1}. Calculate the acceleration.

3. A car accelerates at 1·5 m s^{-2}. If the initial velocity of the car is 2 m s^{-1}, calculate how fast the car would be travelling after:

(a) 2 s;

(b) 2·5 s;

(c) 3·1 s.

4. A lorry in 1st gear accelerates from 0 m s^{-1} to 2 m s^{-1} and covers 20 m. The driver changes into 2nd gear and accelerates from 2 m s^{-1} to 5 m s^{-1} in 12 s.

(a) Calculate the acceleration is 1st gear.

(b) Calculate the acceleration in 2nd gear.

(c) How far did the lorry travel altogether?

5. A car is travelling at a constant velocity of 12 m s^{-1} when a dog runs out onto the road 16 m in front of the car

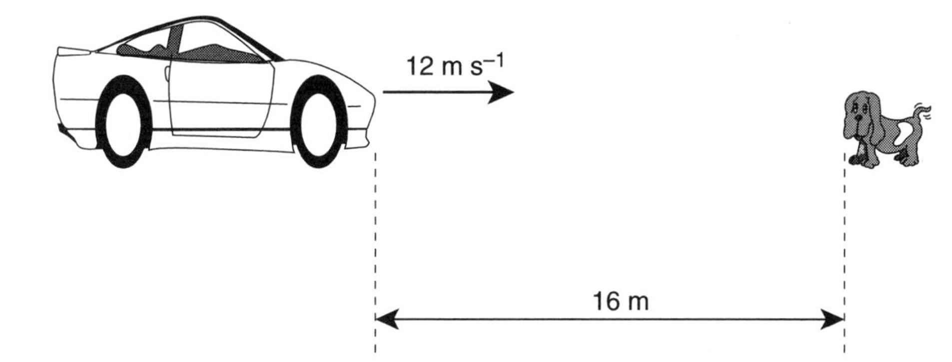

After 0·5 s reaction time, the driver slams on the brakes and the car comes to rest in a further 1·5 s.

(a) How far did the car travel during the driver's reaction time?

(b) Calculate the deceleration of the car.

(c) What was the total braking distance of the car? Include in your answer the "reaction distance" answer to part *(a)*.

(d) Did the car hit the dog?

6. A helicopter is hovering in mid-air. A bag of medical supplies is dropped out and 1·5 s later the bag hits the ground.

How high is the helicopter?

7. A helicopter is travelling upward at a steady velocity of 3 m s^{-1} when a parcel falls out of the door. 2·5 s later the parcel hits the ground.

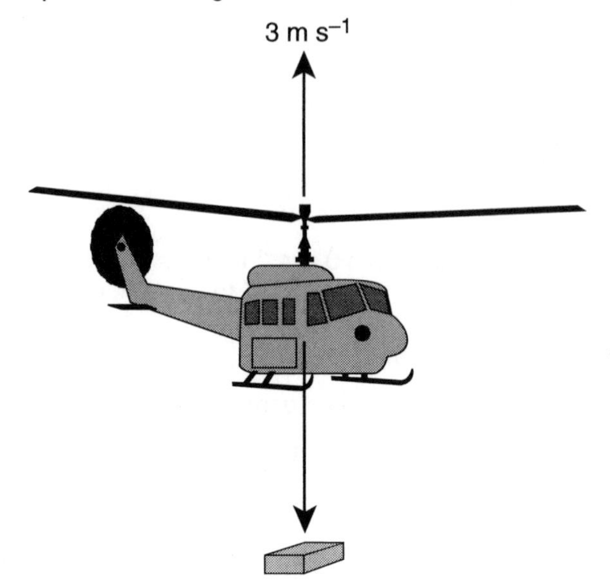

(a) How high was the helicopter when the parcel fell out?

(b) How high was the helicopter when the parcel hit the ground?

8. A race over 100 m is organised between an Olympic athlete and a sports car. The athlete runs the 100 m in 10 s. The car, starting from rest, accelerates constantly at 2·2 m s^{-2}. Where is the car when the athlete crosses the line?

PROJECTILE MOTION

Note: In all problems in this section, air resistance can be ignored.

1. A stone is dropped from the top of a cliff and 5 s later it strikes the ground.

(a) With what velocity did it strike the ground?

(b) What was the average velocity during the 5 s?

(c) How high is the cliff?

(d) Another stone takes 3·9 s to fall from another cliff. How high is this cliff?

2. A bricklayer drops a brick from his scaffolding and 2·5 s later it hits the ground.

(a) With what velocity does the brick strike the ground?

(b) What is the average velocity of the brick during its journey?

(c) How far up the scaffolding is the bricklayer?

3. A stone dropped down a well takes 1·8 s until it hits the bottom.

How deep is the well?

4. In an experiment to find the height of a classroom, a football is dropped out of the window.

If it takes 1·25 s for the football to hit the playground, calculate the height of the classroom.

5. A boy kicks a football horizontally at 4 m s^{-1} from the top of a cliff. At exactly the same moment in time another football is dropped from the top. Both footballs strike the ground after 3 s.

The diagram below shows the motion of both balls.

Copy and complete the diagram and mark in the missing distances and speeds.

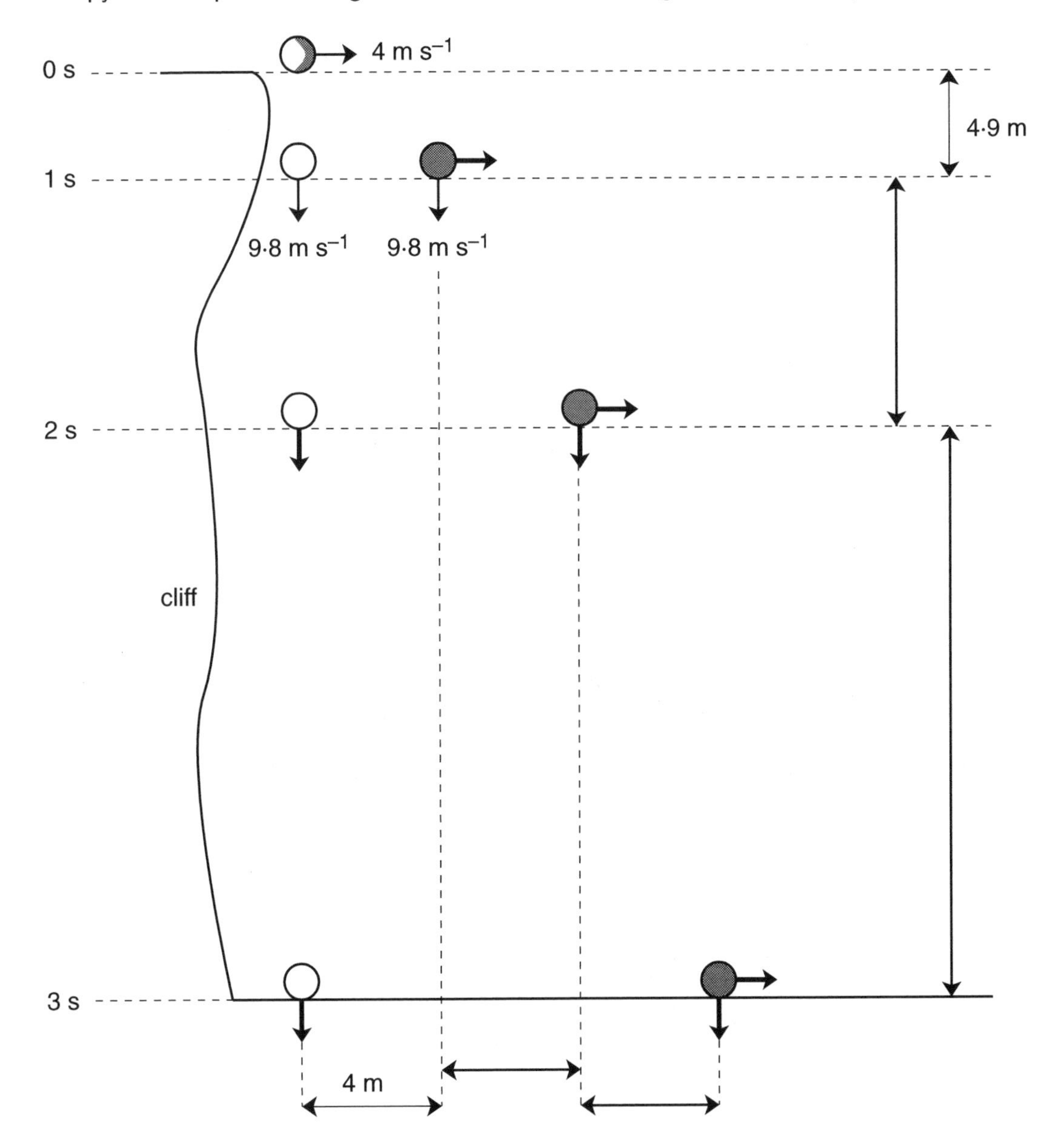

6. A ball is kicked off a cliff with a horizontal velocity of 5 m s^{-1}. Two seconds later it hits the ground.

(a) What is the vertical component of the velocity when the ball hits the ground?

(b) Find the size of X in the diagram.

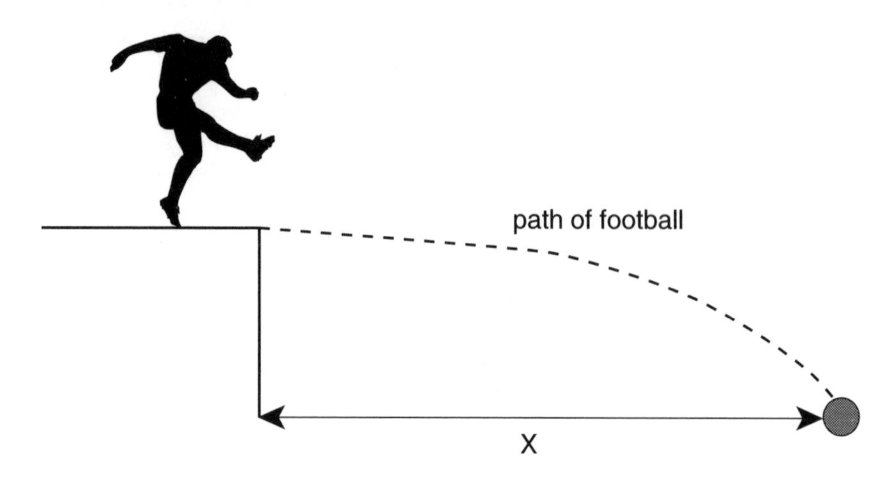

7. An army helicopter is hovering in midair when it fires its machine guns horizontally to strike a target on the ground.

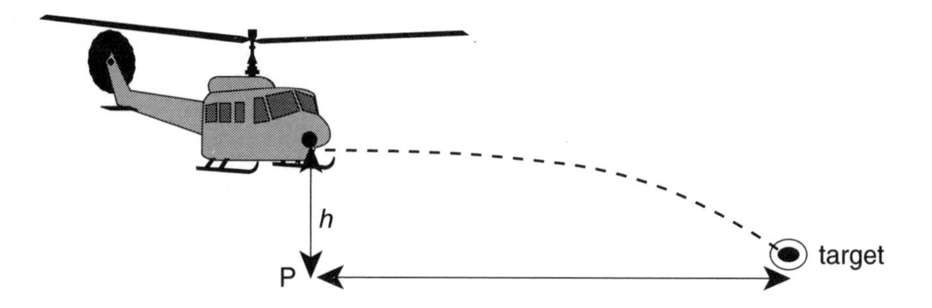

The horizontal velocity of the bullets is 200 m s^{-1}. If each bullet takes 4 s to reach the target,

(a) how far is the target from point P (see diagram)?

(b) how high is the helicopter at the time of firing (h)?

8. An aeroplane flying horizontally with a uniform velocity of 40 m s^{-1} drops a bomb which hits a factory.

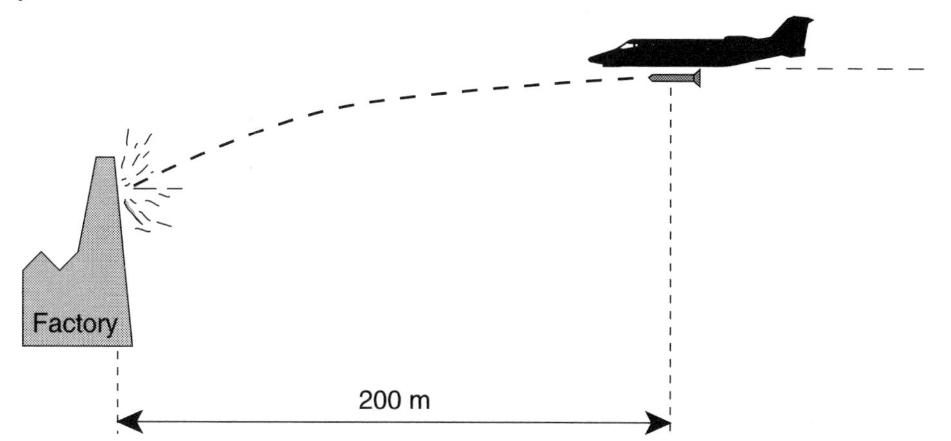

When the bomb is released the horizontal distance between the factory and the aeroplane is 200 m.

(a) What is the time of flight of the bomb?

(b) How high is the aeroplane flying?

(c) Where is the 'plane relative to the factory when the bomb explodes?

9. An aeroplane flying horizontally at 100 m s^{-1} fires a missile horizontally at 400 m s^{-1} (relative to the plane) and scores a direct hit on a tank.

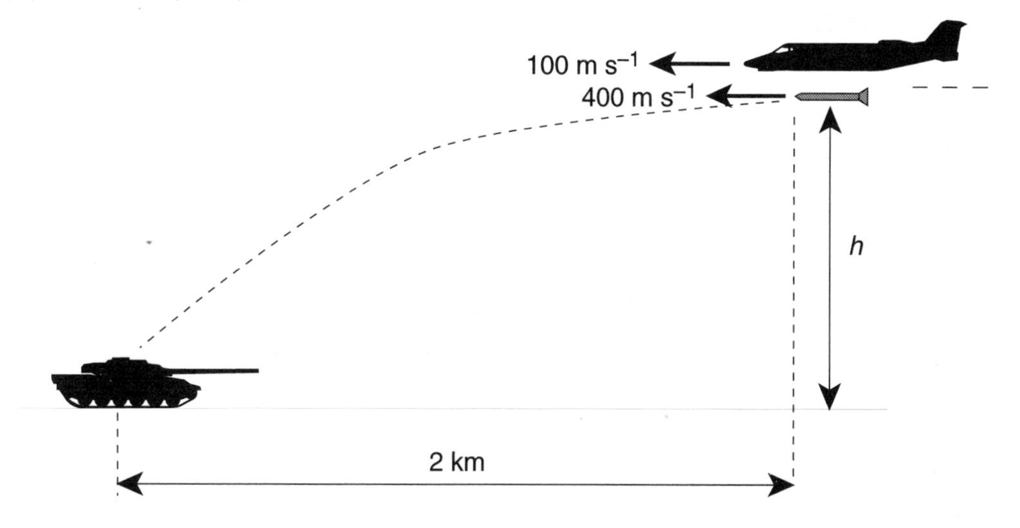

When the missile is fired the horizontal distance between the tank and the aeroplane is 2 km.

(a) What is the time of flight of the missile?

(b) How high is the aeroplane flying (h)?

(c) Where is the aeroplane when the missile explodes? (Use a horizontal reference distance.)

10. An artillery gun fires a shell at an angle to the horizontal. The vertical velocity of the shell is $9{\cdot}8\ \mathrm{m\ s^{-1}}$ and the horizontal velocity of the shell is $60\ \mathrm{m\ s^{-1}}$.

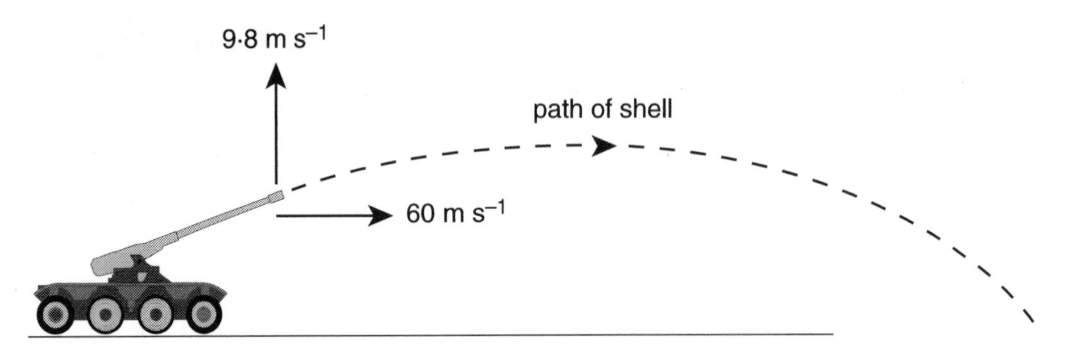

(a) What is the time of flight of the shell?.

(b) What is the maximum height reached by the shell?

(c) What is the horizontal range of the shell?

11. A cannonball is fired horizontally from the top of a cliff towards an enemy ship. The ship is travelling towards the cliff at $5\ \mathrm{m\ s^{-1}}$. The gunner who operates the cannon knows that the cannonball always takes 3 s from the time of firing until it hits the water surface.

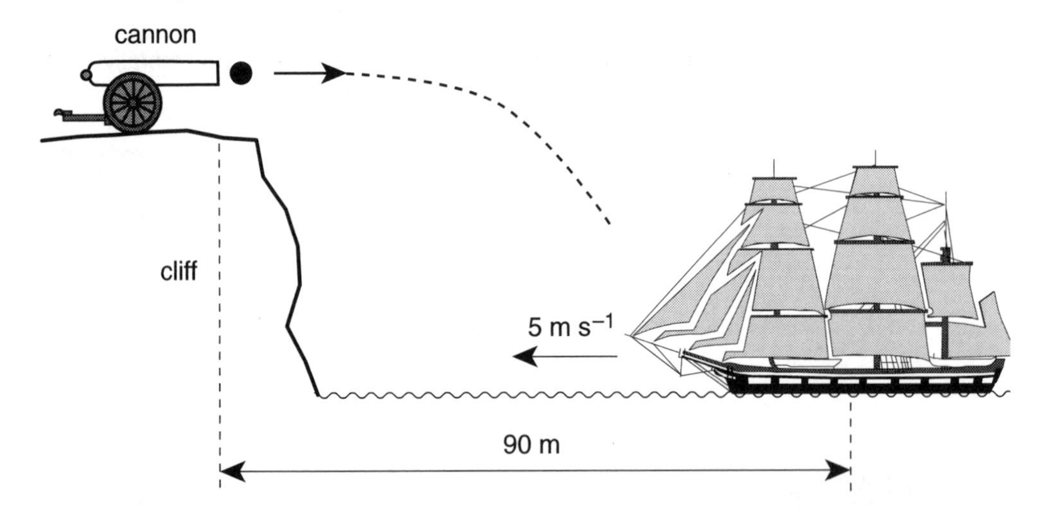

For every 0·5 kg powder the gunner rams down the barrel, the cannonball has a velocity of $5\ \mathrm{m\ s^{-1}}$ (e.g., 1 kg of powder will give the cannonball a velocity of $10\ \mathrm{m\ s^{-1}}$). The gunner fires the cannon while the ship is 90 m away (horizontally — see diagram above). How much powder does he have to ram down the barrel in order to score a direct hit?

12. Using a rifle of muzzle velocity 360 m s^{-1}, a man fires directly at a target 90 m away.

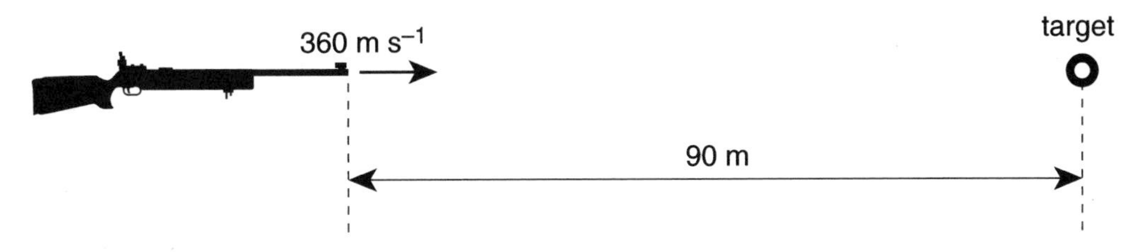

By how much would the bullet pass below the target?

For the following problems, pupils require a knowledge of addition and resolution of vectors.

13. An artillery gun fires a shell at an angle to the horizontal. The vertical component of the shell's velocity is 20 m s^{-1}. The horizontal component of the shell's velocity is 80 m s^{-1}.

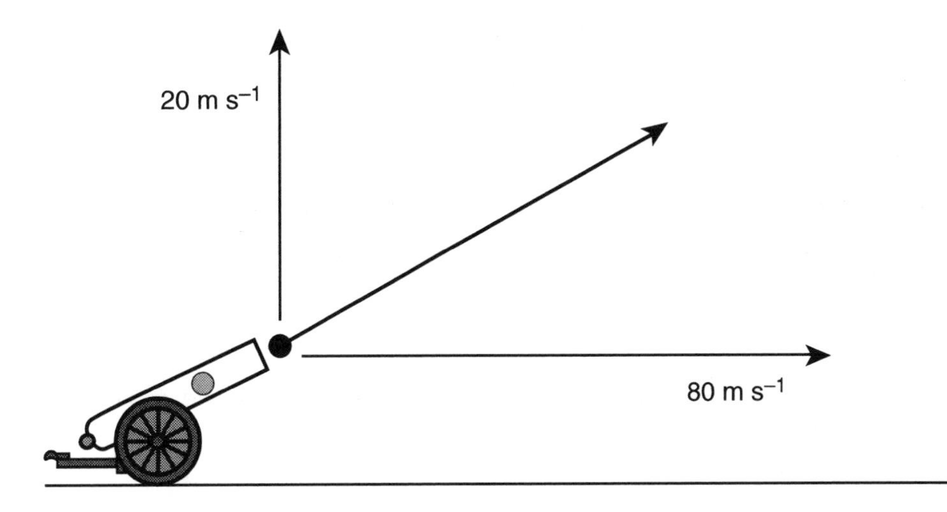

(a) What is the time taken to reach its highest point?

(b) What is the maximum height reached by the shell?

(c) What is the time of flight of the shell?

(d) What is the horizontal range of the shell?

(e) By scale drawing, or otherwise, accurately determine the velocity with which the shell was fired (magnitude and direction).

14. A tank fires a shell at 120 m s^{-1} at an angle of 30° to the horizontal.

(a) Calculate the vertical component of velocity.

(b) Calculate the horizontal component of velocity.

(c) What is the maximum height attained by the shell?

(d) What is the horizontal range of the shell?

15. A shell is fired at 200 m s^{-1} at an angle of 40° to the horizontal.

(a) What is the maximum height attained by the shell?

(b) What is the horizontal range of the shell?

16. A man stands 2·6 m from a dart board, the centre of which is in line with his dart. He throws the dart and scores a bull's eye.

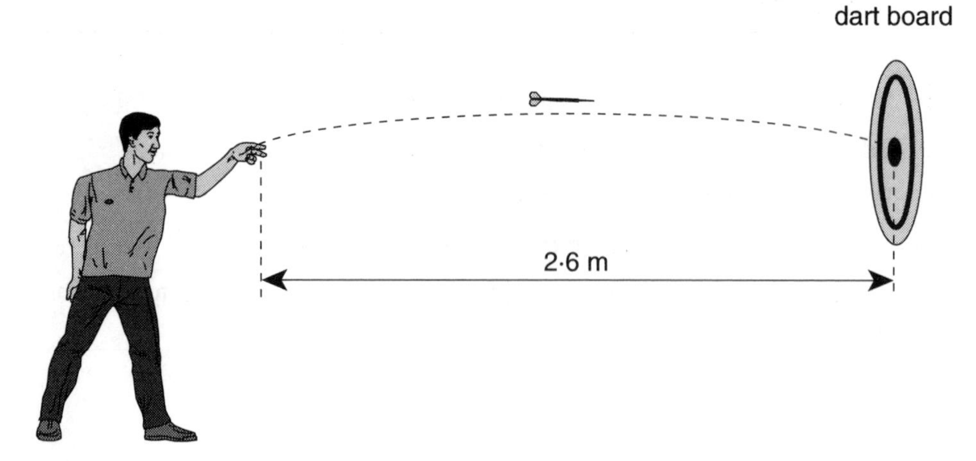

If the time of flight was 0·2 s, calculate the angle to the horizontal at which the dart entered the dart board.

CHAPTER 3

NEWTON'S SECOND LAW, ENERGY AND POWER

NEWTON'S SECOND LAW

1. What unbalanced force is required to accelerate a 2 kg ball at 6 m s^{-2}?

2. A trolley is pulled with a 16 N force. The force of friction acts against this force and has a magnitude of 4 N.

If the mass of the trolley is 1·5 kg, what is the acceleration?

3. Forces act on a 1·5 kg mass as shown.

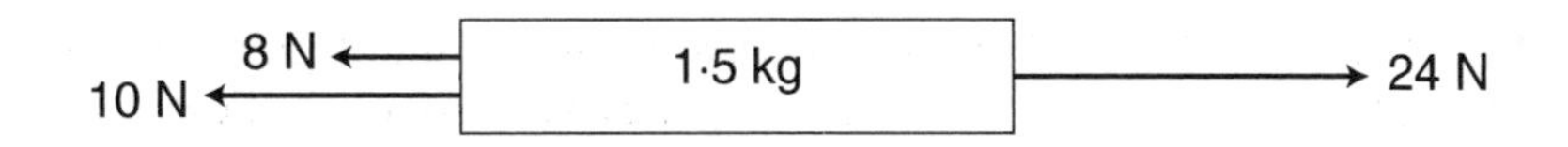

Find:

(a) the resultant force acting on the mass;

(b) the acceleration of the mass;

(c) the velocity of the mass after 3·5 s.

4. A toy car accelerates constantly from 12 m s^{-1} to 20 m s^{-1} in 2 s. The mass of the toy car is 0·9 kg.

(a) Calculate the acceleration.

(b) What unbalanced force is required to cause this acceleration?

5. The graph shows part of the journey of a 1500 kg car (including driver).

(a) Calculate the acceleration during the first 5 s.

(b) Draw the equivalent acceleration-time graph.

(c) Draw the equivalent force-time graph.

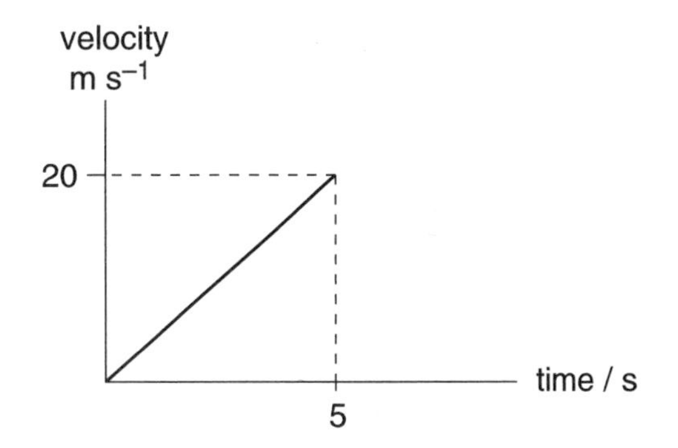

6. The graph shows part of the motion of a 800 kg motorcycle (including rider).

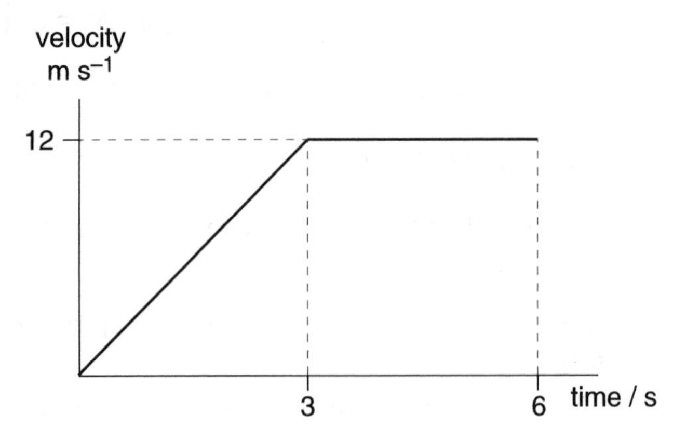

(a) Calculate the acceleration for the first 3 s.

(b) Draw an acceleration-time graph for the 6 s shown.

(c) Draw a force-time graph for the 6 s shown.

In each of the problems 7, 8 and 9, a mass is placed on a frictionless surface. A light string attached to the mass runs over a frictionless pulley to a second mass.

In each problem (numbers 7, 8, 9) calculate:

(a) the acceleration of the system;

(b) the tension *T* in the string.

7. **8.** **9.**

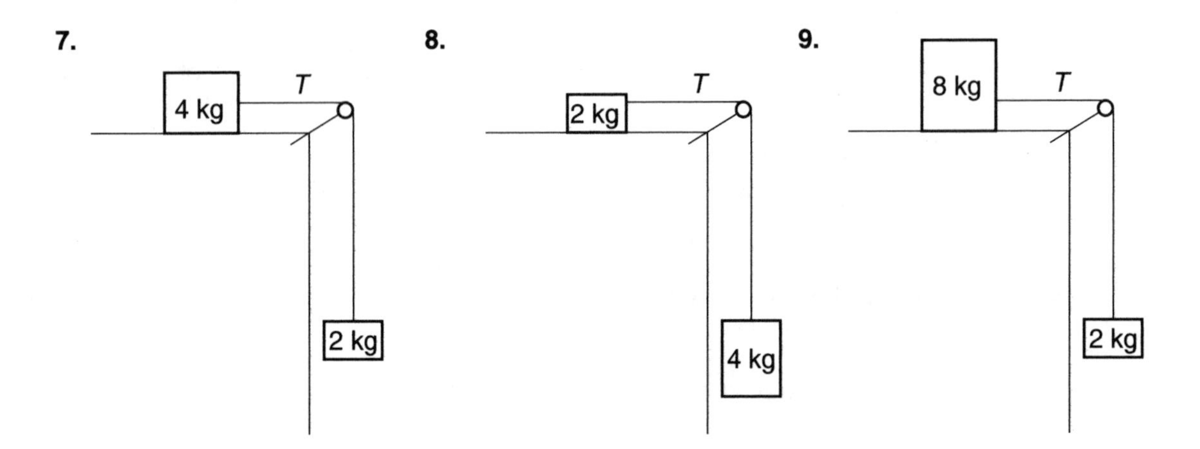

10. A 2 kg mass and a 3 kg mass are linked by a light string passed over a frictionless pulley.

Calculate the acceleration of the system.

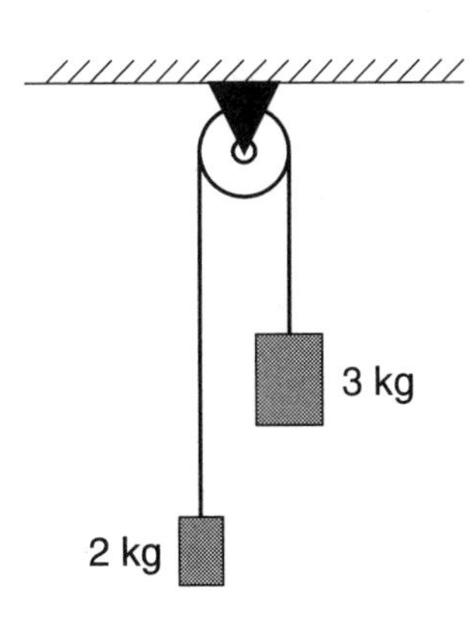

11. A 2·4 kg mass and a 1·6 kg mass are linked by a string passed over a frictionless pulley.

Calculate the acceleration of the system.

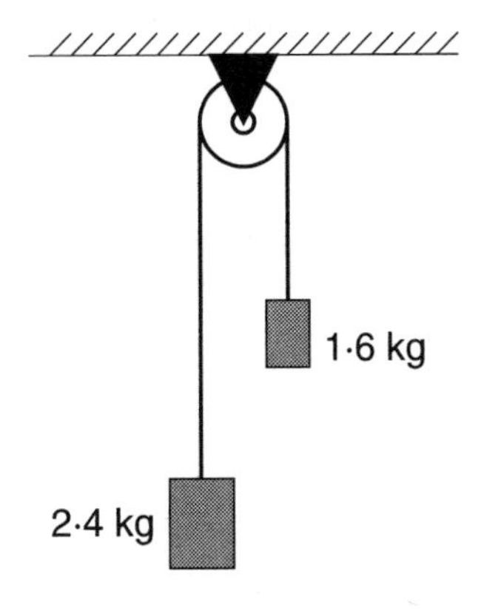

12. A man exerts a force of 192 N on a light rope passed over a single frictionless pulley to a 15 kg mass.

Calculate the acceleration of the mass.

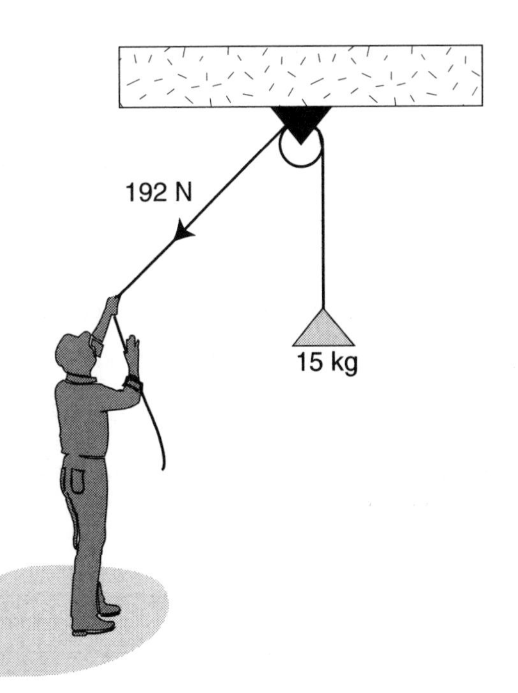

13. Two identical 2 kg trolleys are connected by a light string and pulled by a 12 N force as shown.

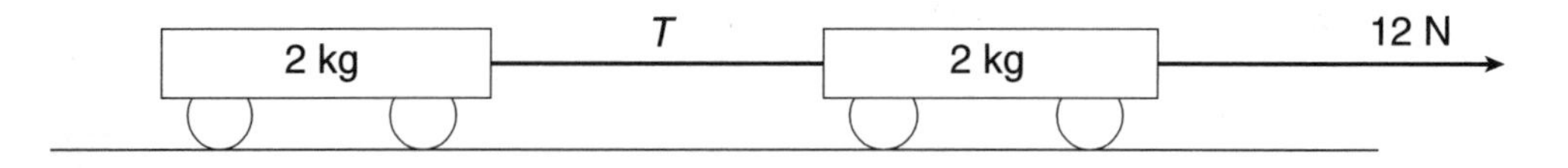

Assuming the surface to be frictionless,

(a) calculate the acceleration of the two trolleys;

(b) find the tension T in the string.

14. A 4 kg trolley and a 2 kg trolley are connected by a light string and pulled by a 12 N force as shown.

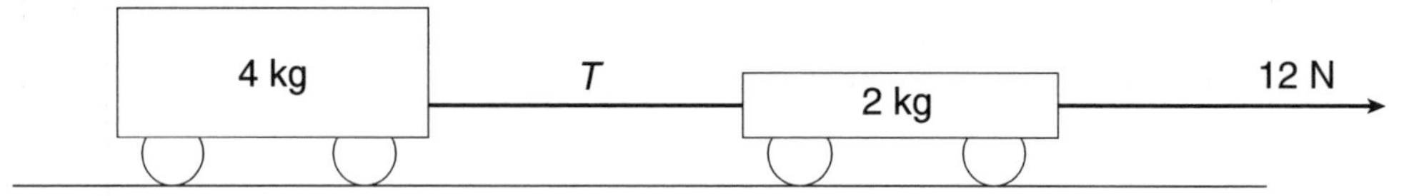

Assuming the surface to be frictionless,

(a) calculate the acceleration of the two trolleys;

(b) find the tension T in the string.

15. Three identical 2 kg trolleys are connected by two light strings and pulled by a 12 N force as shown.

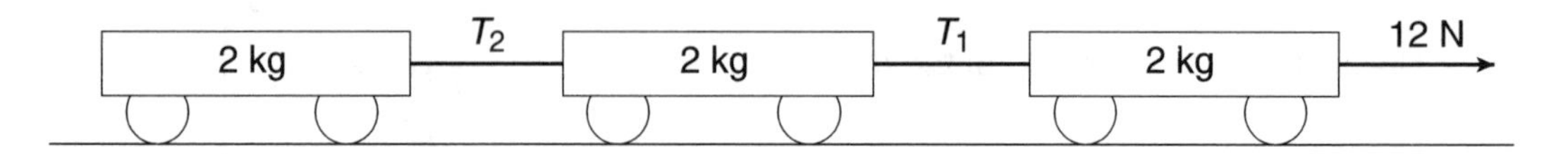

Assuming the surface to be frictionless,

(a) calculate the acceleration of the three trolleys;

(b) find the tension in each string T_1 and T_2.

16. A 4 kg trolley and two 2 kg trolleys are connected by two light strings and pulled by a 12 N force as shown.

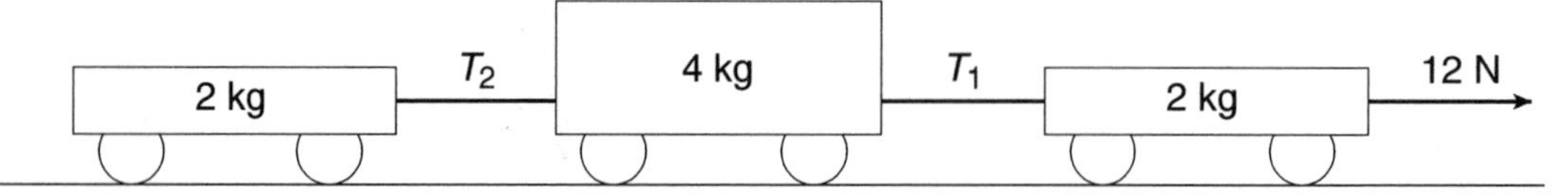

Assuming the surface to be frictionless,

(a) calculate the acceleration of the three trolleys;
(b) find the tension in each string T_1 and T_2.

17. A single light string is used to suspend a pulley with a block attached. If the combined mass of the pulley and block is 5 kg, calculate the tensions T_1 and T_2 in each side of the string.

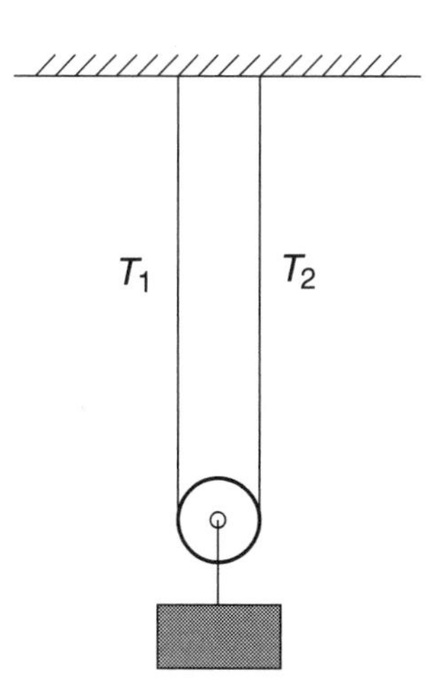

18. Jacqui pushes two blocks A and B (as shown in the diagram) with a 30 N force.

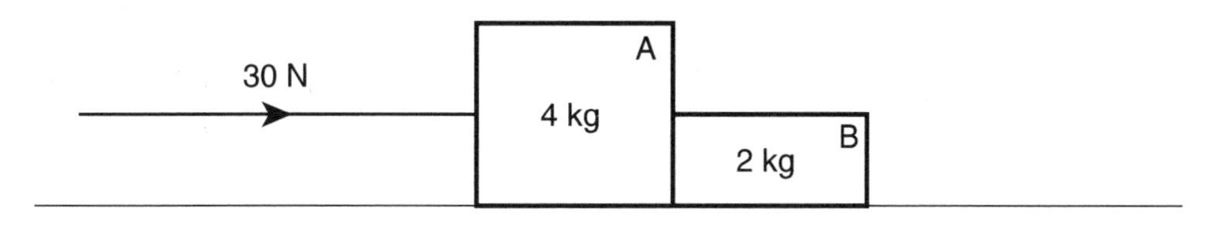

Ignoring friction,

(a) calculate the acceleration of the blocks,

(b) find the force A exerts on B.

19. Lorna-Anne pushes two blocks B and A (as shown in the diagram) with a 30 N force.

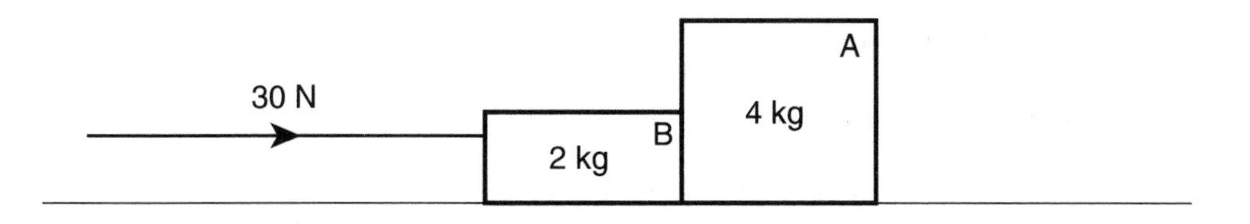

Ignoring friction,

(a) calculate the acceleration of the blocks,

(b) find the force B exerts on A.

20. A model rocket of mass 50 kg is initially accelerated upwards by the thrust of the rocket engine.

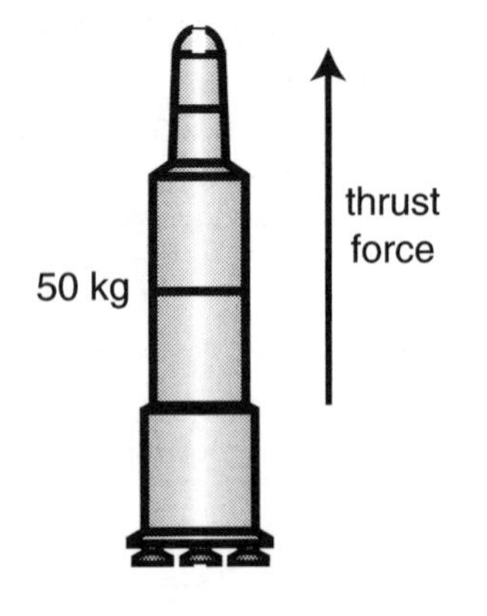

(a) What is the force of gravity acting on the rocket?

(b) If the thrust force is 800 N, calculate the unbalanced force acting on the rocket.

(c) Hence calculate the acceleration of the rocket.

21. A rocket on the launch pad has two forces acting on it as shown in the diagram.

(a) Calculate the initial acceleration of the rocket.

(b) As the rocket rises, what happens to the mass?

(c) How does this affect acceleration?

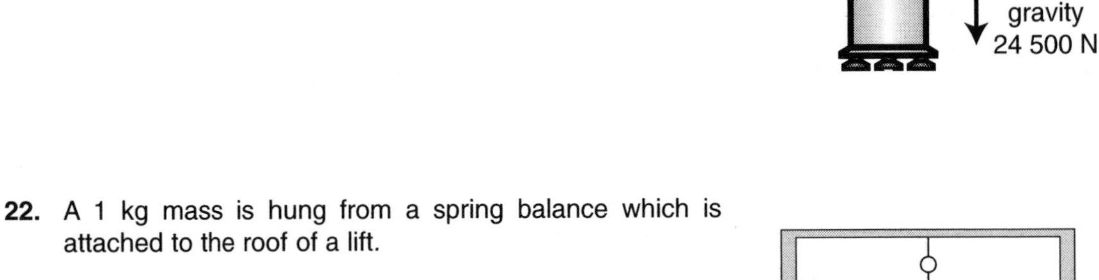

22. A 1 kg mass is hung from a spring balance which is attached to the roof of a lift.

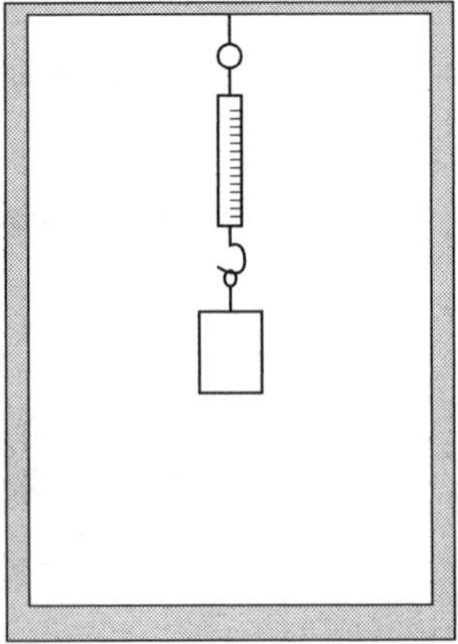

In an upward journey the lift accelerates, moves at constant velocity and decelerates to rest.

Find the reading on the spring balance:

(a) when the lift is stationary;

(b) when the lift is accelerating up at 3 m s^{-2};

(c) when the lift is moving up at constant velocity;

(d) when the lift is decelerating up at 3 m s^{-2}.

23. Duncan (mass 75 kg) stands on bathroom scales inside a lift.

On an upward journey the lift accelerates for 2 s, moves at constant velocity for 6 s and decelerates to rest in a further 2 s.

What does Duncan read on the scales

(a) when the lift is stationary;

(b) when the lift is accelerating up if the acceleration is 2 m s^{-2};

(c) when the lift is moving at constant velocity;

(d) when the lift is decelerating up if the deceleration is 2 m s^{-2}?

24. A 2 kg trolley is placed on a 30° frictionless slope as shown. The force of gravity acting on the trolley is 19·6 N but only a component of this force (parallel to the slope), F_P causes the trolley to accelerate.

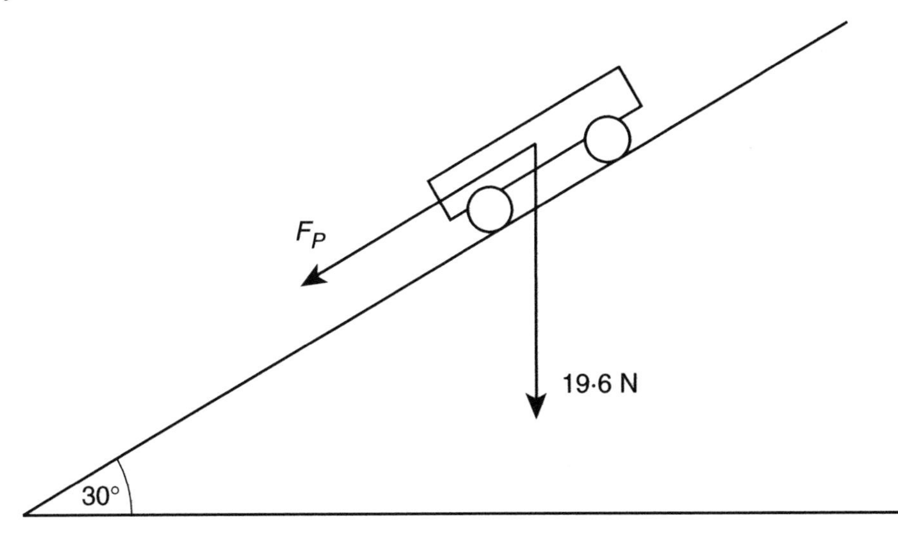

(a) Calculate the size of this accelerating force.

(b) Calculate the acceleration of the trolley (assuming friction is negligible).

25. A 2 kg trolley is placed on a 35° slope. Again only the parallel component causes the trolley to accelerate but this time a frictional force of 1·5 N retards the trolley as shown.

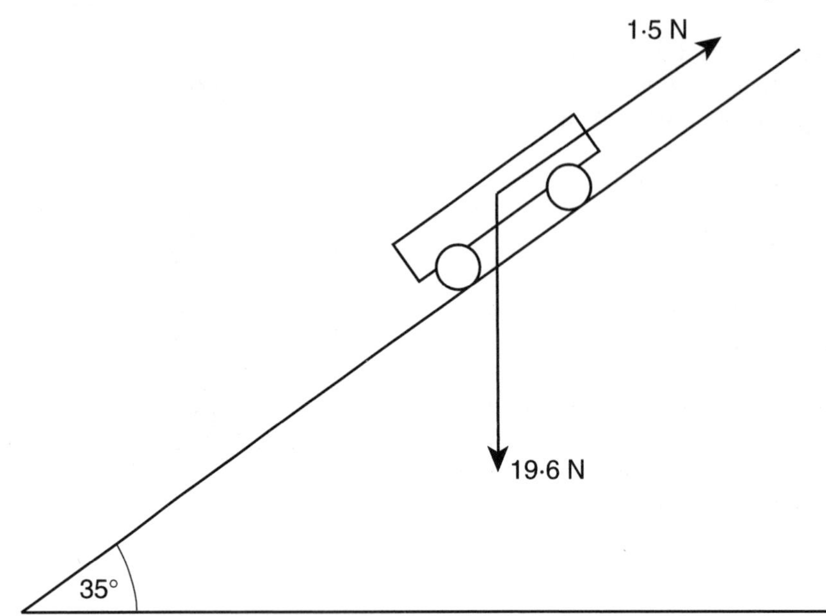

(a) Calculate the accelerating force.

(b) Calculate the acceleration of the trolley.

(c) What effect does increasing the angle of slope have on acceleration?

(d) How large is the normal reaction force?

POTENTIAL AND KINETIC ENERGY, WORK DONE AND POWER

1. A stationary 2 kg mass has an E_P of 313·6 J when it is 16 m above ground. As it falls all the E_P is converted into E_K.

E_P		2 kg	E_K
313·6 J	16 m		0 J
	12 m		
156·8 J	8 m		
	4 m		
0 J	ground level		

Copy and complete the diagram above by filling in the missing E_Ps and E_Ks.

2. An 8 kg mass has a kinetic energy of 1600 J.

How fast is it travelling?

3. A pendulum swings from a point of maximum E_P (X) to the point of minimum E_P (Y) as shown in the diagram.

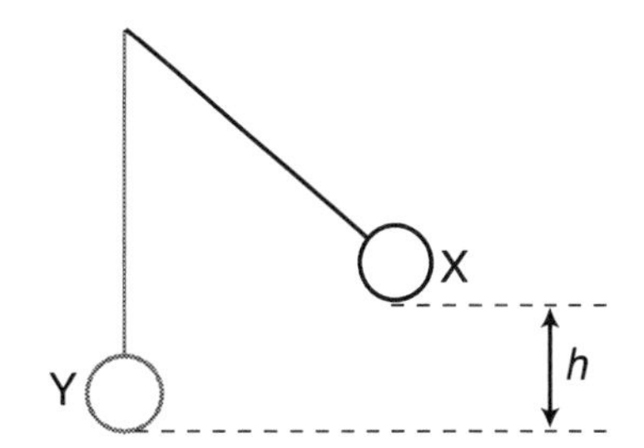

Prove the relationship

$v = \sqrt{2gh}$

for the maximum velocity of the bob.

4. A pendulum swings as shown in the diagram. Points A and C are the extremities of the swing of the pendulum. The mass of the bob is 0·5 kg.

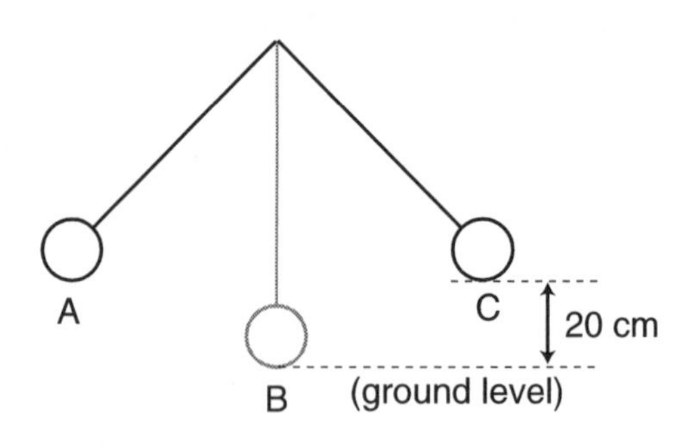

Find:

(a) the maximum potential energy of the bob;

(b) the maximum kinetic energy of the bob;

(c) the top speed of the bob.

5. In an experiment to calculate the power developed by a man, he runs up a flight of stairs as fast as he can.

Given the fact that the man took 5·0 seconds to run up the stairs, use the information in the diagram to calculate his power.

6. A trolley is released from rest at point X and it accelerates down the slope to point Y.

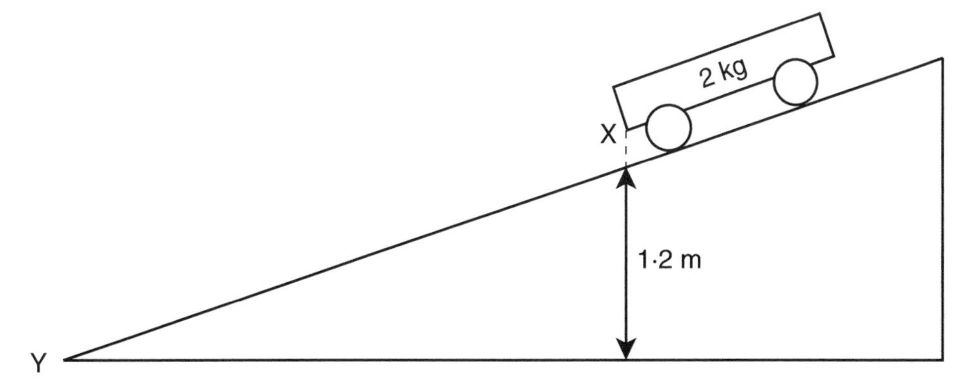

Assuming friction to be negligible, calculate the speed of the trolley at point Y.

7. John releases a block of mass 1 kg initially at rest from a point A 2 m up a slope as shown in the diagram. The block slides down to the point B at the bottom of the slope where its speed is measured. The speed at B is found to be 3·80 m s^{-1}.

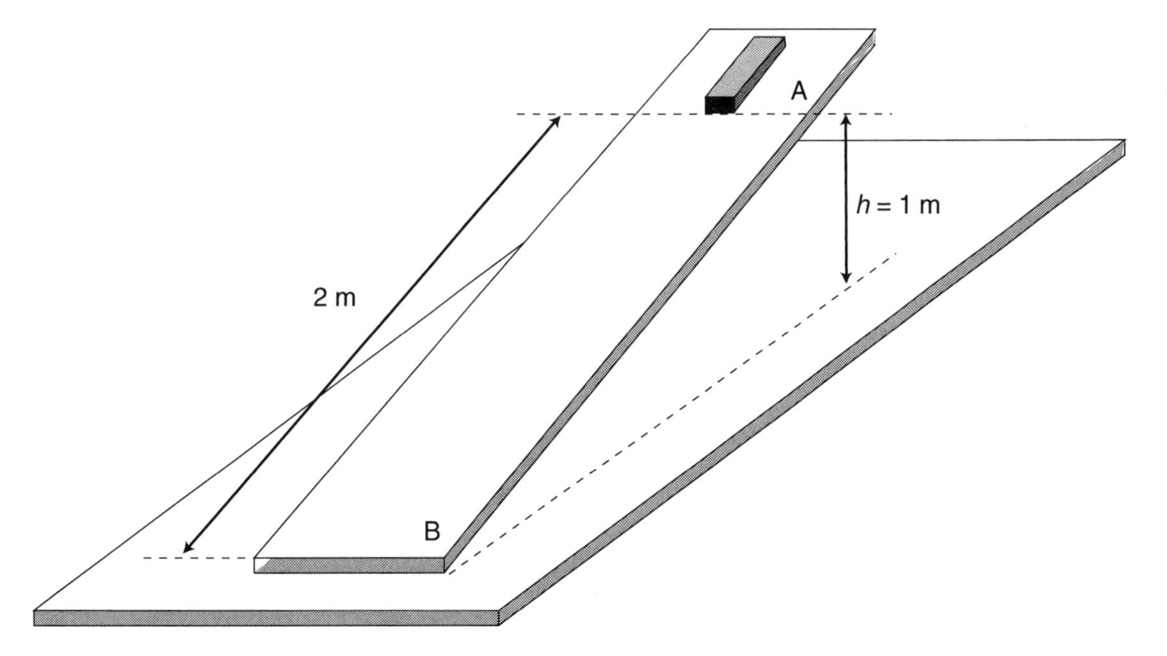

(a) Calculate the potential energy of the block at A.

(b) Calculate the kinetic energy of the block at B.

(c) John is surprised that the answer to *(b)* is not the same as the answer to *(a)*. Explain this to John.

(d) Calculate the average frictional force acting on the block between A and B.

Note: Before attempting problems 8 and 9, students would require a knowledge of momentum.

8. In a test designed to calculate the velocity of an air pellet, the pellet (mass 20 g) was fired horizontally at a lump of plasticine (mass 0·98 kg) suspended by a long string.

The plasticine moved up a height

$h = 3{\cdot}2$ cm

before swinging back.

v

20 g

0·98 kg

$h = 3{\cdot}2$ cm

Calculate the velocity of the air pellet before it hit the plasticine.

9. The bob of a pendulum (mass m_1) swings from (stationary) point X to point Y where it strikes an identical mass (m_2). The pendulum bob stops and the identical mass is projected forwards and lands on the floor.

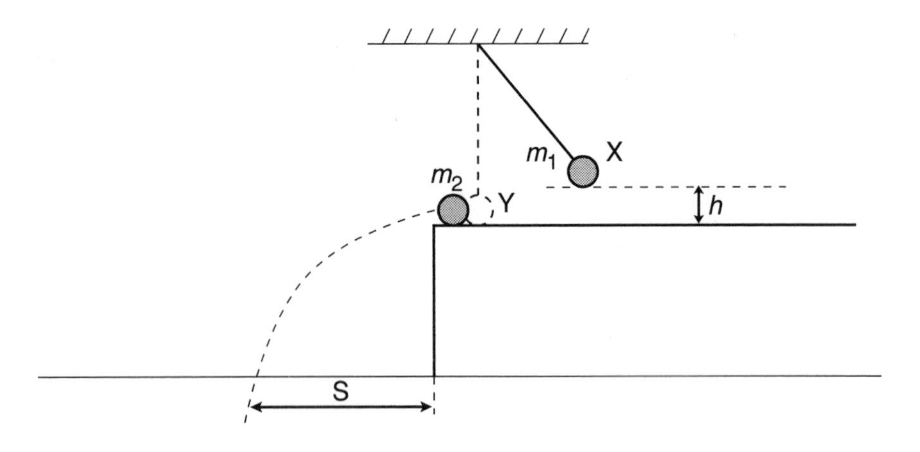

(a) Given only the height $h = 45$ cm, calculate the velocity of the mass m_2 immediately after the collision.

(b) If the mass took 0·5 s to strike the ground, find S, the distance from the foot of the table.

(c) How high is the surface of the table above the ground?

CHAPTER 4

MOMENTUM AND IMPULSE

MOMENTUM (A) — INELASTIC COLLISIONS

1. How much momentum does a 40 kg boy have when he is moving at:

(a) 6 m s^{-1};
(b) 4 m s^{-1};
(c) 1·0 m s^{-1};
(d) 0·6 m s^{-1};
(e) 150 cm s^{-1}?

2. A rugby player has a mass of 75 kg. How fast does he have to run to have a momentum of 525 kg m s^{-1}?

3. A car has a mass of 1000 kg. How fast is it moving when its momentum is 6200 kg m s^{-1}?

4. A wheelbarrow has a momentum of 177 kg m s^{-1} when it is moving at 3 m s^{-1}. What is the mass of the wheelbarrow?

5. A radio-controlled car has a momentum of 1·5 kg m s^{-1} when travelling at 2 m s^{-1}. What is the mass of the car?

6. A trolley of mass 2 kg moving at 4 m s^{-1} collides with, and sticks to, an identical stationary trolley. What is the velocity of the two trolleys immediately after the collision?

7. A boy of mass 54 kg runs at 4 m s^{-1} and jumps onto a stationary skateboard (mass 6 kg) and both move off together.

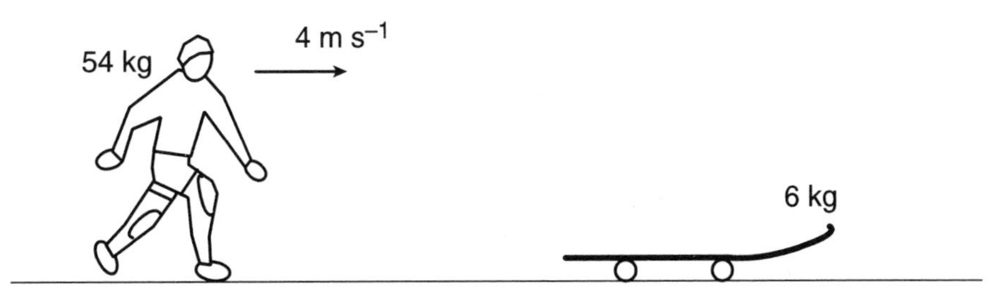

With what velocity does the skateboard (and boy) move?

8. A trolley of mass 2 kg is moving along a horizontal plane at 3 m s^{-1}. When the trolley passes a certain point, a mass *m* is dropped on top of it.

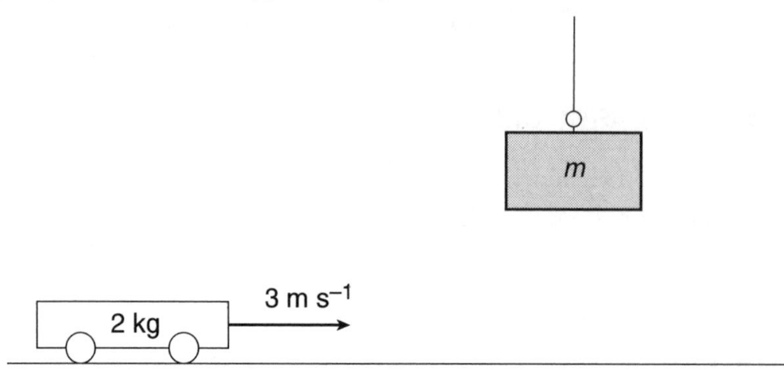

What is the velocity of the trolley and mass coupled together if the mass is 1 kg?

In problems 9 to 12, a 2 kg trolley travelling at 6 m s^{-1} collides with and sticks to a stationary trolley. Calculate the speed *v* of the combination immediately after the collision in each case.

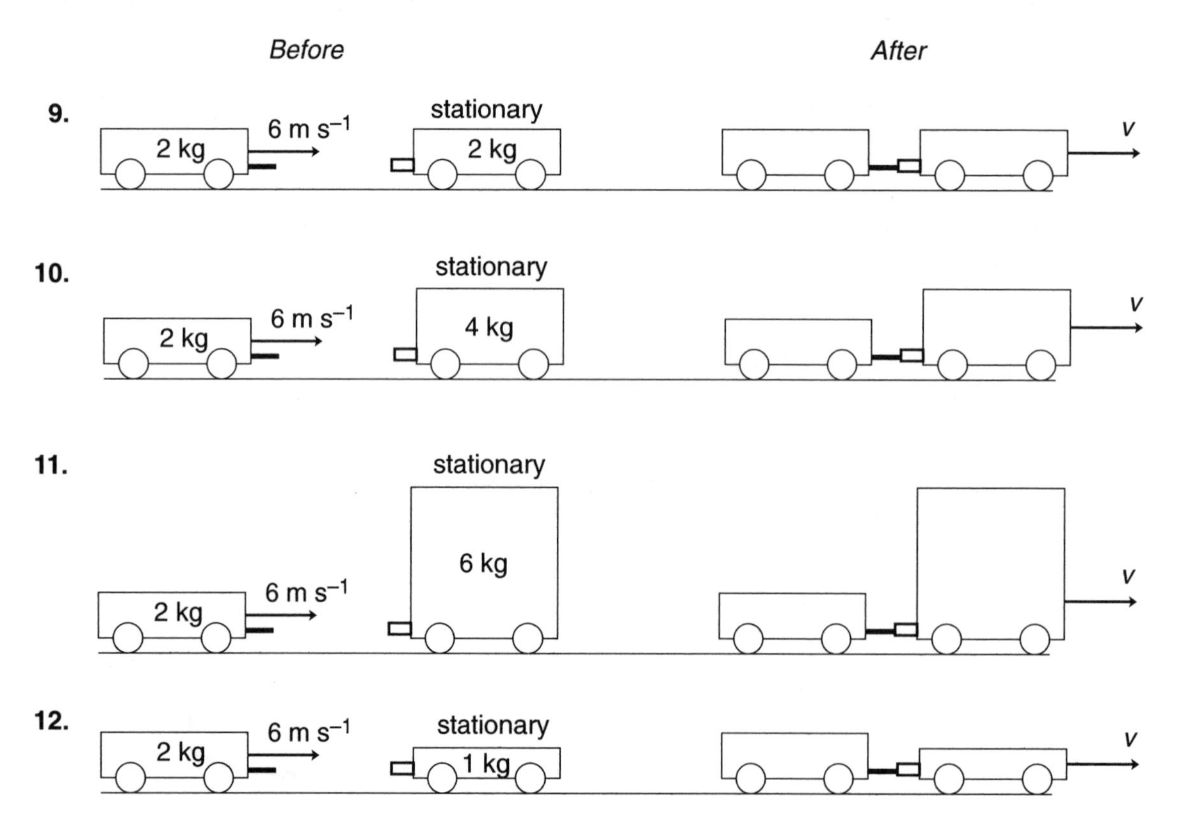

13. A 2 kg trolley travelling at 6 m s^{-1} collides with and sticks to an identical stationary trolley. After the collision both trolleys move off at 3 m s^{-1}.

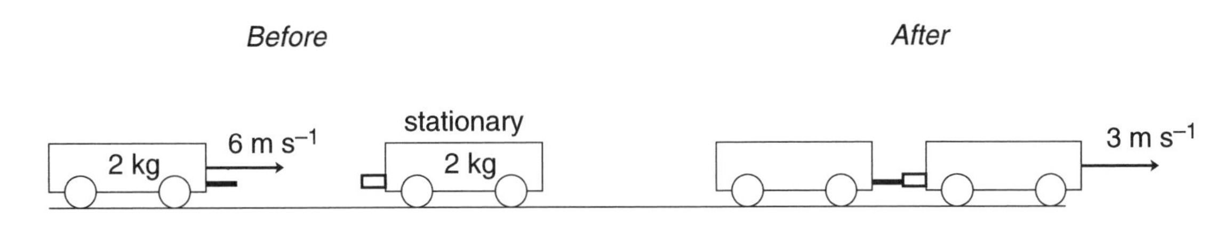

(a) Prove that momentum is conserved.

(b) Find the kinetic energy before the collision.

(c) Find the kinetic energy after the collision.

14. A 2 kg trolley travelling at 6 m s^{-1} collides with and sticks to a stationary 3 kg trolley.

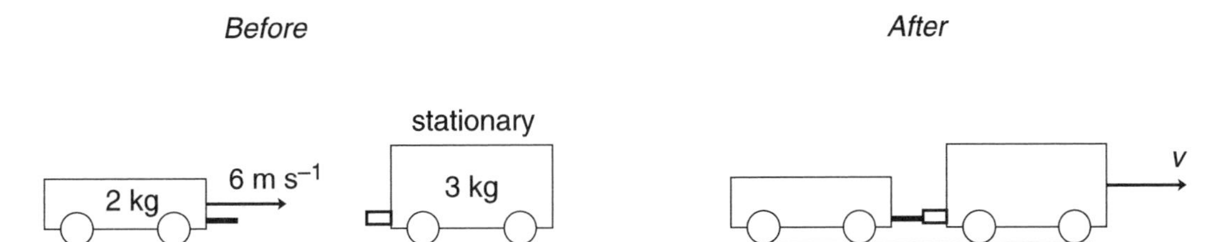

(a) Find the speed v of the trolleys immediately after the collision.

(b) Find the kinetic energy before the collision.

(c) Find the kinetic energy after the collision.

(d) What type of collision is it?

15. Car A (mass 600 kg) collides with and sticks to car B (mass 800 kg) which is parked at the side of the road. If both cars move off together at 10 m s^{-1}, how fast was car A travelling before the collision?

16. A car of mass 700 kg collides with and sticks to a stationary van of mass 1400 kg and both move off together at 11 m s^{-1}. Was the car driver exceeding the speed limit of 30 m s^{-1} before the accident?

17. A 4 kg rock falls off the edge of a cliff. Taking the acceleration of gravity as 9·8 m s^{-2}, calculate the momentum of the rock after it has been falling for

(a) 1 s,

(b) 2·5 s,

(c) 3·9 s.

18. A 800 kg car accelerates from rest at a rate of 5 m s^{-2} for 4 s when it has a head-on collision with a 1200 kg car travelling at 5 m s^{-1}.

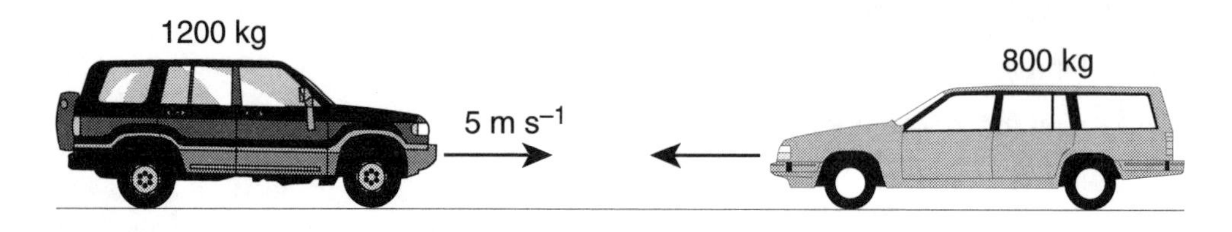

Assuming both cars lock together on impact, find:

(a) the direction that they move in after the collision;

(b) the velocity of the wreckage immediately after impact;

(c) the average force of friction acting on the cars after collision if the wreckage comes to rest in 2 s.

19. A 700 kg car moving at 20 m s^{-1} runs into the back of a 1000 kg car moving at 11·5 m s^{-1}. Both cars lock together on impact.

(a) What is the velocity of the two cars immediately after the collision?

(b) If it takes the two cars 4 s to slow down to 9 m s^{-1} after the collision, what is the average force of friction acting against them?

20. A hammer of mass 500 kg is allowed to fall freely from rest on to a pile of mass 1500 kg which is 19·6 m below it (see diagram).

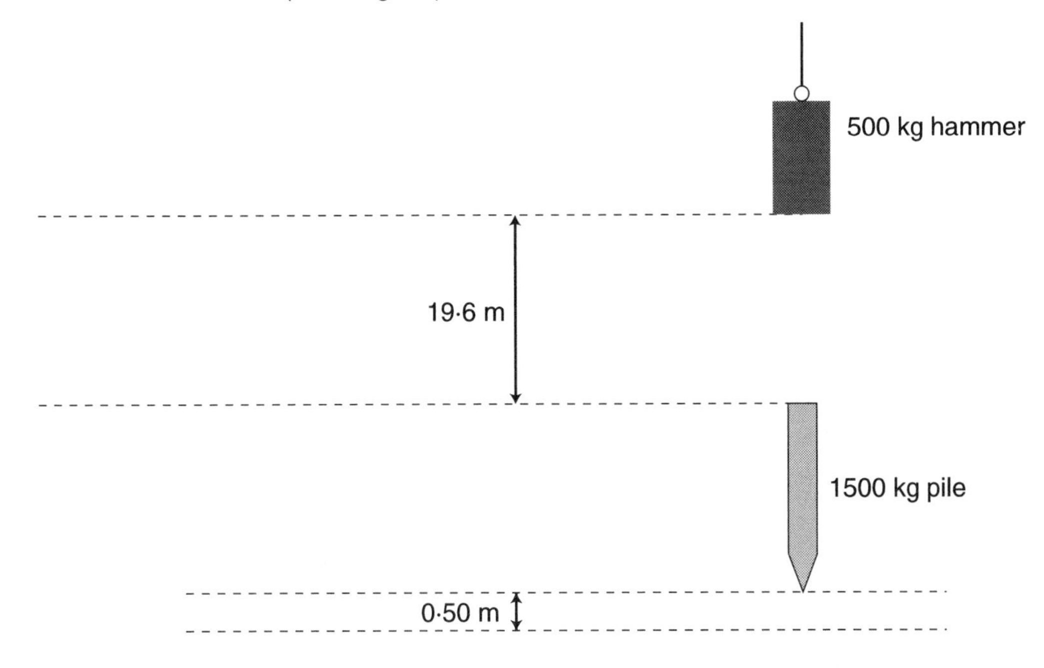

The hammer and pile then move together as the pile is driven 0·50 m into the ground.

(a) With what speed does the hammer hit the pile?

(b) Calculate the common velocity of pile and hammer immediately after collision.

(c) How long does it take the pile to travel the 0·50 m into the ground?

21. An air pellet of mass 0·02 kg travelling at 40 m s^{-1} collides with and becomes embedded in a block of wood mounted on a stationary trolley.

mass of trolley = 1·50 kg

mass of wood = 0·48 kg

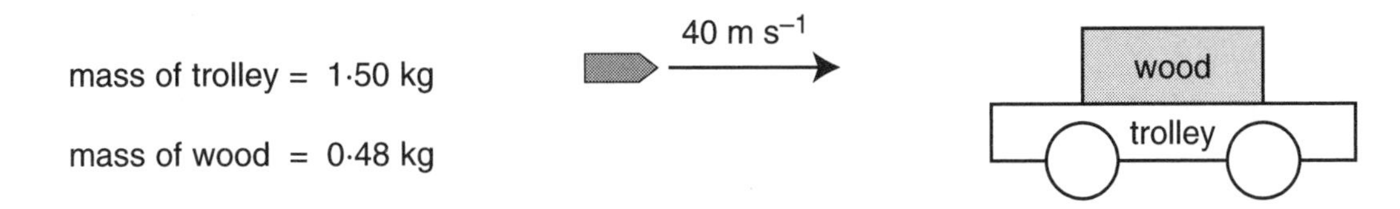

Calculate the velocity of the trolley, wood and bullet immediately after impact.

22. In an experiment to find the velocity of an air pellet of mass 0·02 kg the 1·50 kg trolley and 0·48 kg block of wood shown in question 21 were used.

(a) What additional apparatus would be necessary to perform the experiment?

(b) Describe, in some detail, how to perform the experiment and **list** the readings necessary to find the velocity of the bullet.

(c) Given that the combined mass of trolley and wooden block plus bullet moves off at 1 m s^{-1}, calculate the initial velocity of the bullet

MOMENTUM (B) — ELASTIC COLLISIONS

1. Complete the sentence:

In all collisions .... is conserved but .... is only conserved in elastic collisions.

2. In a collision, a 0·2 kg ball (A) strikes an identical stationary ball (B).

After the collision, A stops.

(a) Calculate the velocity of B immediately after the collision.

(b) Calculate the kinetic energy before the collision.

(c) Calculate the kinetic energy after the collision.

(d) Is the collision elastic or inelastic?

3. On a linear air track, vehicle A (0·02 kg), moving at 1·0 m s^{-1}, collides with vehicle B (0·04 kg), which is initially stationary.

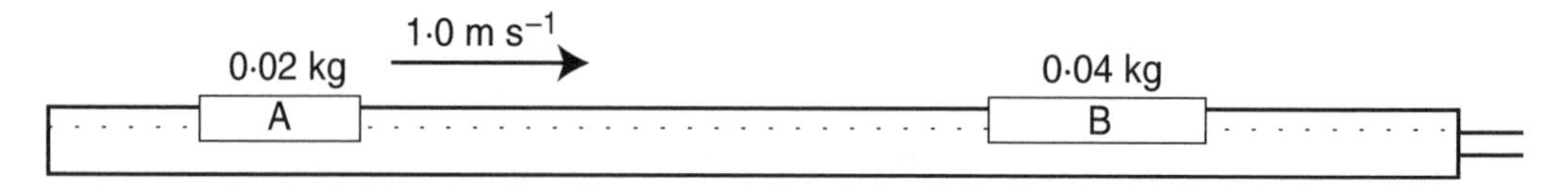

After the collision, vehicle A bounces back to the left at 0·1 m s^{-1} and vehicle B moves to the right.

(a) Find the momentum before the collision.

(b) Find the momentum of A after the collision.

(c) Hence calculate the speed of B after the collision.

(d) Is the collision elastic or inelastic? You must justify your answer with calculations.

MOMENTUM (C) — EXPLOSIONS

In problems 1 to 4, two trolleys are exploded apart so that they move in opposite directions. Calculate the speed *v* of the left-hand trolley in each case.

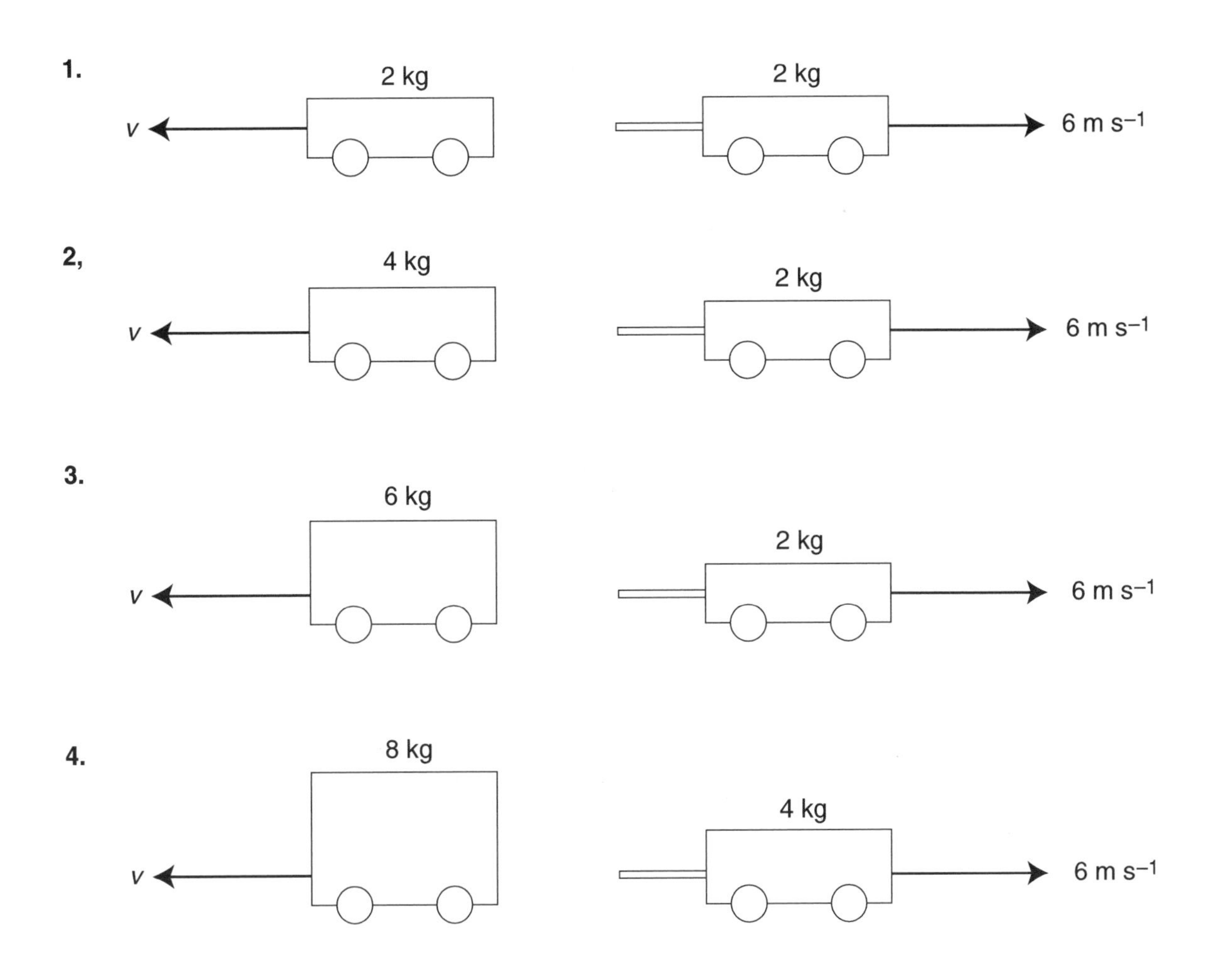

5. A bullet of mass 100 g is fired from a 5 kg gun at 50 m s^{-1}.

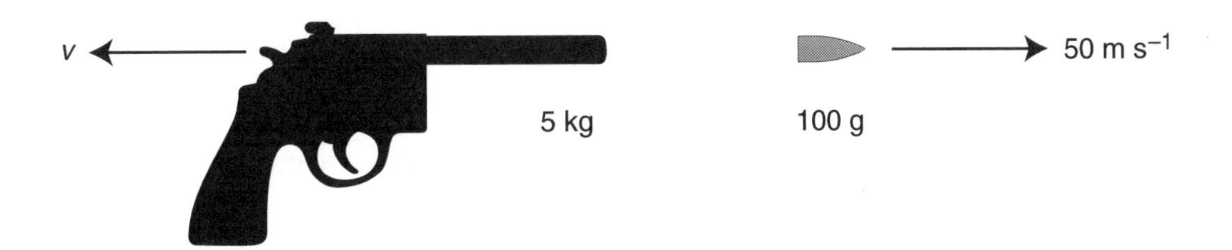

Calculate the recoil speed of the gun.

6. A 40 g bullet fired from an 8 kg gun has a velocity of 150 m s^{-1}. With what speed does the gun recoil?

7. A Uranium nucleus has a mass of 238 a.m.u. It decays by emitting an alpha particle of mass 4 a.m.u., leaving a Thorium nucleus of mass 234 a.m.u.

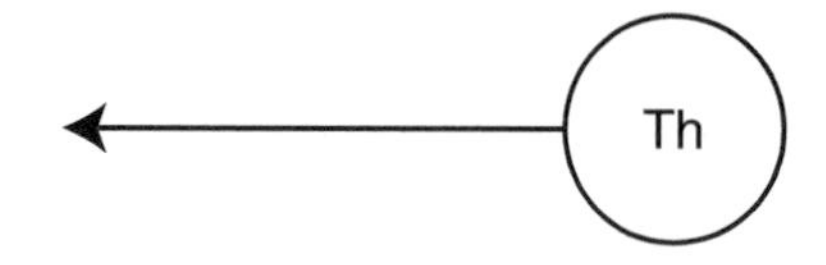

If the alpha particle is emitted with a velocity of $1 \cdot 17 \times 10^7$ m s^{-1}, calculate the recoil velocity of the Thorium nucleus formed.

8. Two astronauts are floating in "weightless" conditions inside a simulator.

Astronaut A has a mass of 80 kg.

Astronaut B has a mass of 90 kg.

A pushes B and he (A) moves backwards at 3 m s^{-1}.

Calculate the speed of B in the opposite direction.

IMPULSE

1. Copy and complete the sentence:

> In a car accident an air bag will protect a driver from injury because it .... the time of contact and .... the average force acting on the driver.

2. A 50 kg boy jumps from a platform and lands in a sand pit at 3 m s^{-1}. If he comes to rest 0·25 s after he hits the sand, calculate:

(a) the change in momentum of the boy;

(b) the average force acting to slow the boy down.

3. A trolley of mass 2 kg travelling at 4 m s^{-1} strikes a cushion and comes to rest in 0·6 s. Calculate the average resistive force acting on the trolley.

4. A bullet of mass 6 g is acted upon by a force of 3000 N for 1·5 m s in the barrel of a rifle. Calculate the velocity of the bullet as it leaves the barrel.

5. A stationary snooker ball (mass 0·2 kg) is struck by a cue.

The graph shows how the force varies during the time of contact of 40 ms.

How fast does the ball move off?

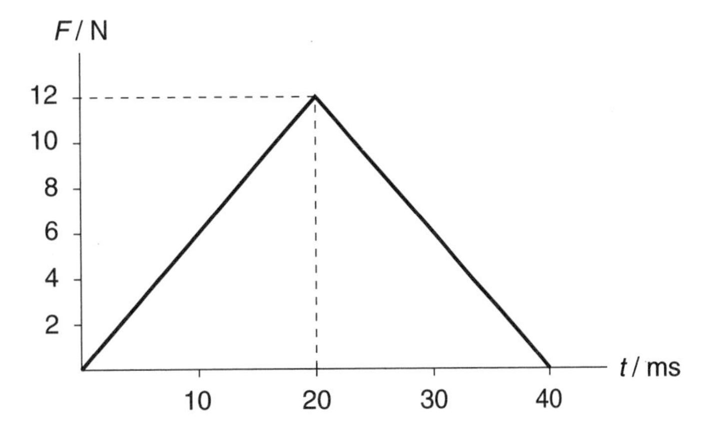

6. In an experiment to calculate the force exerted on a football kicked by Rocket Shot Roberts of United Rovers, the apparatus below was used.

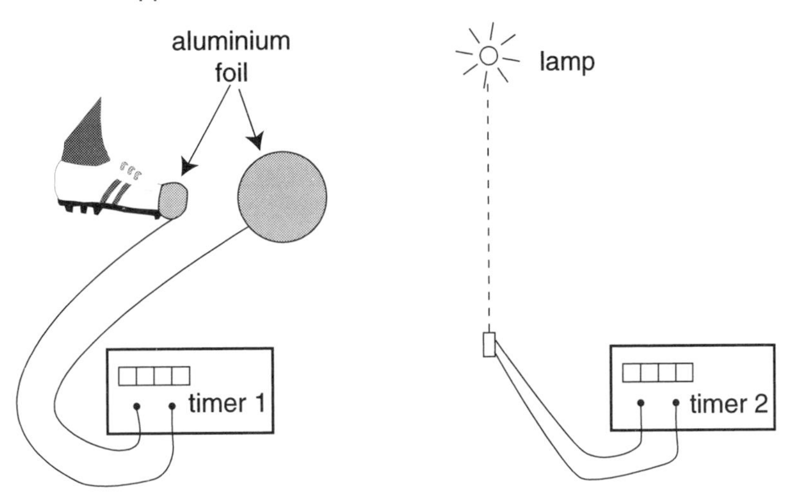

(a) What is the purpose of the aluminium foil?

(b) When does timer 1 start?

(c) When does timer 1 stop?

(d) What time appears on timer 2?

7. Data for the experiment detailed in question 6 is shown below.

Time on timer 1	=	0·008 s
Time on timer 2	=	0·05 s
Diameter of football	=	20 cm
Mass of football	=	0·80 kg

(a) Calculate the speed of the football as it passes through the light beam.

(b) What was the average force exerted on the football?

(c) Use Newton's second law to calculate the acceleration of the ball.

8. A ball of mass 0·6 kg travelling at 8 m s^{-1} strikes a wall perpendicularly and rebounds at 7 m s^{-1} back the way it came.

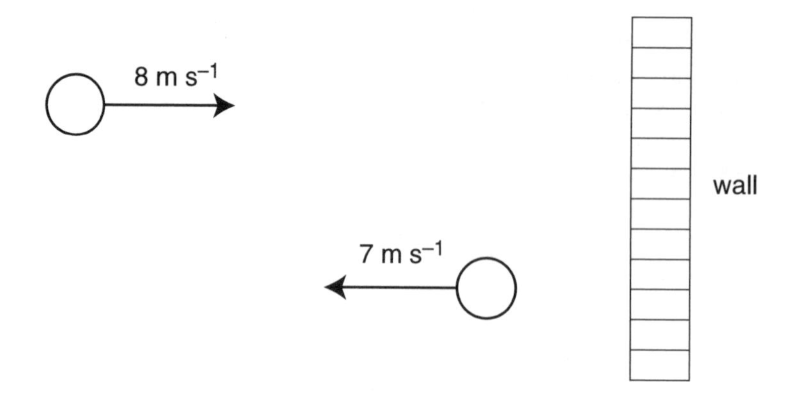

If the time of contact between ball and wall is 0·05 s, calculate:

(a) the change in momentum of the ball;

(b) the average force acting on the wall.

9. A cricketer exerts a resistive force of 25 N for 0·125 s to stop a ball of mass 0·50 kg.

(a) What impulse does the cricketer exert?

(b) What was the initial speed of the ball?

(c) Through what distance does the cricketer exert the force?

10. A tennis ball of mass 0·1 kg moves through the air at 4 m s^{-1} horizontally.

A tennis player strikes the ball so that it returns the way it came at 5 m s^{-1}.

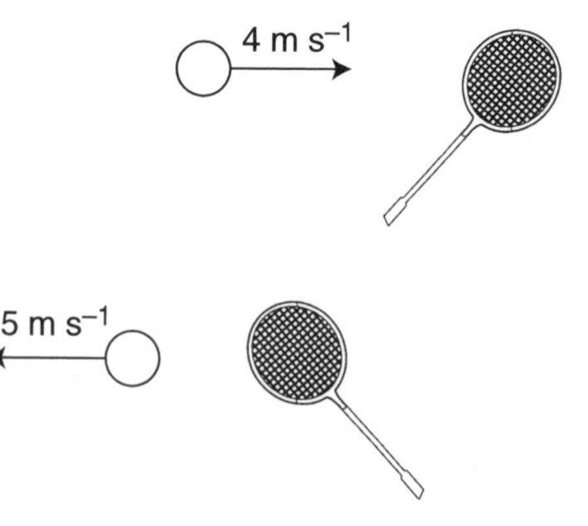

If the average force exerted by the tennis racquet on the ball was 30 N, calculate the time during which the racquet was in contact with the tennis ball.

CHAPTER 5

DENSITY AND PRESSURE

DENSITY AND PRESSURE

1. The area of a room wall is 25 m^2. If the force of air molecules on the wall is $2{\cdot}5 \times 10^6$ N, what is the air pressure in the room?

2. Air molecules exert an average force of 6×10^5 N on a wall. The wall measures 2 m $\times$ 3 m. What is the air pressure on the wall?

3. A cube of side 3 m is sitting on a bench. If the mass of the cube is 27 kg, what is the pressure on the bench?

4. Hydrogen molecules at low pressure exert an average force of 3×10^4 N on one wall of a cubic container. One edge of the cube measures 2 m. Calculate the low pressure of the hydrogen.

5. *(a)* What is the pressure of air at sea level?
(b) What is the average force air molecules exert on a seaside wall measuring 3 m $\times$ 5 m?
(c) Comment on the force exerted on an identical wall 1000 feet above sea level.

6. A man of mass 70 kg is standing still on both feet. The average area of each foot is $0{\cdot}025$ m^2.
(a) Calculate the pressure exerted by the man on the ground.
(b) If the man now stands on only one foot, calculate the pressure this time.

7. *(a)* A man of mass 60 kg stands on a block of wood measuring 28 cm $\times$ 8 cm. Calculate the pressure on the ground.

(b) A woman of mass 60 kg stands on one high heel shoe. The area of the sole in contact with the ground is $1{\cdot}2 \times 10^{-3}$ m^2. The area of the heel in contact with the ground is $2{\cdot}5 \times 10^{-5}$ m^2. Calculate the pressure on the ground.

(c) Although the man and the woman had the same mass, they did not have the same pressure. Explain why this is the case.

(d) Why is it necessary to wear snow shoes to walk over soft snow?

8. Air is enclosed in a cylinder by a gas-tight piston which can move freely. The cross-sectional area of the piston is 2×10^{-3} m^2.

With only atmospheric pressure of 100 kPa acting on the piston, it settles 6 cm from the end of the cylinder (see Figure 1).

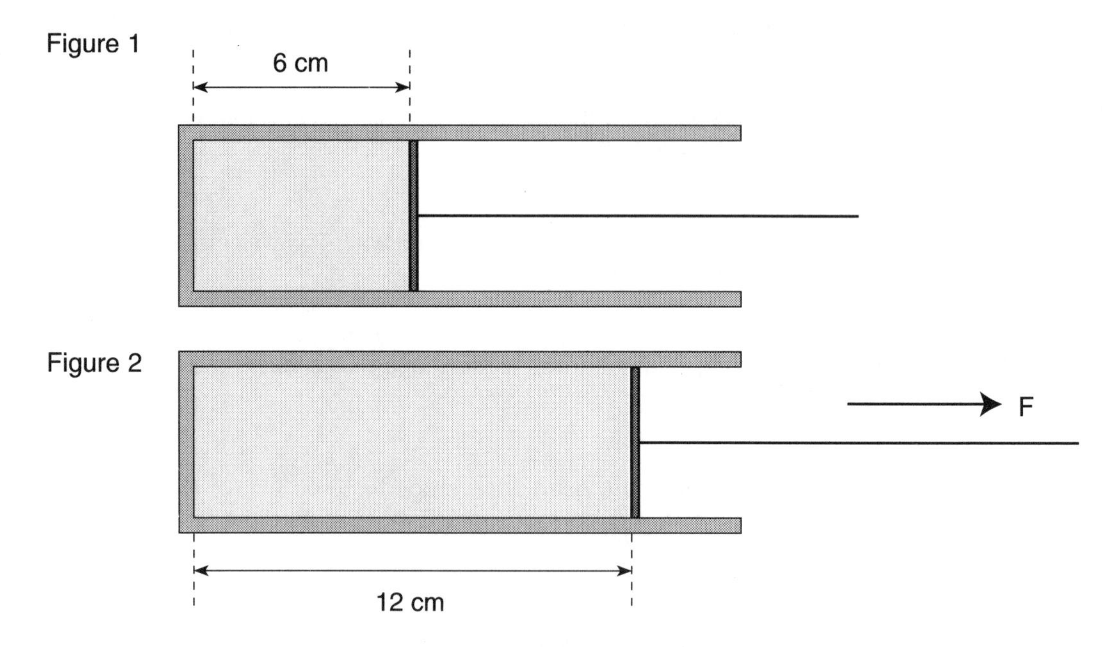

The piston is slowly pulled out until it is 12 cm from the end of the cylinder (see Figure 2). If the expansion takes place at constant temperature, find the force *F* required to hold the piston in its new position.

9. Find the density of:

(a) a 20 kg mass occupying a volume of 8 m^3;

(b) a 10 kg mass occupying a volume of 8 m^3;

(c) a 5 kg mass occupying a volume of 8 m^3;

(d) a 1 kg mass occupying a volume of 8 m^3;

(e) a 0·1 kg mass occupying a volume of 8 m^3;

(f) a 5 kg mass occupying a volume of 10 m^3;

(g) a 5 kg mass occupying a volume of 5 m^3;

(h) a 5 kg mass occupying a volume of 2 m^3;

(i) a 5 kg mass occupying a volume of 0·5 m^3;

(j) a 5 kg mass occupying a volume of 1000 cm^3.

10. In an experiment designed to measure the density of air, a container full of air is attached to a balance and the mass recorded (mass m). More air is now pumped into the container and the new mass recorded (mass M).

(a) A pupil thinks that by subtracting the masses ($M - m$) he will find the mass of air in the container. Explain why this is wrong. What mass does ($M - m$) represent?

The next part of the experiment uses a gas jar filled with water standing upside down in a tank of water.

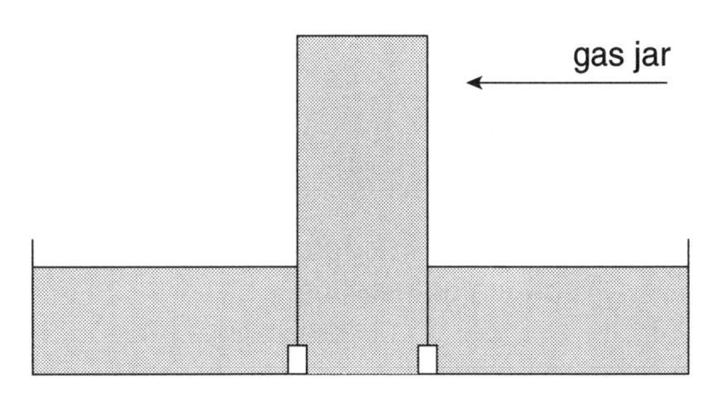

(b) Explain how this is used to find the volume (V) of the "extra" air in the container.

(c) Why does all the air not leave the container?

(d) How are the results used to calculate the density of air? Your answer should include an equation for density in terms of m, M and V.

The following problems require a knowledge of pressure, depth and density.

The density of water is 1000 kg m^{-3}.

11. Calculate the pressure on a diver at a depth of 6 m.

12. Calculate the pressure at the bottom of a swimming pool:

(a) at the shallow end (0·9 m);

(b) at the deep end (2·2 m).

13. A cube of side 10 cm is completely submerged in water so that the top of the cube is level with the top surface of the water.

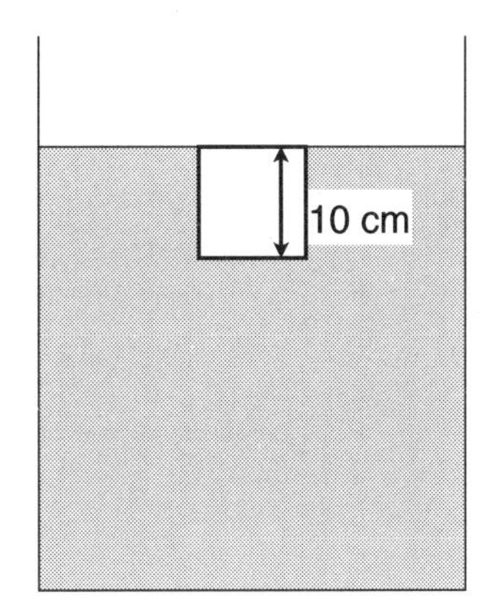

(a) Calculate the pressure at a depth of 10 cm.

(b) Calculate the area of the bottom surface of the cube.

(c) Calculate the force exerted on the bottom surface of the cube.

14. A cube of side 14 cm is completely submerged in water so that the top of the cube is level with the top surface of the water.

(a) Calculate the pressure at a depth of 14 cm.

(b) Calculate the force exerted on the bottom surface of the cube.

15. A cube of side 20 cm is submerged to a depth of 40 cm (see diagram).

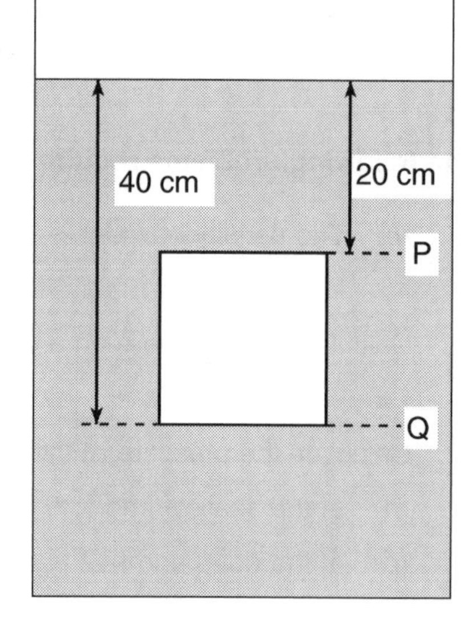

(a) Calculate the pressure at P.

(b) Calculate the pressure at Q.

(c) Find the force acting on the top surface of the cube.

(d) Find the force acting on the bottom surface of the cube.

(e) Calculate the resultant force acting on the cube.

CHAPTER 6

GAS LAWS

BOYLE'S LAW

1. The diagram shows the apparatus used in the Boyle's law experiment.

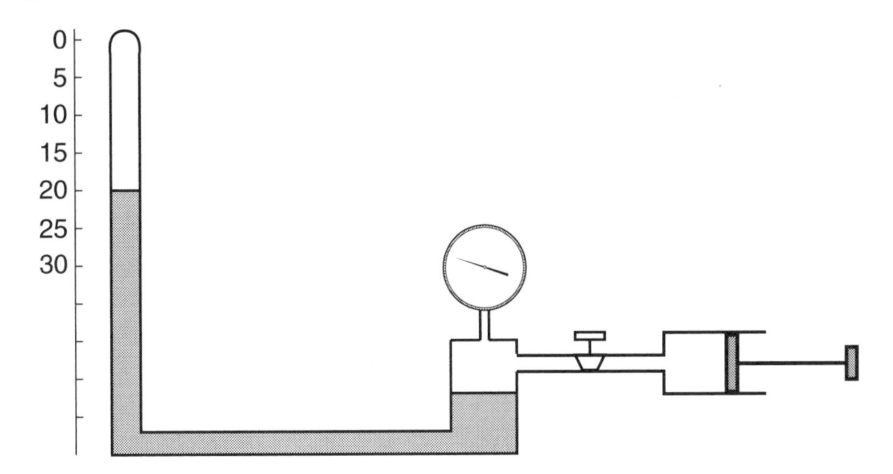

(a) Copy the diagram and label the trapped gas, the Bourdon gauge and the oil.

(b) What happens to the volume of gas as the pressure increases?

(c) What (apart from the mass of the gas) remains constant during the experiment?

(d) Sketch the graph of p against V.

2. 100 cm^3 of gas is expanded to 200 cm^3 at constant temperature. If the initial pressure was $1{\cdot}0 \times 10^5$ Pa, calculate the final pressure.

3. Find the missing pressures and volumes in the table below.

	p_1	V_1	p_2	V_2
(a)	1×10^5 Pa	42 cm^3	2×10^5 Pa	
(b)	3×10^5 Pa		$4{\cdot}5 \times 10^5$ Pa	60 cm^3
(c)	$1{\cdot}2 \times 10^5$ Pa	16 cm^3		12 cm^3
(d)		15 cm^3	$2{\cdot}8 \times 10^5$ Pa	75 cm^3

4. In the diagram below, the piston is moved from A to B. The enclosed gas is therefore compressed by 30 cm^3.

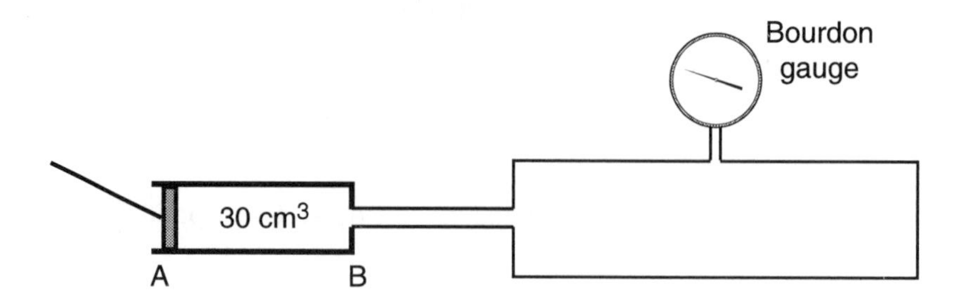

With the piston at A, pressure $= 2{\cdot}0 \times 10^5$ Pa.

With the piston at B, pressure $= 3{\cdot}0 \times 10^5$ Pa.

Calculate the initial volume of the gas.

Instructions for problems 5 to 9

When the tap is opened, the gas flows until the pressure is equalised in both containers.
Assume a constant temperature.
Find the pressure **after** the tap is opened.

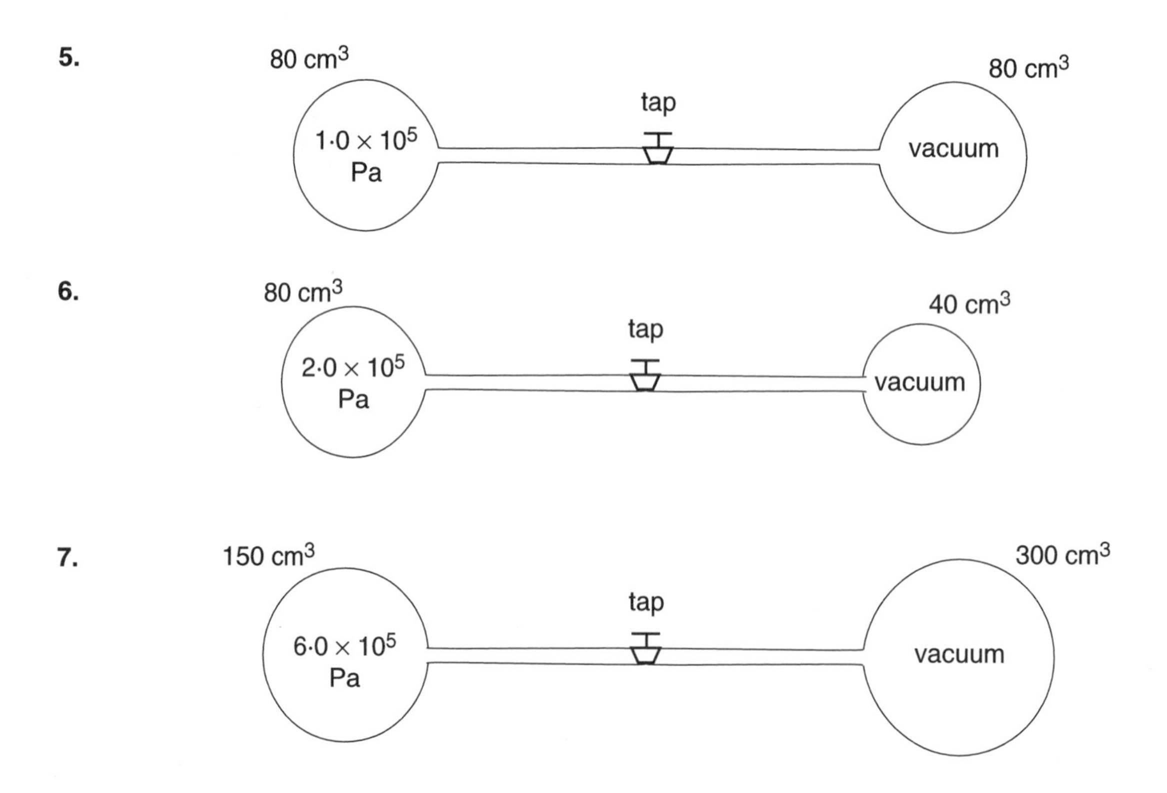

8.

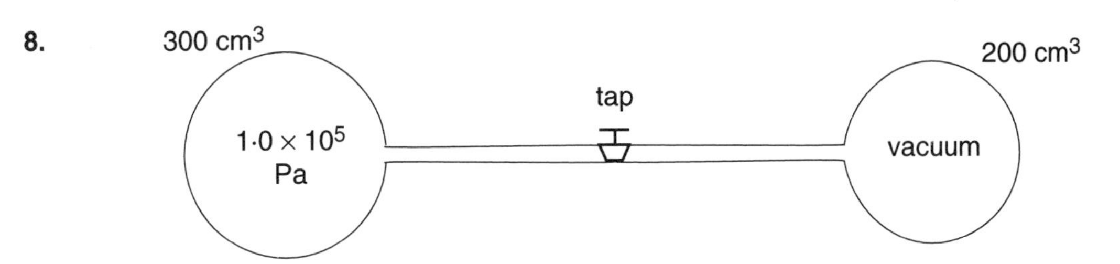

9. Note that there is gas in both containers before the tap is opened.

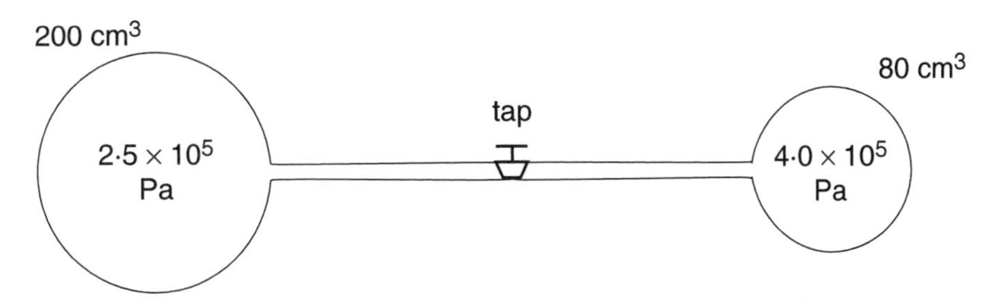

PRESSURE LAW

1. The diagram shows the apparatus used in the pressure law experiment.

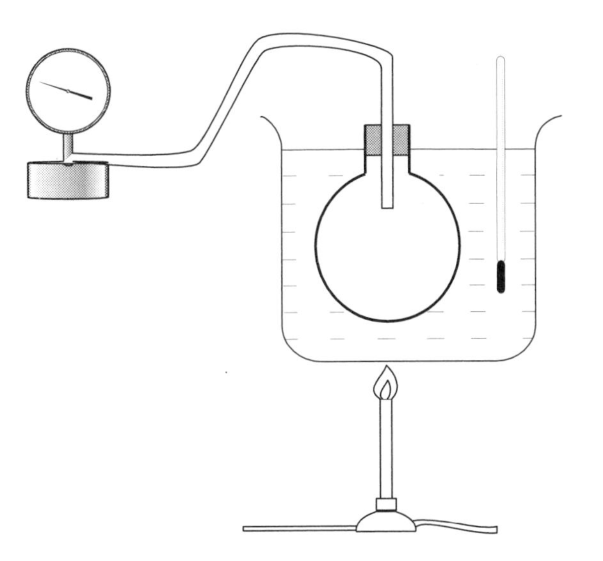

(a) Copy the diagram and label the trapped gas, Bourdon gauge and thermometer.

(b) What happens to the pressure of the gas as the temperature increases?

(c) What (apart from the mass of the gas) remains constant during the experiment?

(d) Sketch a graph of pressure against temperature and show how it can be used to find absolute zero.

2. A sealed flask (constant volume) is heated from 27 °C to 77 °C. If the initial pressure of the gas inside was $1{\cdot}0 \times 10^5$ Pa, calculate the final pressure.

3. Find the missing pressures and volumes in the table below.

	p_1	T_1	p_2	T_2
(a)		200 K	3×10^5 Pa	400 K
(b)	$2{\cdot}5 \times 10^5$ Pa	250 K	1×10^5 Pa	
(c)	1×10^5 Pa	27 °C		127 °C
(d)	$0{\cdot}9 \times 10^5$ Pa		$1{\cdot}5 \times 10^5$ Pa	77 °C

4. In the pressure law experiment (see question 1), the pressure changes from $1{\cdot}00 \times 10^5$ Pa at 20 °C to $1{\cdot}20 \times 10^5$ Pa at 79 °C.

(a) Show that these results are consistent with the pressure law.

(b) Comment on the criticism that the air in the tube is cooler than the air in the flask.

(c) Should the thermometer be inside the flask?

CHARLES' LAW

1. The diagram shows the apparatus used in the Charles' law experiment.

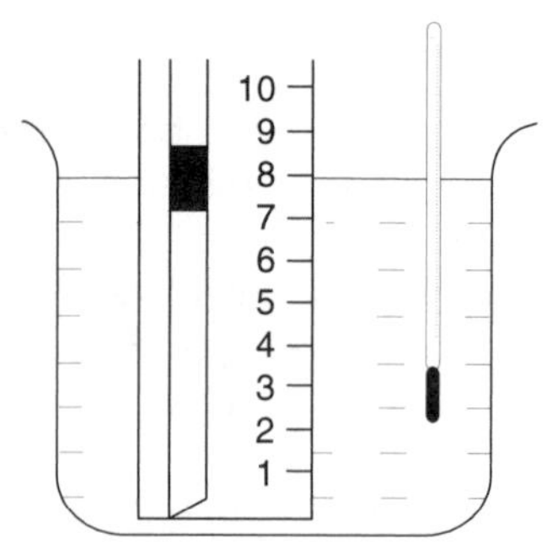

(a) Copy the diagram and label the trapped gas, the mercury and the hot water.

(b) What happens to the volume of gas as the temperature falls?

(c) What (apart from the mass of the gas) remains constant during the experiment?

(d) Sketch a graph of volume against temperature (°C) for this experiment and show how it can be used to find absolute zero.

2. A fixed mass of gas is cooled from 100 °C to 20 °C. The pressure is kept at atmospheric pressure throughout. If the initial volume is 6 cm^3, calculate the final volume.

3. Find the missing volumes and temperatures in the table below.

	V_1	T_1	V_2	T_2
(a)	8 cm^3	300 K		600 K
(b)		200 K	100 cm^3	250 K
(c)	100 cm^3	27 °C	120 cm^3	
(d)	48 cm^3		60 cm^3	77 °C

4. In the Charles' law experiment (see question 1), the column of mercury rises from 6·00 cm at 20 °C to 7·25 cm at 81 °C

(a) Show that these results are consistent with Charles' law.

(b) Comment on the use of **length** of the air column instead of **volume** of air.

THE GENERAL GAS EQUATION

1. 200 cm^3 of carbon dioxide at 27 °C is heated to 127 °C. If the initial pressure is 6×10^5 Pa and the final pressure is 1×10^6 Pa, what is the volume after heating?

2. Hydrogen in a sealed container was heated from 77 °C to 400 K. If the gas was allowed to expand during heating from 50 cm^3 to 120 cm^3 and the pressure after expansion was 2×10^5 Pa, what was the pressure before the container was heated?

3. The pressure of a fixed mass of nitrogen is increased from $1{\cdot}5 \times 10^5$ Pa to $2{\cdot}5 \times 10^5$ Pa. At the same time, the container is compressed from 125 cm^3 to 100 cm^3. If the initial temperature of the gas was 30 °C, find the final temperature of the gas.

4. Oxygen at atmospheric pressure is heated from 400 K to 500 K in a sealed container. If the volume increases during heating from 80 cm^3 to 100 cm^3, find the final pressure of the oxygen.
(**N.B.** Take atmospheric pressure as 1×10^5 Pa.)

5. 150 cm^3 of a petrol and air mixture are compressed to a quarter of the original volume as shown in the diagram.

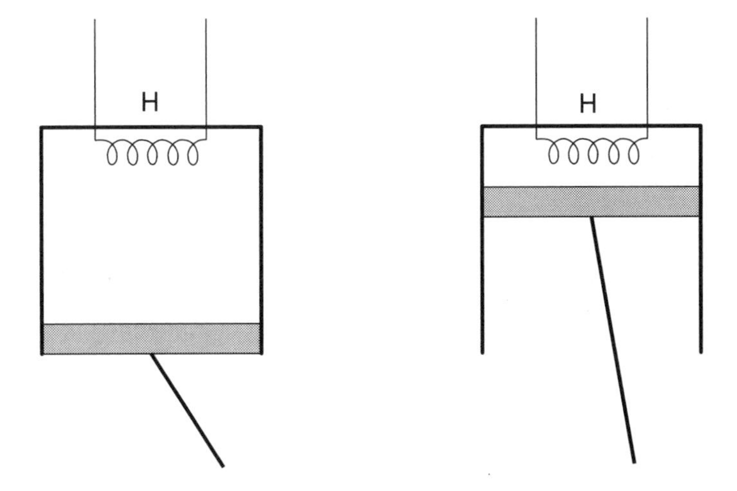

During the compression, the heater H heats the gas from 17 °C to 127 °C. If the pressure of the petrol / air mixture was $2{\cdot}5 \times 10^5$ Pa originally, what is the pressure of the compressed gas?

UNIT 2

ELECTRICITY AND ELECTRONICS

CHAPTER 7

ELECTRIC FIELDS AND RESISTORS IN CIRCUITS

CHARGES MOVING IN ELECTRIC FIELDS

Data necessary for some problems.

Mass of electron = $9{\cdot}11 \times 10^{-31}$ kg
Charge of electron = $(-)1{\cdot}6 \times 10^{-19}$ C

1. A proton (charge $1{\cdot}6 \times 10^{-19}$ C) is moved from A to B through a potential difference of 20 V.

How much work is done?

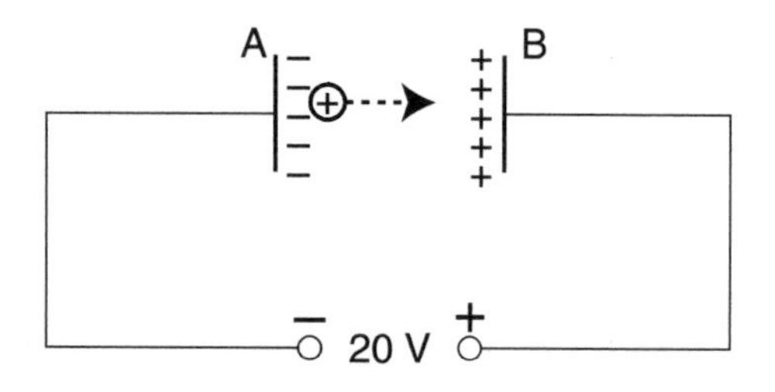

2. A positive charge of $12{\cdot}8 \times 10^{-19}$ C is moved from A to B through a potential difference of 8 V.

How much work is done?

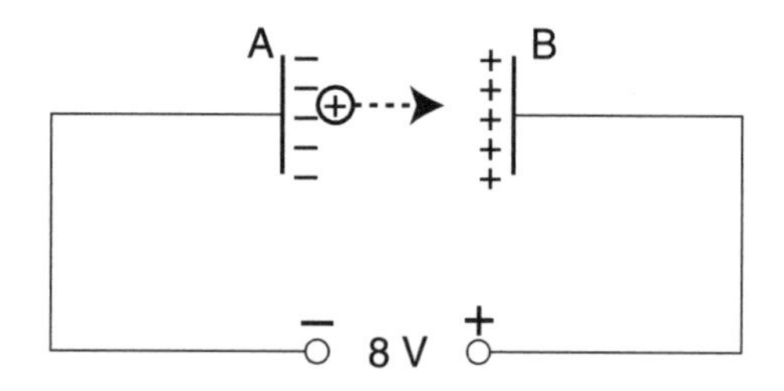

3. It takes $1{\cdot}92 \times 10^{-17}$ J of energy to move a positive charge of $9{\cdot}6 \times 10^{-19}$ C from A to B.

Calculate the potential difference between the plates.

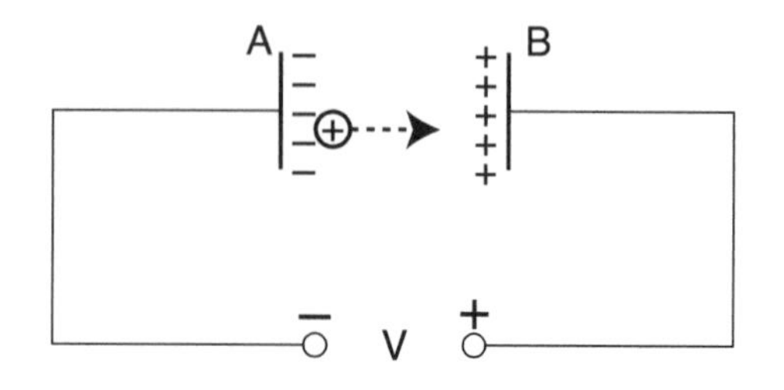

4. A negative charge of (–)1·6 × 10^{-19} C is moved from B to A through a potential difference of 500 V.

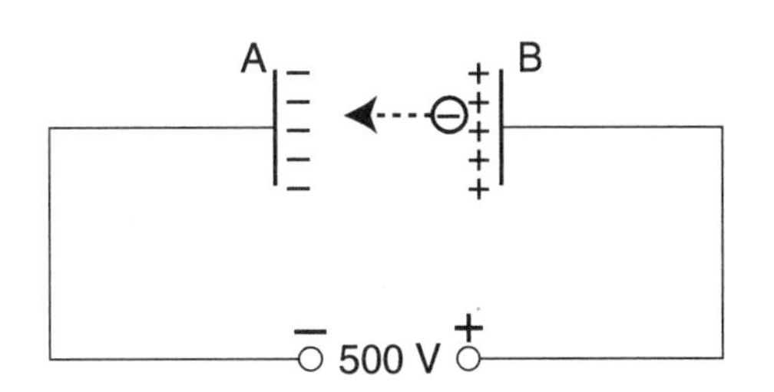

(a) How much work is done? (N.B. Answer must be positive.)

(b) How much potential energy does this negative charge have at plate A?

5. An electron is accelerated (from rest) in an electron gun by a voltage of 1000 V.

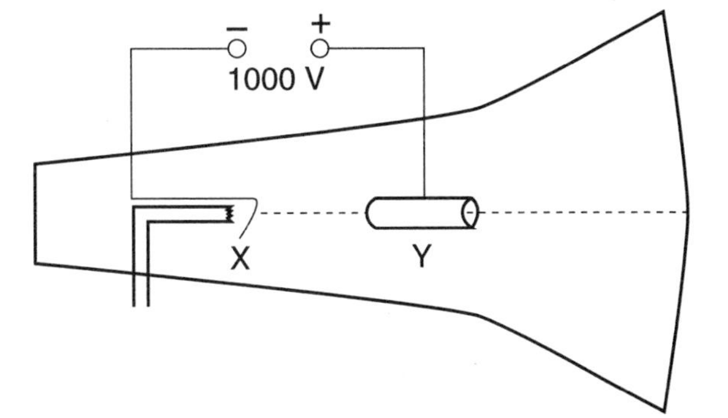

(a) Calculate the potential energy of the electron at X.

(b) What is the kinetic energy of the electron at Y?

(c) Calculate the maximum velocity of the electron.

6. An electron is accelerated (from rest) in an electron gun by a voltage of 3000 V.

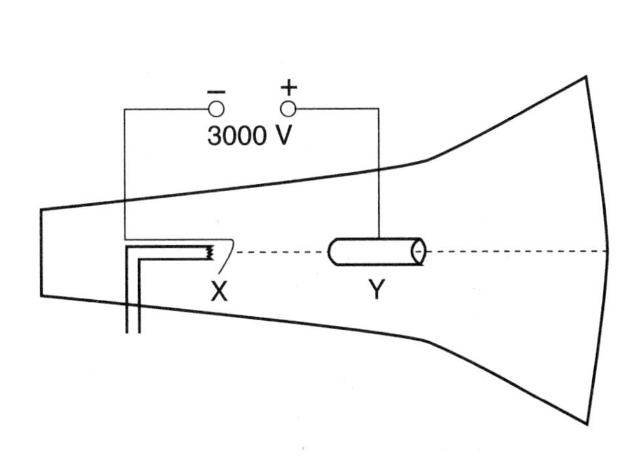

(a) Calculate the potential energy of the electron at X.

(b) What is the kinetic energy of the electron at Y?

(c) Calculate the maximum velocity of the electron.

7. An electron is accelerated (from rest) in an electron gun by a voltage of 4000 V.

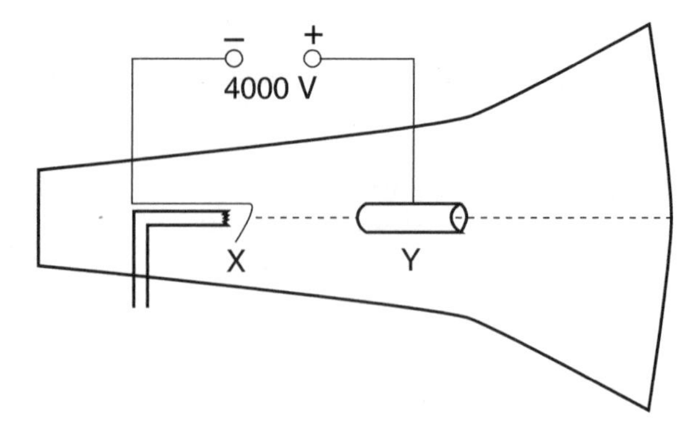

(a) Calculate the potential energy of the electron at X.

(b) What is the kinetic energy of the electron at Y?

(c) Calculate the maximum velocity of the electron.

8. An electron is accelerated (from rest) in an electron gun by a voltage of 4500 V.

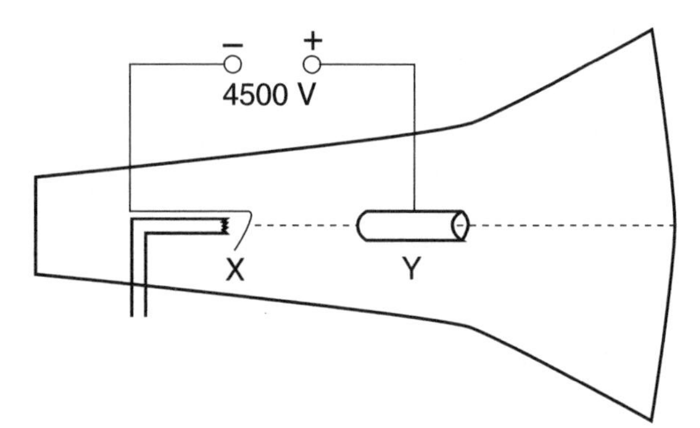

(a) Calculate the potential energy of the electron at X.

(b) What is the kinetic energy of the electron at Y?

(c) Calculate the maximum velocity of the electron.

9. Electrons are accelerated (from rest) in an electron gun by a voltage supply which can be altered using a rheostat.

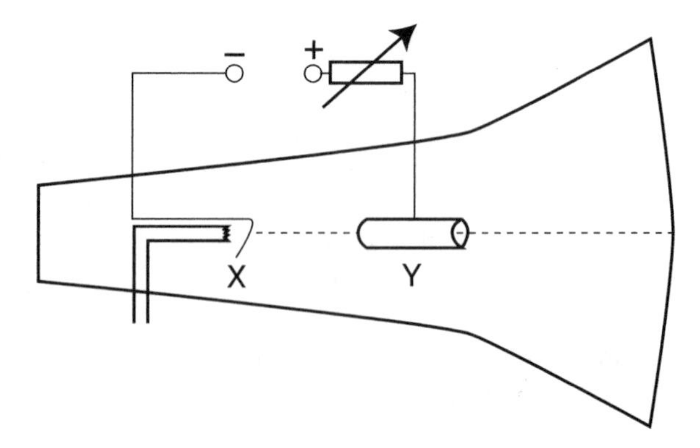

(a) When the voltage of the anode (Y) is set at 2500 V, calculate the velocity of an electron at Y.

(b) When the voltage of the anode (Y) is set at 5000 V, calculate the velocity of an electron at Y.

(c) Doubling the voltage from 2500 V to 5000 V does not double the velocity of the electrons. Why not?

10. An oscilloscope has one electron gun. The impact velocity v of an electron on the screen is 3×10^7 m s^{-1}.

What is the voltage of the anode (Y) necessary to accelerate the electron (from rest) to this velocity?

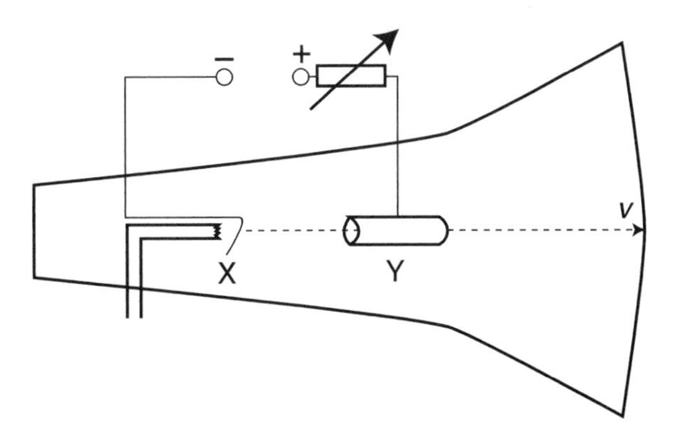

11. In an X-ray tube, electrons are fired at a target. The maximum energy of the X-ray is produced by one electron being brought to rest in a single collision.

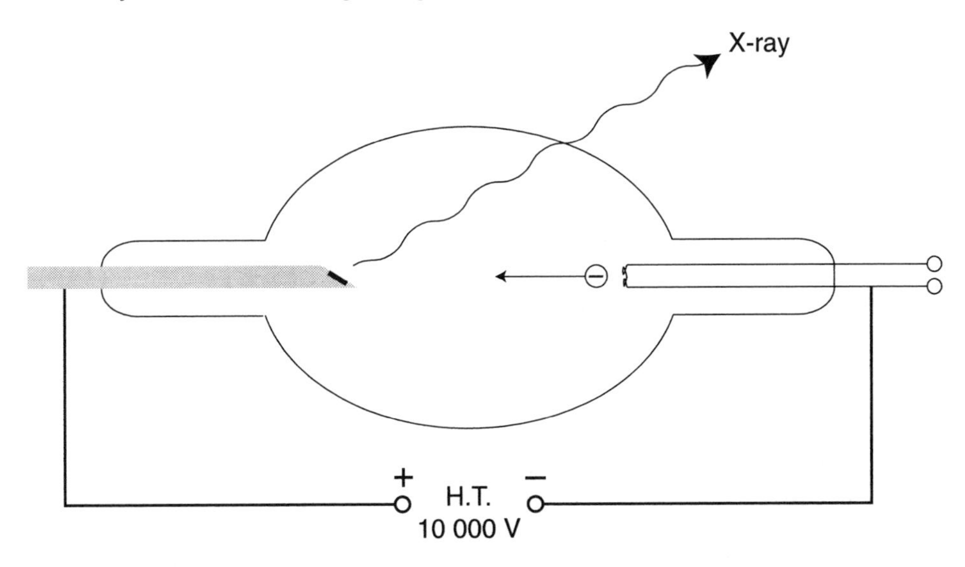

(a) Find the maximum energy of X-ray that could be produced by a 10 000 V supply.

(b) With what velocity do the electrons strike the target?

12. The power ouput of a TV screen is 24 W. If the accelerating voltage is 12 000 V, calculate the number of electrons striking the screen per second.

E.M.F. AND INTERNAL RESISTANCE

1. The e.m.f. of a cell is 12 V. When a 5 Ω resistor is connected across the ends of the cell, a 2 A current flows in the circuit.

(a) What is the voltage between the ends of the cell (A and B)?

(b) How many volts have been "lost" across the internal resistance *r*?

(c) Calculate the internal resistance of the cell *r*.

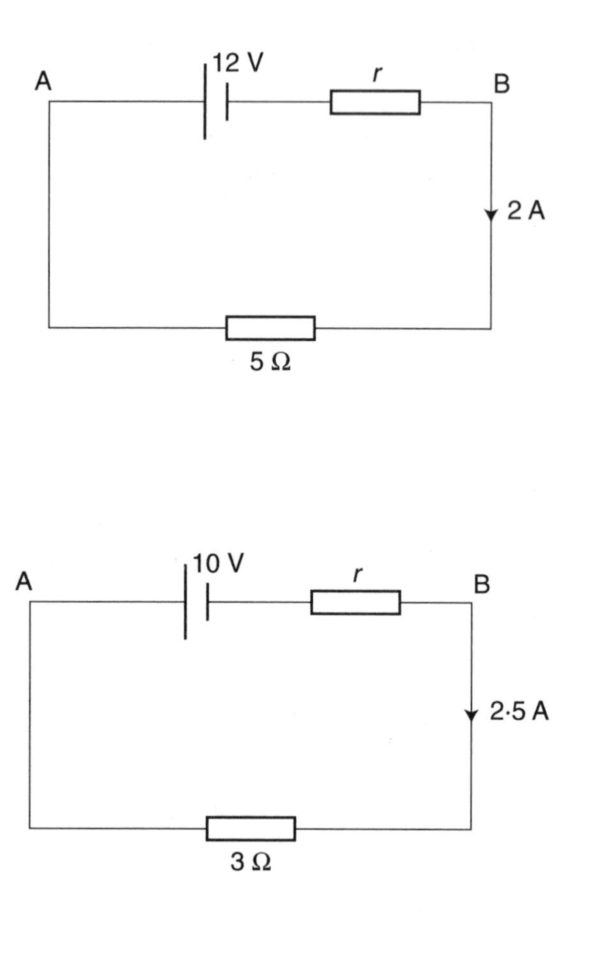

2. The e.m.f. of a cell is 10 V. When a 3 Ω resistor is connected across the ends of the cell, a 2·5 A current flows in the circuit.

(a) What is the voltage between the ends of the cell (A and B)?

(b) How many volts have been "lost" across the internal resistance *r*?

(c) Calculate the internal resistance of the cell *r*.

3. The e.m.f. of a cell is 6 V. When a 12 Ω resistor is connected across the ends of the cell, a 0·4 A current flows in the circuit.

(a) What is the voltage between the ends of the cell (A and B)?

(b) How many volts have been "lost" across the internal resistance *r*?

(c) Calculate the internal resistance of the cell *r*.

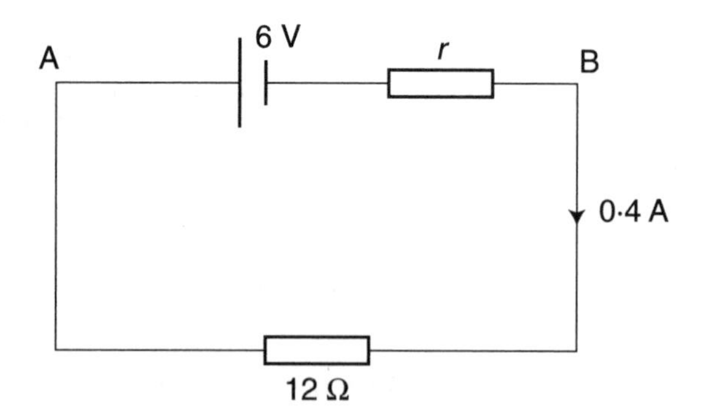

4. The e.m.f. of a cell is 1·5 V. When a 4 Ω resistor is connected across the ends of the cell, a current of 0·3 A flows in the circuit.

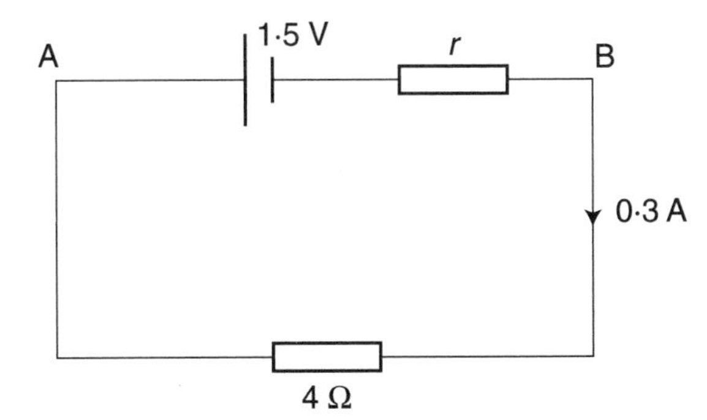

(a) What is the voltage between the ends of the cell (A and B)?

(b) How many volts have been "lost" across the internal resistance *r*?

(c) Calculate the internal resistance of the cell *r*.

5. In the three circuits shown, the e.m.f., the current and the "external" resistance are marked.

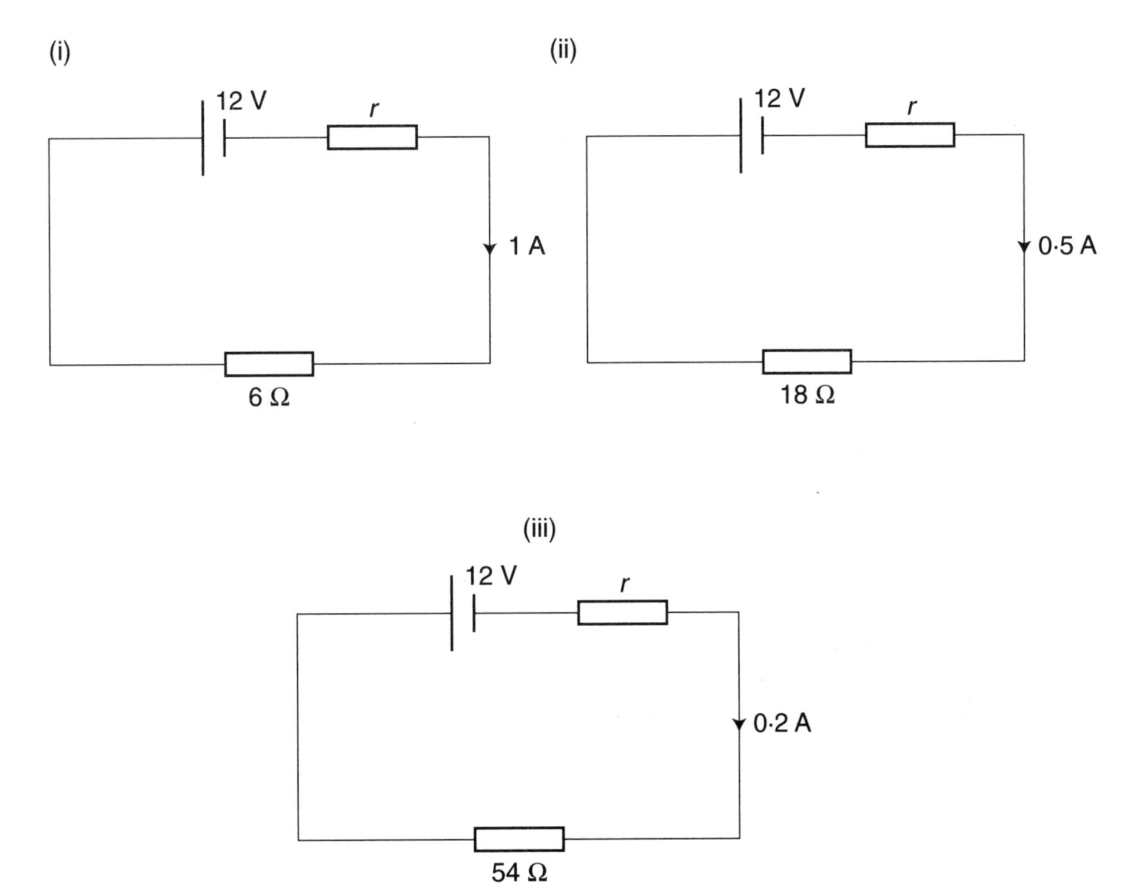

(a) Calculate the internal resistance, *r*, of each cell.

(b) Comment on how the "lost volts" are affected by increasing the external resistance connected across a cell.

6. In the three circuits shown, the e.m.f., the terminal potential difference and the external resistance are marked.

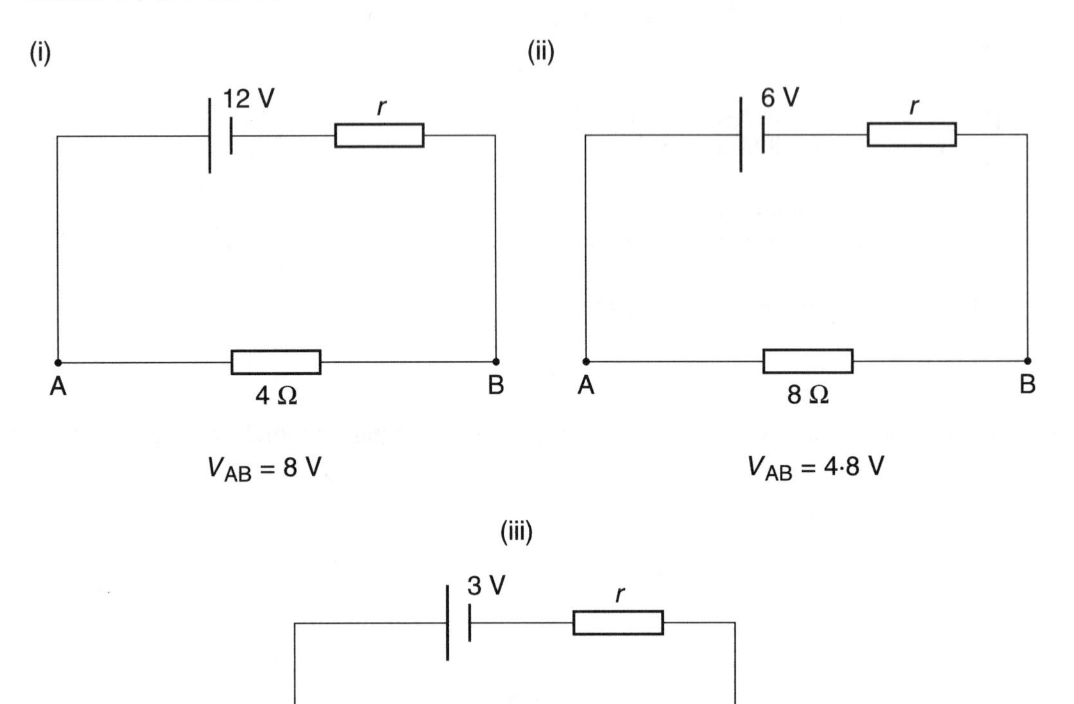

(a) Calculate the internal resistance, *r*, of each cell.

(b) Calculate the fraction of the e.m.f. lost across the internal resistance in each circuit.

(c) Which circuit is the most efficient at delivering maximum voltage available?

7. In the three circuits shown, the terminal potential difference V_{AB} is marked together with the internal and external resistances.

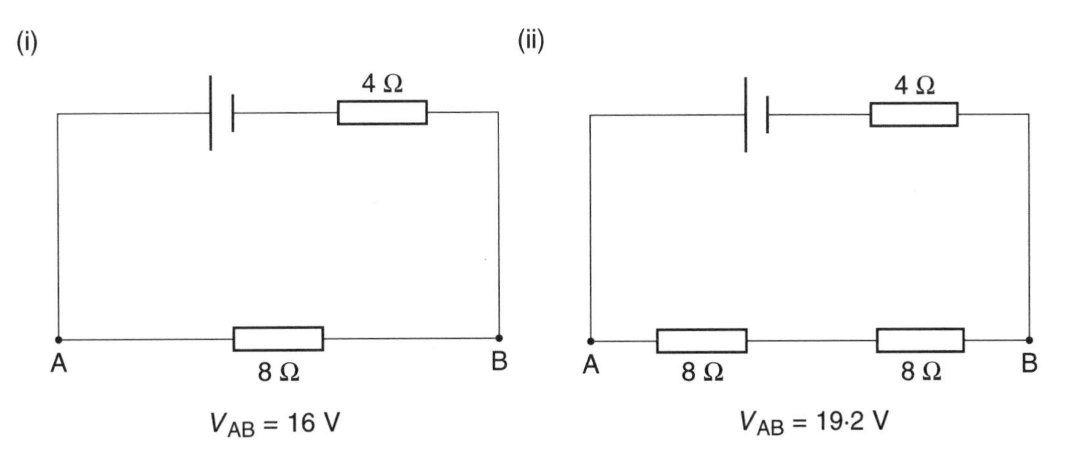

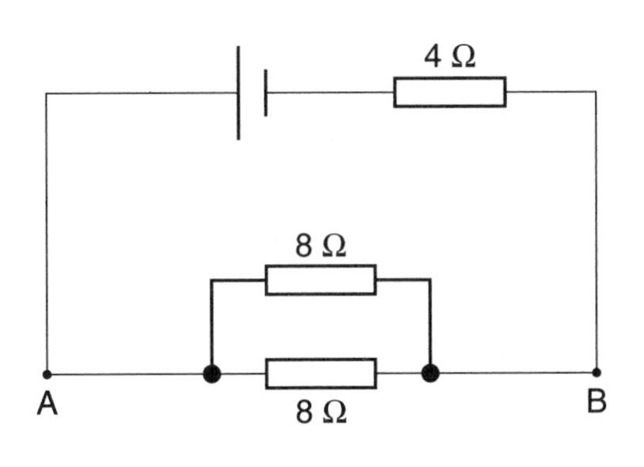

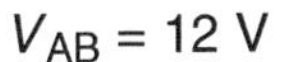

(a) Calculate the e.m.f. of each cell.

(b) Which circuit is the most efficient at delivering maximum voltage available?

(c) Which circuit develops the greatest (external) power?

8. A 3 Ω resistor is connected across the terminals of a cell of e.m.f. 2 V and internal resistance 1 Ω.

A voltmeter is connected across the cell. What is the reading on the voltmeter?

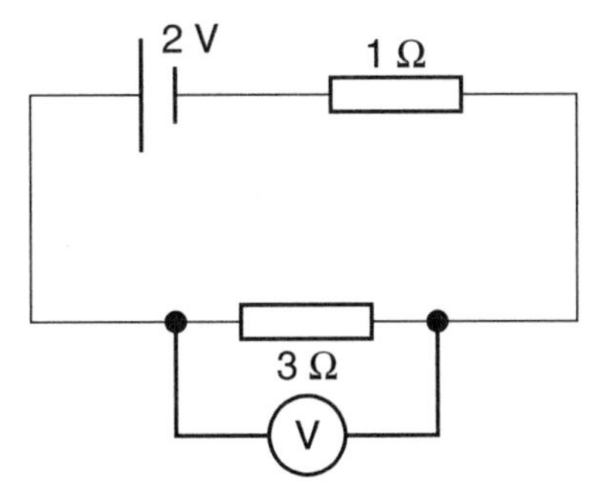

9. A resistor R is connected across the terminals of a cell of e.m.f. 12 V and internal resistance 1 Ω. A voltmeter connected across the cell reads 10·5 V.

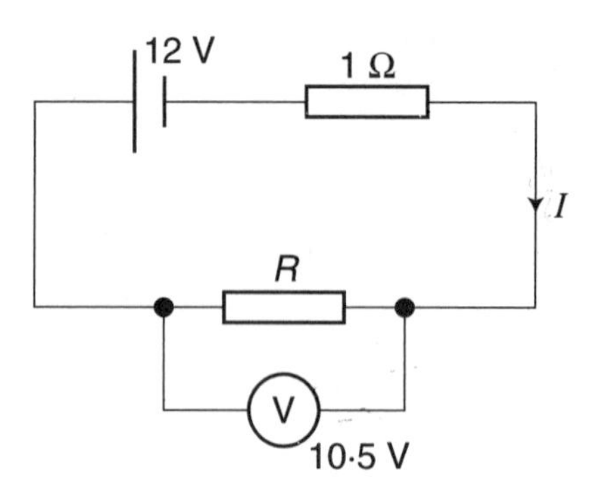

(a) Calculate the current from the cell, I.

(b) What is the resistance of R?

10. In an experiment to find the internal resistance of a cell, a rheostat is varied and corresponding readings on the voltmeter and ammeter in the circuit below are taken. The results are plotted in the graph shown.

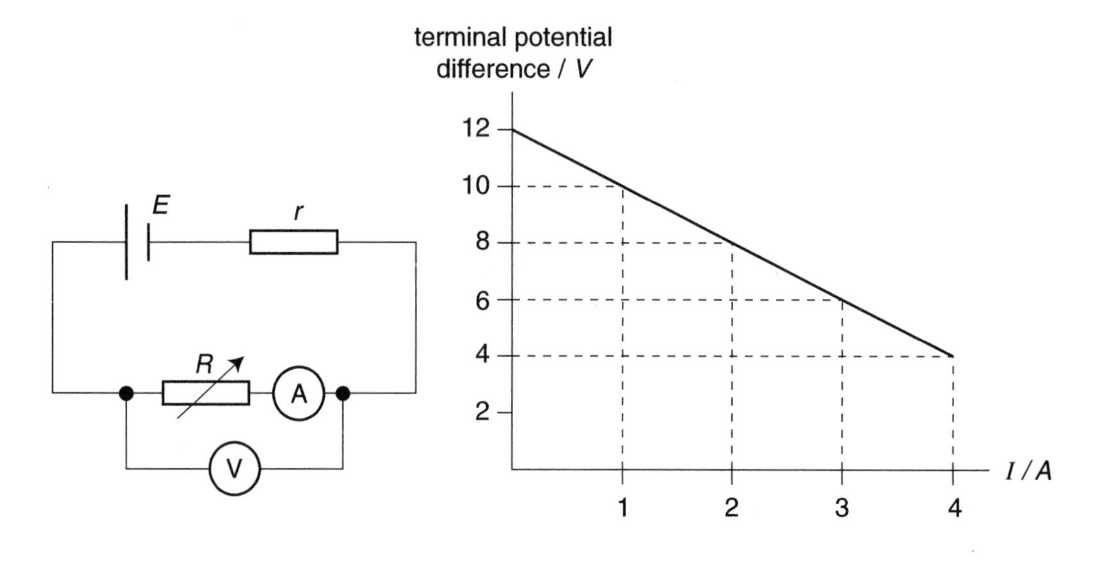

(a) From the graph, find the e.m.f. of the cell.

(b) When $I = 2$ A, what is the reading on the voltmeter?

(c) When $I = 2$ A, what is the voltage "lost" across r?

(d) When $I = 2$ A, calculate R.

(e) Calculate the internal resistance r.

11. In an experiment to find the internal resistance of a cell, a rheostat is varied and corresponding readings on the voltmeter and ammeter in the circuit below are taken. The results are plotted in the graph shown.

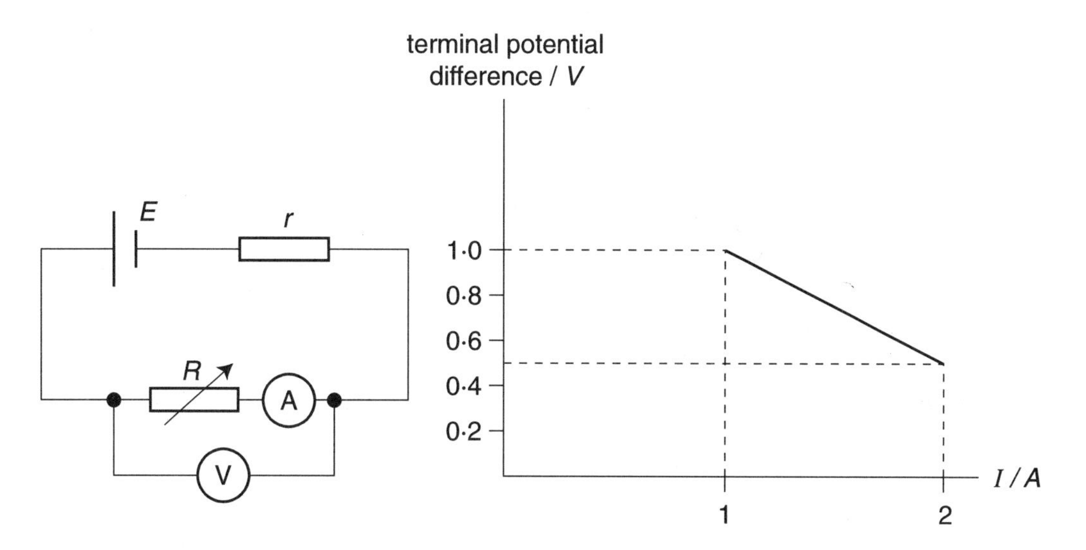

(a) Copy the graph on to graph paper and complete it.

(b) What is the e.m.f. of the cell?

(c) Calculate the internal resistance *r*.

12. John is changing the rheostat in the circuit shown. Sometimes he gets a big voltage (but the current is small). Sometimes he gets a small voltage (but the current is big).

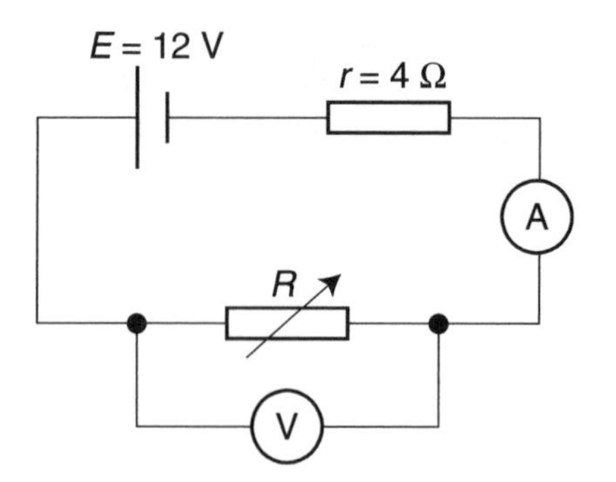

"What's best?" John asks his teacher.

"Let's find out!", John's teacher replies.

Together they produce this table of results.

$\frac{R}{\Omega}$	$\frac{V}{V}$	$\frac{P = \frac{V^2}{R}}{W}$
2		
4	6·00	
6	7·20	
8	8·00	8·00
10		

(a) Find the two missing numbers in the voltage column.

(b) Copy and complete the power column.

(c) Plot a graph of *P* (*y*-axis) against *R* (*x*-axis).

(d) John's teacher says it's not maximum voltage or maximum current that is important but maximum power.

From your graph, what is **the condition for maximum power transfer**?

RESISTORS IN CIRCUITS

1. In the circuit shown, calculate the resistance between A and B.

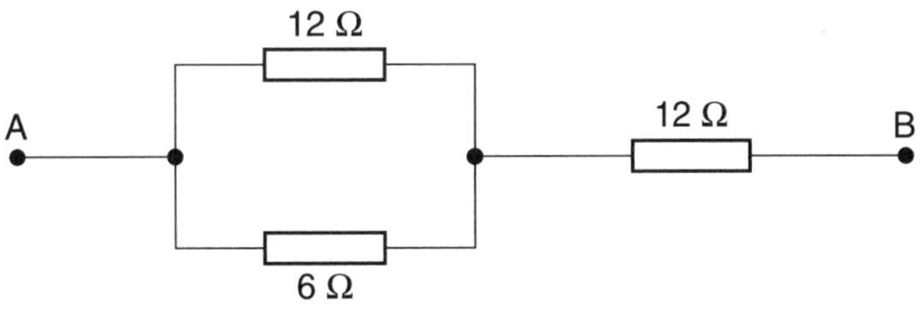

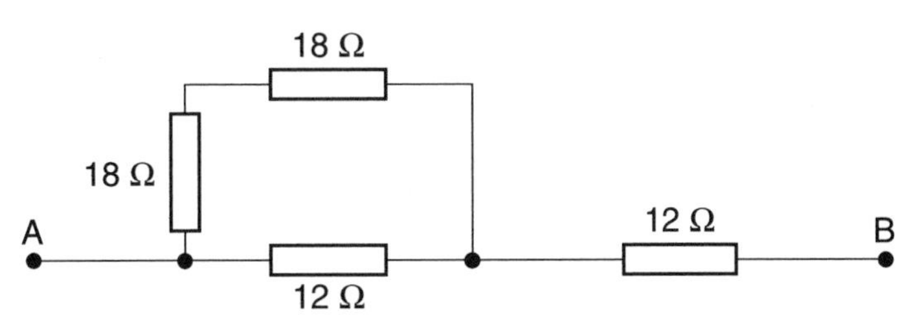

2. In the circuit shown, calculate the resistance between A and B.

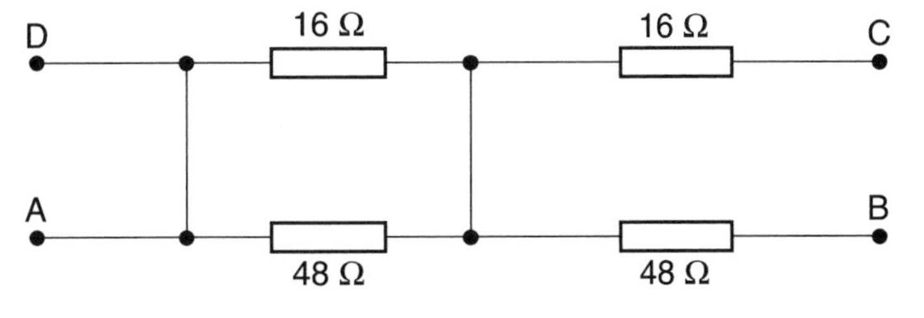

3. In the circuit shown, calculate the resistance:

(a) between A and B and

(b) between A and C.

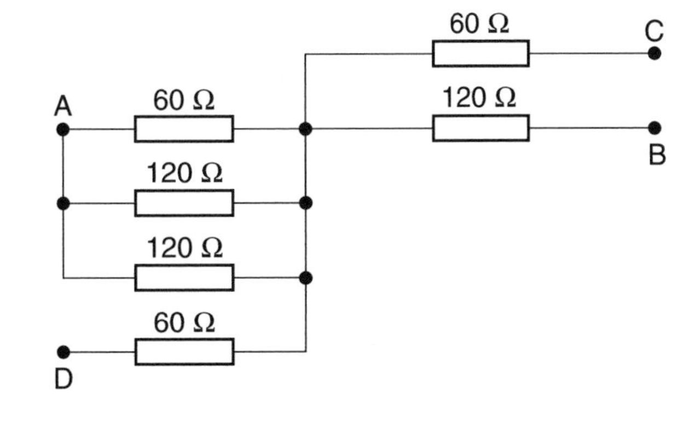

4. In the circuit shown, calculate the resistance:

(a) between A and B and

(b) between A and C.

5. The circuit shows a network of resistors with four terminals, A, B, C, and D. Calculate the resistance:

(a) between terminals A and B;

(b) between terminals A and C;

(c) between terminals B and D.

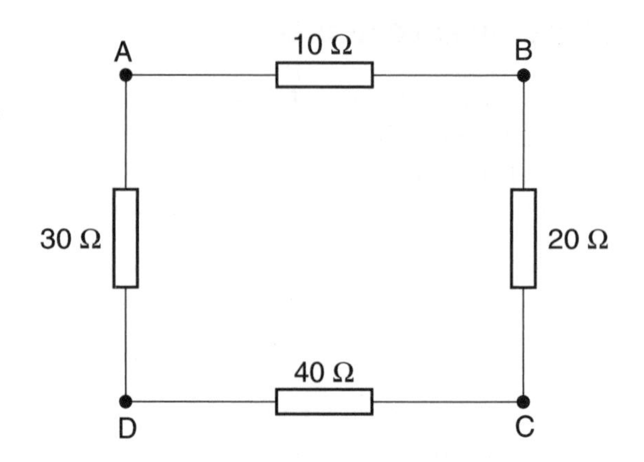

6. Calculate the value of each resistor in the circuit shown, given that all three resistors (R) are equal.

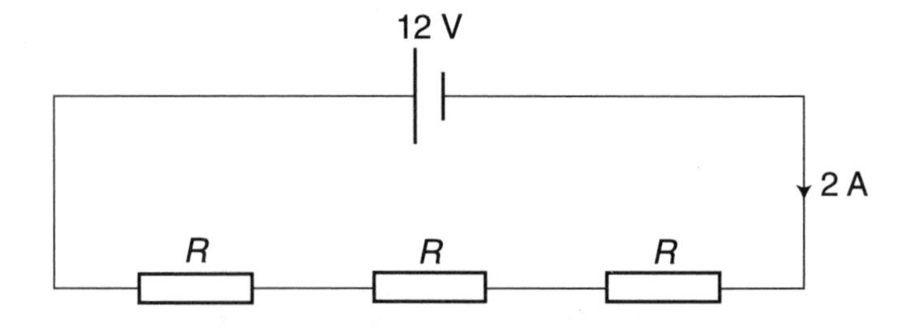

7. Calculate the value of each resistor in the circuit shown, given that all three resistors (R) are equal.

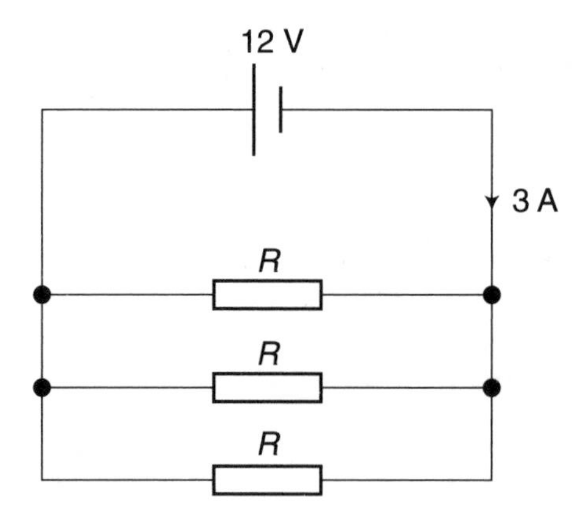

8. Calculate the value of each resistor in the circuit shown, given that all three resistors (R) are equal.

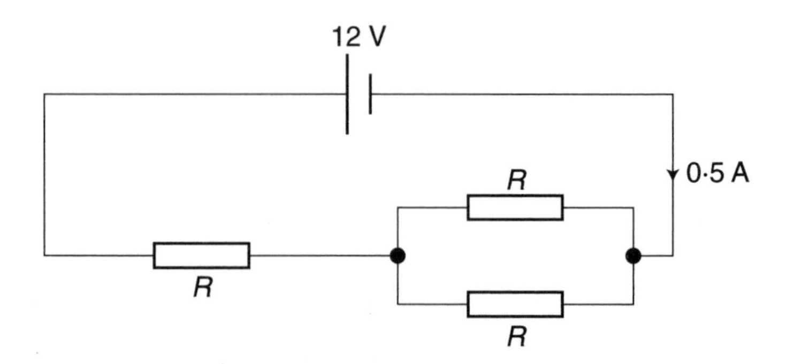

In the following problems, students need to know how a switch can change the resistance of a circuit.

9. In the circuit shown, switch S is open and the ammeter reads 0·5 A.

(a) Calculate *R*.

(b) When switch S is closed, calculate the reading on the ammeter.

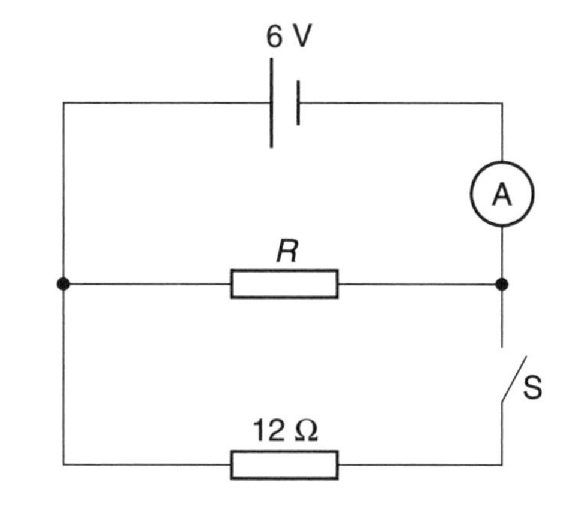

10. In the circuit shown:

(a) calculate the reading on the ammeter when S is open;

(b) calculate the reading on the ammeter when S is closed.

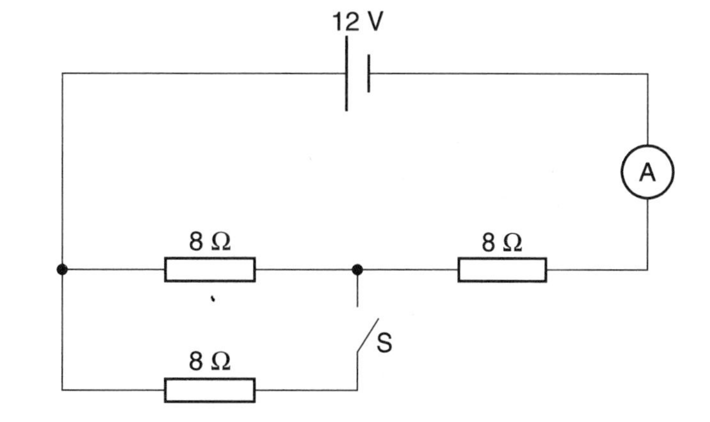

11. In the circuit shown:

(a) calculate the reading on the ammeter when S is open;

(b) calculate the reading on the ammeter when S is closed.

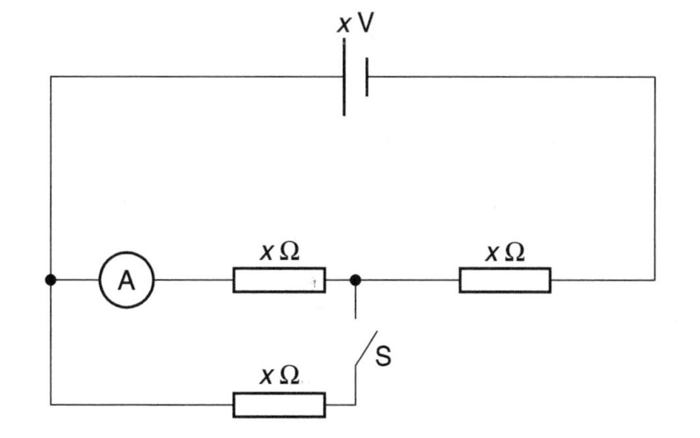

12. In the circuit shown:

(a) calculate the reading on the voltmeter when S is open;

(b) calculate the reading on the voltmeter when S is closed.

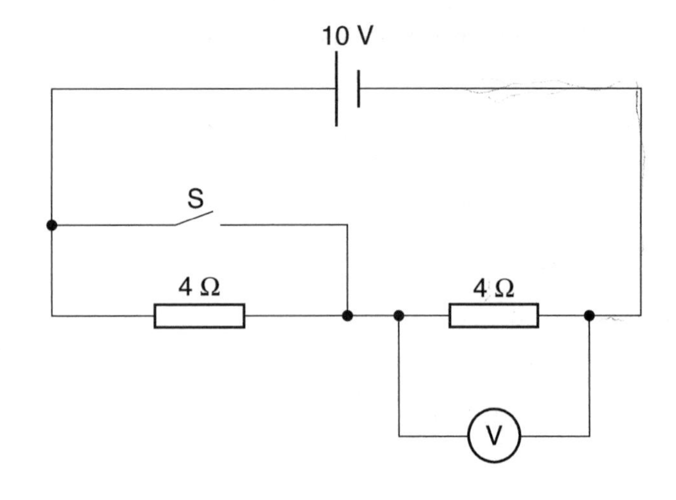

13. In the circuit shown:

(a) calculate the reading on the voltmeter when S is open;

(b) calculate the reading on the voltmeter when S is closed.

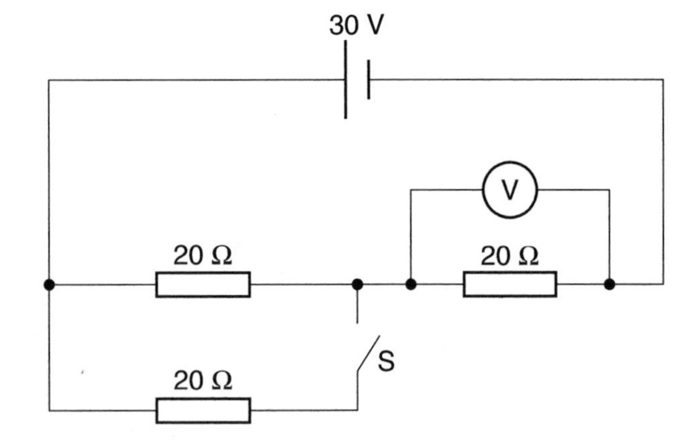

14. In the circuit shown:

(a) calculate the reading on the voltmeter when S is open;

(b) calculate the reading on the voltmeter when S is closed.

12 V
6 Ω
V
18 Ω
S
18 Ω

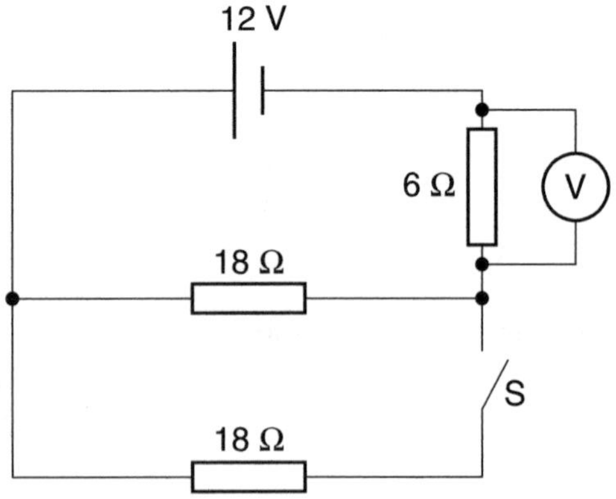

OHM'S LAW AND POWER (ADVANCED PROBLEMS)

Some revision of Ohm's Law and Power at 'S' Grade level is advised before the student progresses to these advanced problems.

1. In the circuit shown:

(a) calculate the total resistance of the circuit;

(b) calculate the readings on the ammeters A_1, A_2 and A_3.

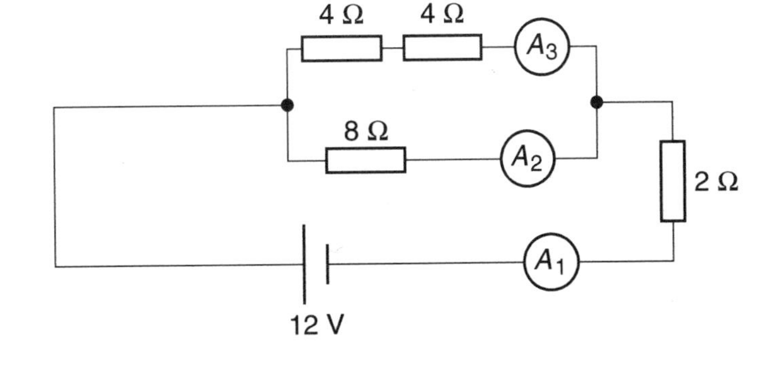

2. In the circuit shown:

(a) calculate the total resistance of the circuit;

(b) calculate the voltage of the supply.

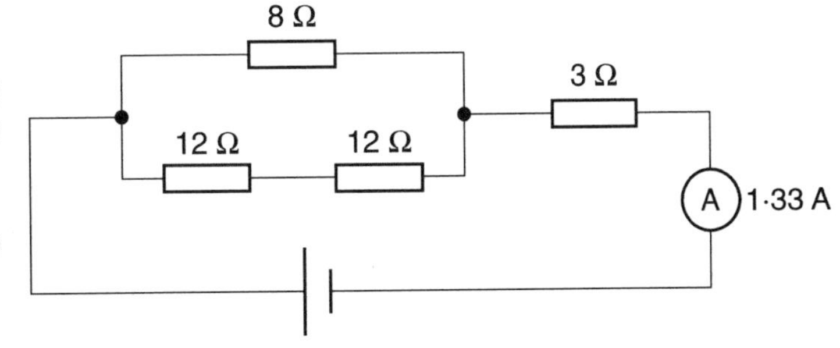

3. In the circuit shown:

(a) calculate the total resistance of the circuit;

(b) what is the potential difference between X and Y?

(c) Find the readings on ammeters A_1, A_2 and A_3.

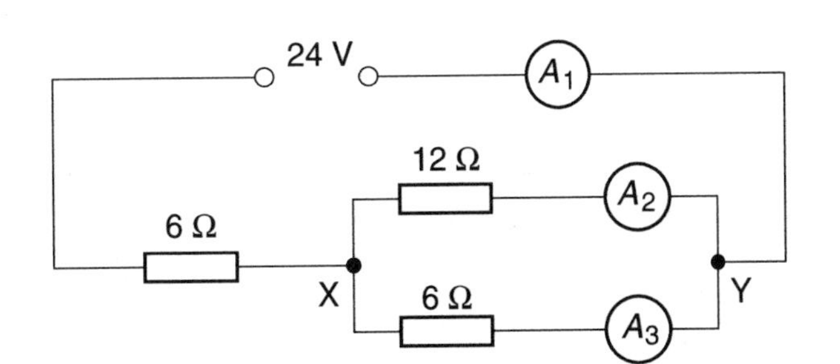

4. In the circuit shown:

(a) calculate the total resistance of the circuit;

(b) find the readings on ammeters A_1 and A_2;

(c) find the reading on the voltmeter.

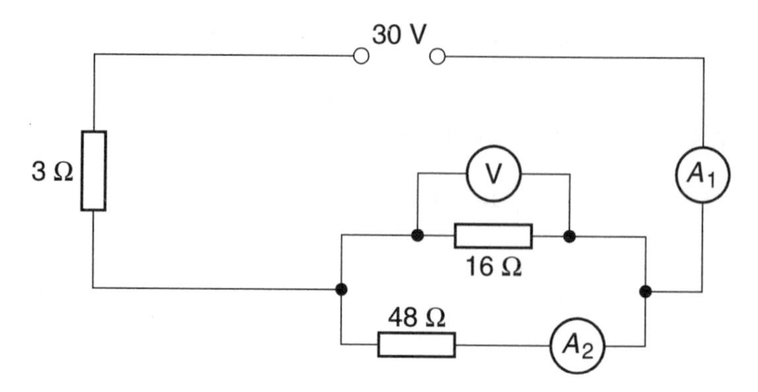

5. In the circuit shown, the ammeter reads 1 A.

(a) Find the readings on voltmeters V_1 and V_2.

(b) Calculate R.

(c) Calculate the total resistance of the circuit.

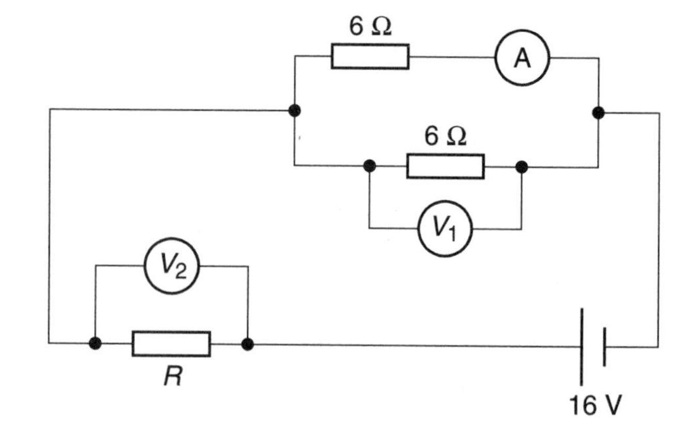

6. A 6 W bulb is connected to a 12 V supply. If the bulb is working normally, calculate the resistance of the filament.

7. A resistor R is used to protect a 6 V 12 W bulb in the circuit shown.

(a) Calculate the current in the bulb if it is working normally.

(b) What is the potential difference across R?

(c) Calculate R.

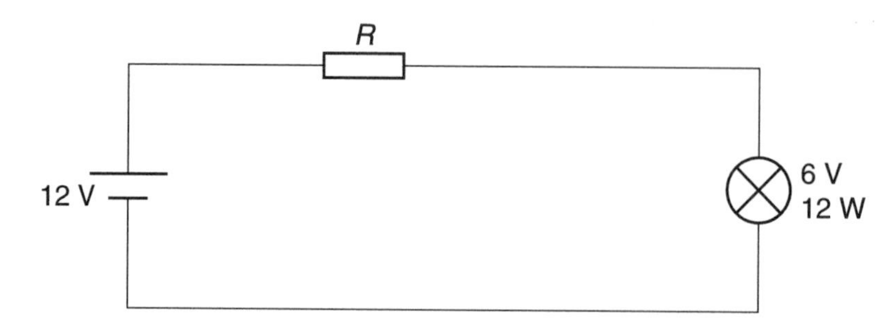

8. A resistor, *R*, is used to protect both bulbs in the circuit shown.

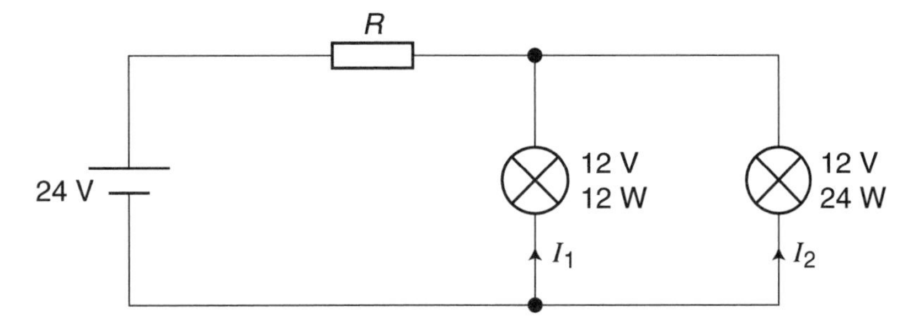

If both bulbs are working normally:

(a) calculate current I_1;

(b) calculate current I_2;

(c) calculate *R*.

9. A resistor, *R*, is used to protect a 12 V bulb in the circuit shown.

If the bulb is working normally, calculate the power dissipated in resistor *R*.

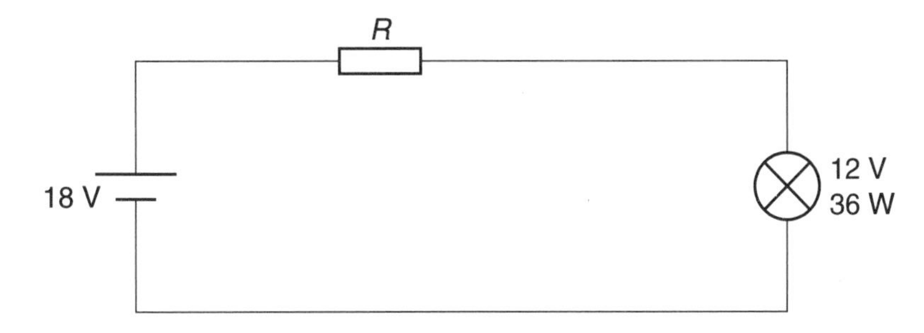

10. Given the circuit below, calculate the power dissipated in each resistor.

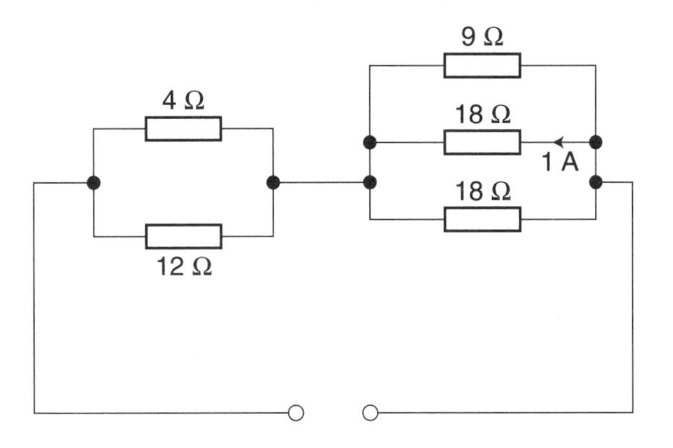

THE WHEATSTONE AND METER BRIDGES

1. The circuit shown is balanced.

(a) What is the reading on the voltmeter?

(b) Given the figures shown, calculate R_4.

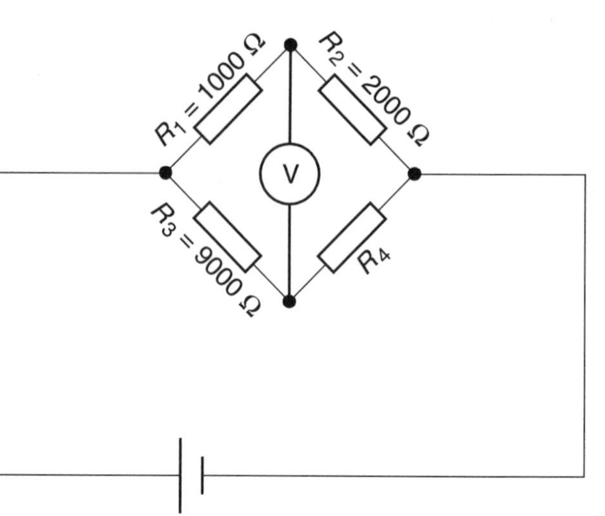

2. The circuit shown is balanced.

(a) What is the reading on the voltmeter?

(b) Given the figures shown, calculate R_3.

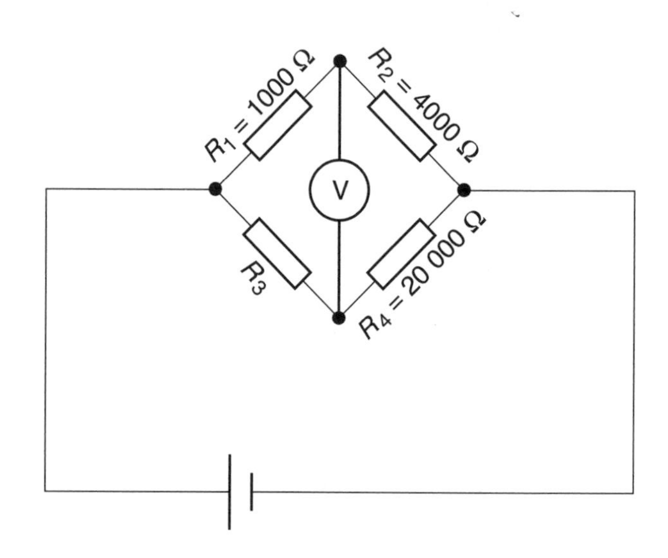

3. The circuit shown is balanced.

(a) What is the reading on the voltmeter?

(b) Given the figures:
$R_1 = 250\ \Omega$,
$R_3 = 1750\ \Omega$,
$R_4 = 5250\ \Omega$,
calculate R_2.

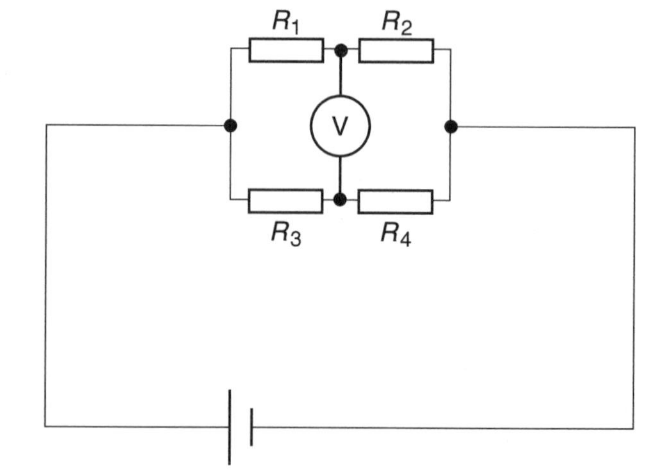

4. The circuit shown is balanced.

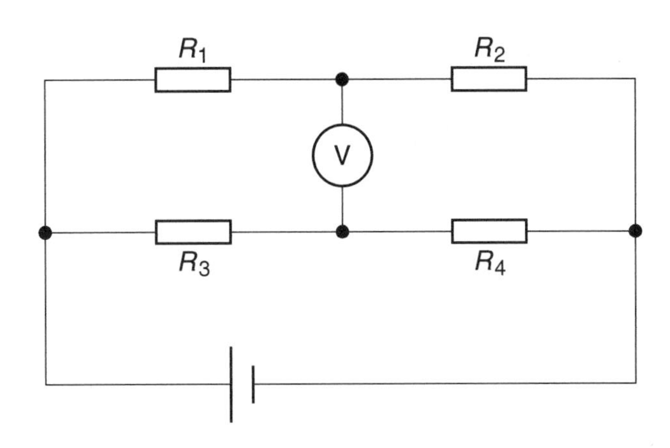

(a) What is the reading on the voltmeter?

(b) Given the figures:
R_2 = 2·4 kΩ,
R_3 = 5 kΩ,
R_4 = 300 Ω,
calculate R_1.

5. The circuit shown is balanced when R_1 = 900 Ω
R_2 = 1200 Ω
and R_3 = 30 Ω

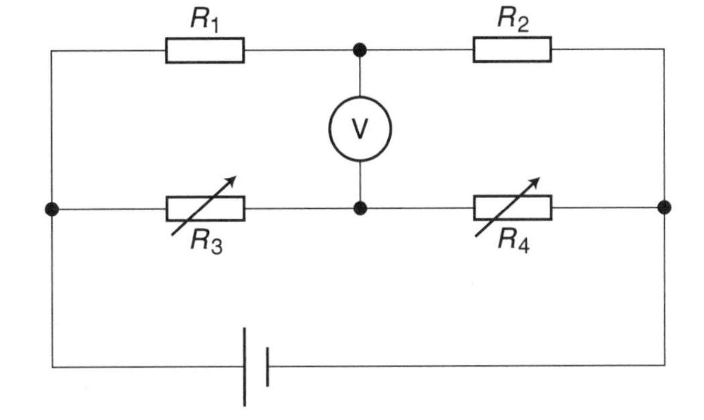

(a) Calculate R_4 when the circuit is balanced.

(b) R_4 is now increased and the circuit is knocked out of balance. To obtain balance again should R_3 be increased or decreased?

6. The circuit shown is balanced.

$R_1 = R_2 = R_3 = R_4 = 2$ kΩ.

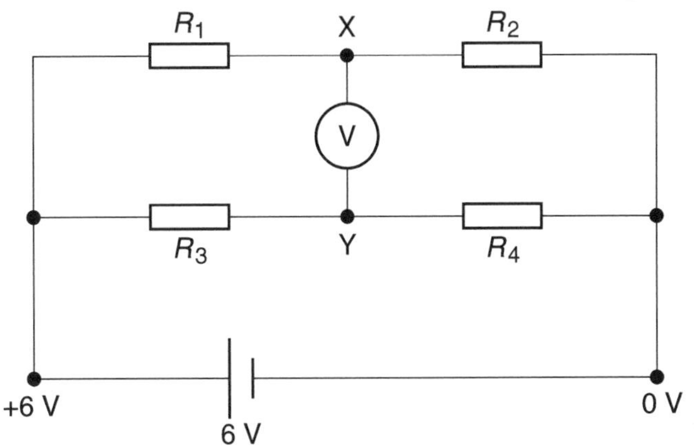

(a) What is the voltage across R_1?

(b) What is the voltage across R_2?

(c) What is the voltage across R_3?

(d) What is the voltage across R_4?

(e) What is the voltage at point X?

(f) What is the voltage at point Y?

(g) What is the p.d. between X and Y?

7. The meter bridge shown is balanced when $l_1 = 20$ cm.

(a) What is the reading on the voltmeter?

(b) Given that $R_1 = 10\ \Omega$, calculate R_2.

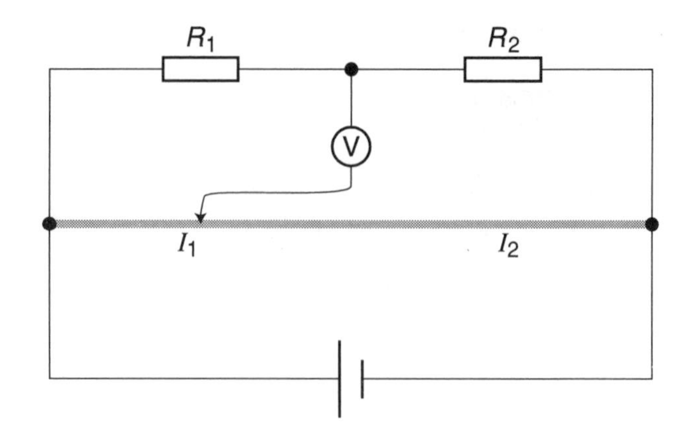

8. The meter bridge shown is balanced when $l_1 = 25$ cm.

(a) What is the reading on the voltmeter?

(b) Given that $R_1 = 100\ \Omega$, calculate R_2.

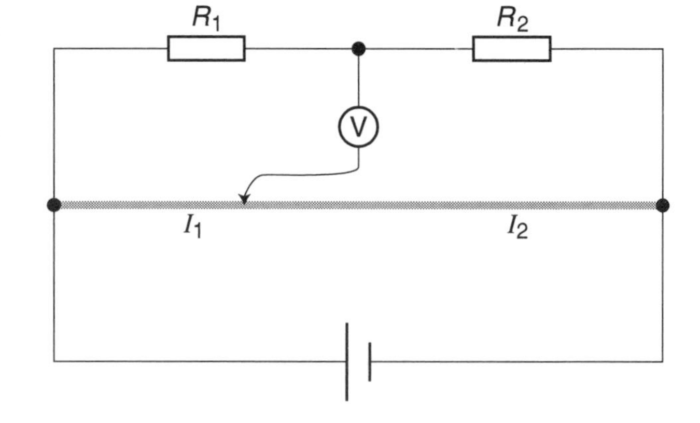

9. The meter bridge shown is balanced when $l_2 = 33{\cdot}3$ cm.

(a) What is the reading on the voltmeter?

(b) Given that $R_2 = 4{\cdot}7\ \mathrm{k}\Omega$, calculate R_1.

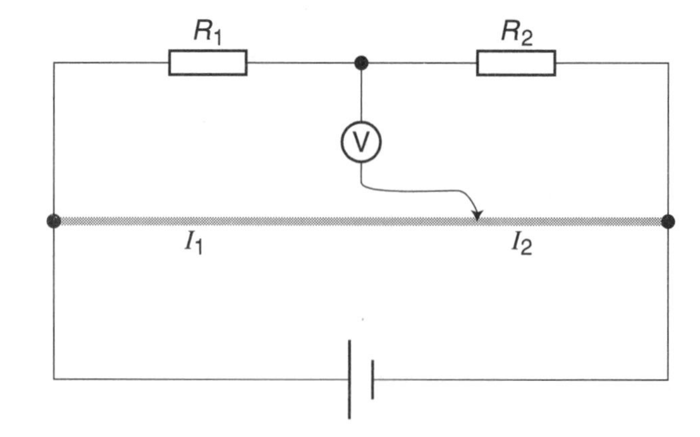

10. The meter bridge shown is balanced when l_2 = 40 cm.

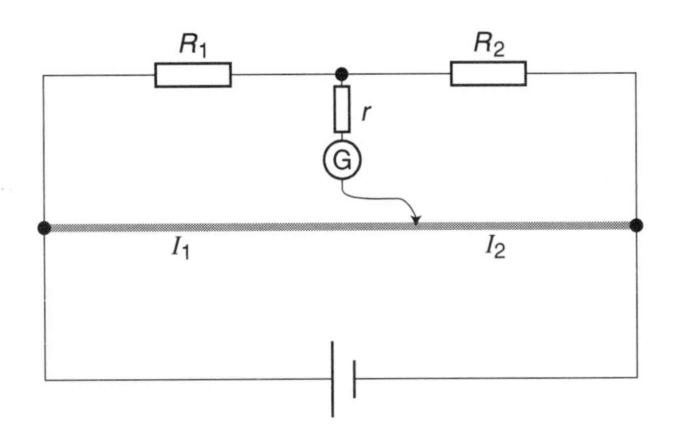

(a) What is the reading on the centre zero galvanometer?

(b) Given that R_2 = 1000 Ω calculate R_1.

(c) What is the purpose of resistor r?

11. The meter bridge shown is balanced.

Given that R_1 = 75 Ω
and R_2 = 175 Ω,
calculate the point of balance (l_1).

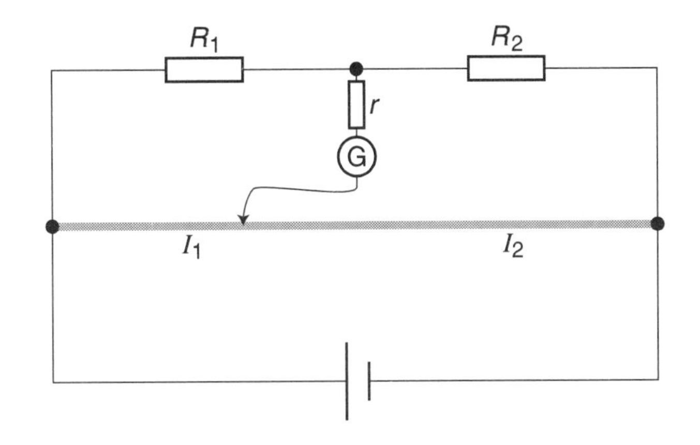

12. The meter bridge shown is balanced.

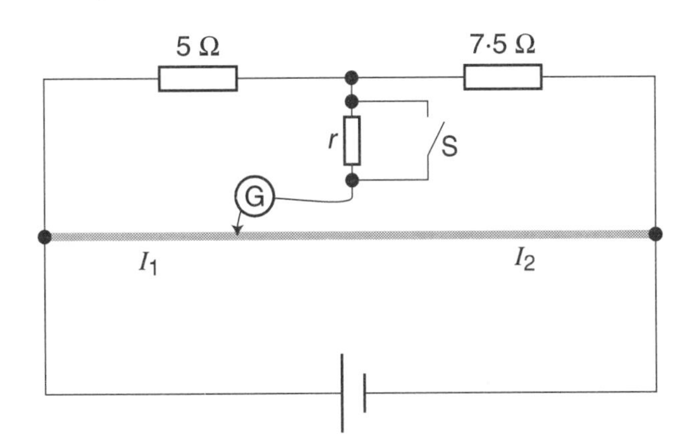

(a) Calculate the point of balance (l_1).

(b) If another 5 Ω resistor is connected **in parallel** across the 5 Ω resistor shown, calculate the new point of balance (l_1).

(c) What is the purpose of switch S?

THE UNBALANCED WHEATSTONE BRIDGE

1. A Wheatstone bridge circuit is set up as shown in the diagram and R_4 is adjusted until the bridge is balanced. At balance $R_4 = 1000\ \Omega$.

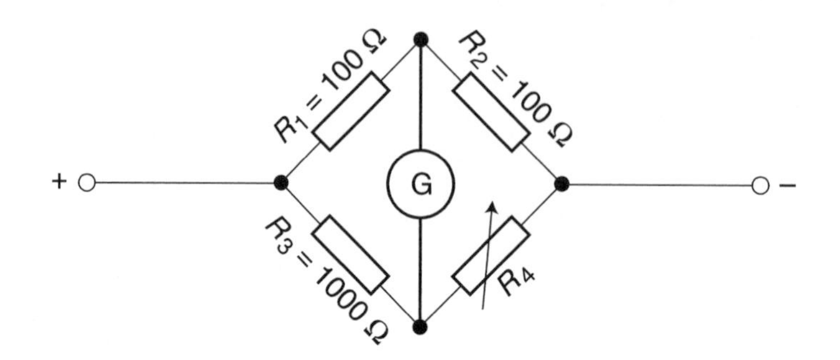

R_4 is now increased by constant amounts and the reading on the galvanometer is noted.

Results:

$\frac{R_4}{\Omega}$	1000	1020	1040	1060	1080	1100
$\frac{I}{\mu A}$	0	8	16	24	32	40
change in $\frac{R_4}{\Omega}$	0	20	40			

(a) Find the three missing numbers in the table above.

(b) Plot a graph of galvanometer current (y-axis) against change in resistance (x-axis).

(c) What mathematical relationship between current and change in R_4 can be deduced from the graph?

2. The resistance of R_4 in question 1 is now reduced to 980 Ω then 960 Ω, etc.

Results

$\frac{R_4}{\Omega}$	1000	980	960	940	920	900
$\frac{I}{\mu A}$	0	–8				
Change in $\frac{R_4}{\Omega}$	0	–20				

(a) Copy and complete the last two rows in the table above.

(b) Plot a graph of galvanometer current against change in R_4.

(c) What is the mathematical relationship between current and change in R_4 this time?

3. The graphs in questions 1 and 2 are really two parts of the same graph. If the change in resistance was large, e.g., 500 Ω, would the current on the galvanometer be proportional to the change in resistance? Give a reason for your answer.

4. The circuit shown has five voltmeters.

(a) What is the reading on V_1?

(b) What is the reading on V_2?

(c) What is the reading on V_3?

(d) What is the reading on V_4?

(e) What is the reading on V_5?

(f) What is the potential at point X?

(g) What is the potential at point Y?

(h) If a voltmeter was connected between X and Y, what would be the reading on the voltmeter?

5. Given the circuit shown.

(a) Find the potential of point X.

(b) Find the potential of point Y.

(c) What is the reading on the voltmeter?

(d) Is the circuit balanced?

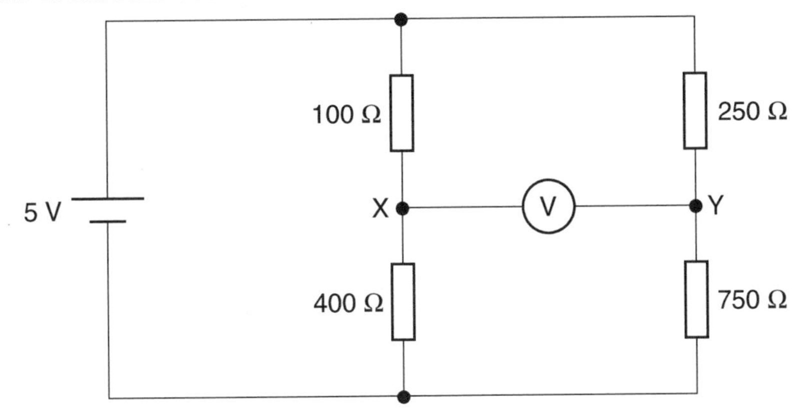

CHAPTER 8

ALTERNATING CURRENT AND VOLTAGE

OSCILLOSCOPES AND VOLTAGE

1. Copy and complete the oscilloscope pictures for each of the circuits below.

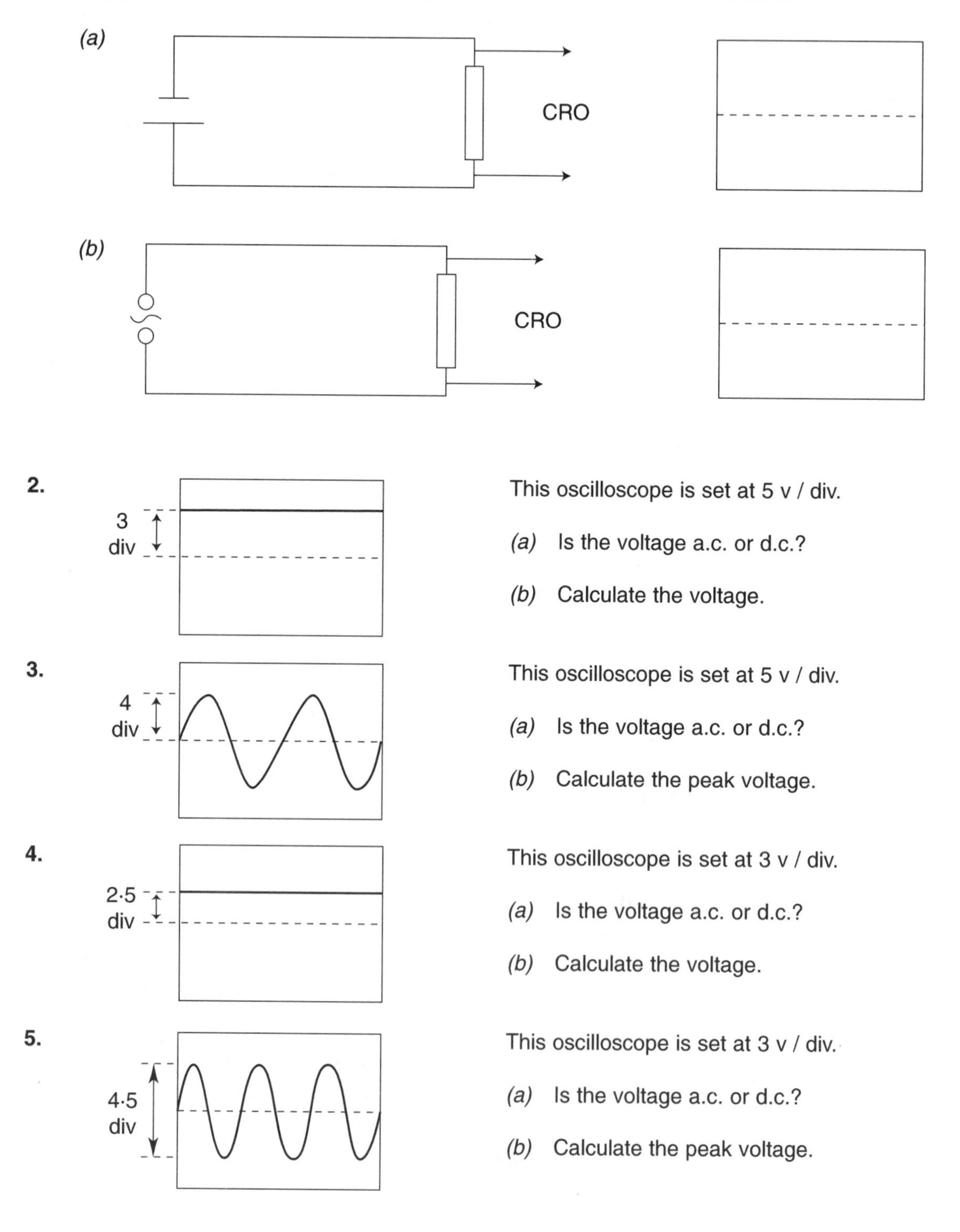

2. This oscilloscope is set at 5 v / div.

   (a) Is the voltage a.c. or d.c.?

   (b) Calculate the voltage.

3. This oscilloscope is set at 5 v / div.

   (a) Is the voltage a.c. or d.c.?

   (b) Calculate the peak voltage.

4. This oscilloscope is set at 3 v / div.

   (a) Is the voltage a.c. or d.c.?

   (b) Calculate the voltage.

5. This oscilloscope is set at 3 v / div.

   (a) Is the voltage a.c. or d.c.?

   (b) Calculate the peak voltage.

OSCILLOSCOPES AND FREQUENCY

1. An a.c. source of frequency 200 Hz is connected across an oscilloscope and the pattern shown is obtained.

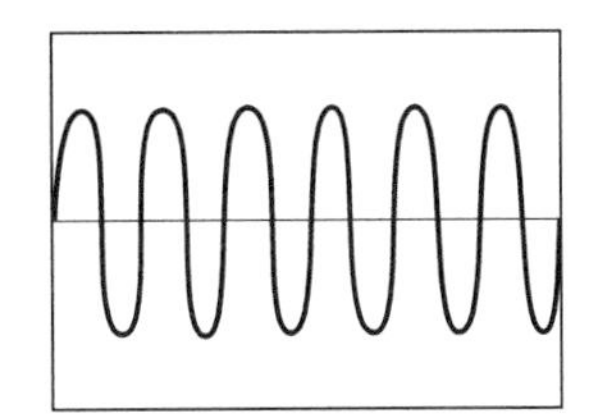

(a) With the oscilloscope controls unaltered, a signal of frequency 400 Hz is connected to the input. Draw the new pattern obtained.

(b) Repeat (a) for an input of 100 Hz.

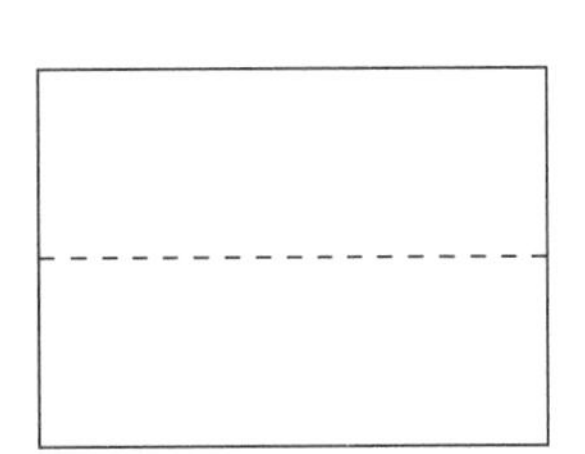

2.

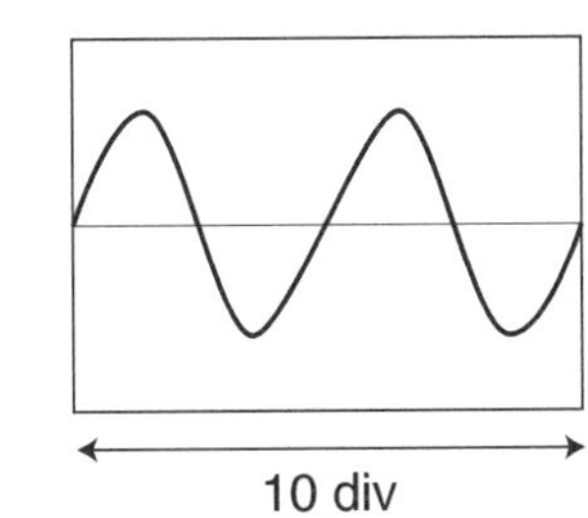

10 div

This oscilloscope time base is set at 10 m s / div.

(a) What is the time for 1 wave on the screen?

(b) Calculate the frequency.

3.

10 div

This oscilloscope time base is set at 1 m s / div.

(a) What is the time for 1 wave on the screen?

(b) Calculate the frequency.

4.

10 div

This oscilloscope time base is set at 10 m s / div.

(a) What is the time for 1 wave on the screen?

(b) Calculate the frequency.

5. 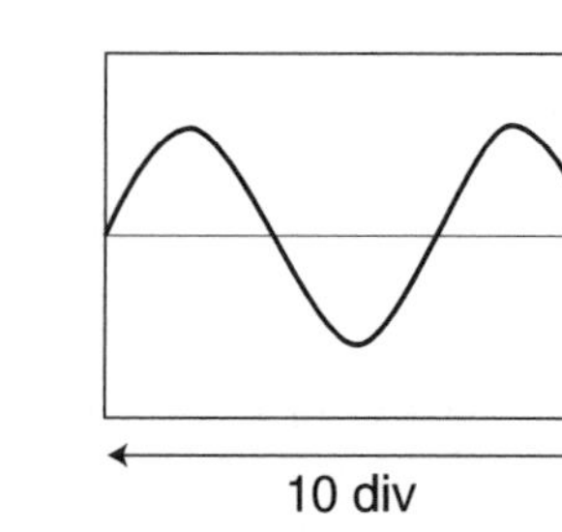

This oscilloscope time base is set at 100 m s / div.

(a) What is the time for 1 wave on the screen?

(b) Calculate the frequency.

PEAK AND R.M.S. VOLTAGE

1. An a.c. supply has a peak voltage of 10 V. The a.c. supply can be replaced with a d.c. supply. What is the voltage of the equivalent d.c. supply?

2. A d.c. supply has a constant voltage of 24 V. The d.c. supply can be replaced with an a.c. supply. What is the peak voltage of the equivalent a.c. supply?

3. Copy and complete the table below by calculating the r.m.s. voltages which are equivalent to the peak voltages shown.

Peak voltage	*r.m.s. voltage*
15 V	
50 V	
75 V	
240 V	

4. Copy and complete the table below by calculating the peak voltages which correspond to the r.m.s. voltages shown.

Peak voltage	*r.m.s. voltage*
	6 V
	20 V
	100 V
	230 V

CHAPTER 9

CAPACITANCE

CAPACITANCE, CHARGE, VOLTAGE, CURRENT, TIME

1. In an experiment designed to examine the relationship between voltage and charge, an electrophorus disc is used to charge a can. An electroscope measures the voltage of the can each time a unit of charge is delivered (1 electrophorus).

Results

Charge / No. of units	*Voltage / V*
1	2·5
2	5·0
3	7·5

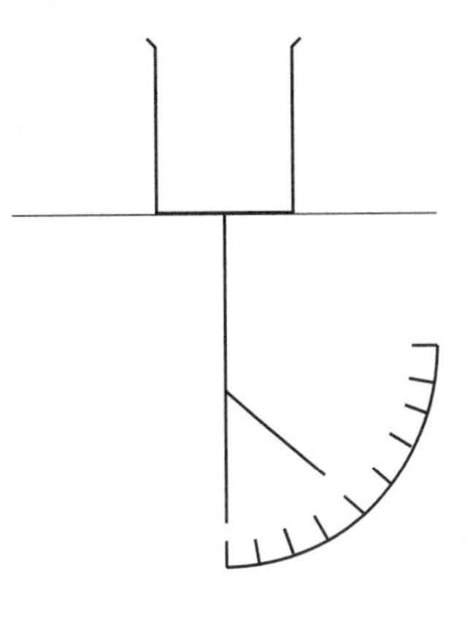

(a) Plot a graph of the results.

(b) What is the relationship between charge and voltage?

(c) Has capacitance been kept constant during the experiment?

2. In an experiment designed to examine the relationship between capacitance and voltage, an electrophorus disc is used to put one unit of charge on to a can which is attached to an electroscope. The electroscope measures the voltage of the can. One, two and three cans are attached in turn to alter the capacitance while the electrophorus always delivers only one unit of charge.

Results

Capacitance / No. of cans	*Voltage / V*
1	3·0
2	1·5
3	1·0

(a) Plot a graph of the results.

(b) What is the relationship between capacitance and voltage?

(c) What quantity was held constant during the experiment?

3. A capacitor has a capacitance of 10^{-9} F. If it is charged to a voltage of 90 V, how much charge is stored?

4. A 6 μF capacitor is given a charge of 9×10^{-4} C. What is the potential difference across it?

5. A parallel plate capacitor is charged to 25 V with a charge of $0{\cdot}5 \times 10^{-3}$ C. What is the capacitance of the capacitor?

6. Calculate the unknown (Q, C or V) in the table below.

	Q	C	V
(a)	?	0·1 F	15 V
(b)	$2{\cdot}4 \times 10^{-3}$ C	?	12 V
(c)	$6{\cdot}0 \times 10^{-3}$ C	3 μF	?
(d)	1·5 C	?	3000 V
(e)	?	1·5 μF	$3{\cdot}5 \times 10^{3}$ V

7. A parallel plate capacitor has a capacitance of 1 F. A single electron on one plate induces a positive charge on the opposite plate. Calculate the potential difference between the plates. (Charge on the electron is $-1{\cdot}6 \times 10^{-19}$ C.)

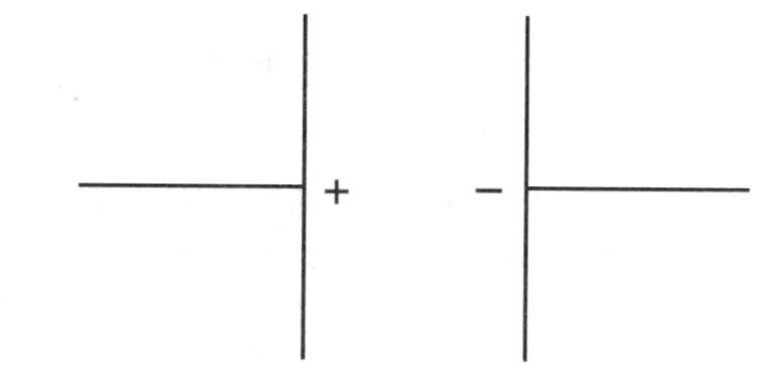

8. A capacitor reads 300 μF, 50 V.

(a) How much charge is on the capacitor when the voltage across it is 50 V?

(b) How much charge is on the capacitor when the voltage across it is 40 V?

9. A capacitor reads 500 μF, 25 V.

(a) How much charge is on the capacitor when the voltage across it is 25 V?

(b) How long would it take to charge using an average current of 5 A?

(c) Explain why the current is not steady.

10. A capacitor is marked 0·25 μF. How long will it take an average current of 20 A to charge it to 300 V?

CAPACITANCE AND ENERGY

1. The equation energy $= \frac{1}{2} QV$ is proved from the graph shown.

Copy and complete the graph by labelling the axes.

Show how the equation comes from the graph.

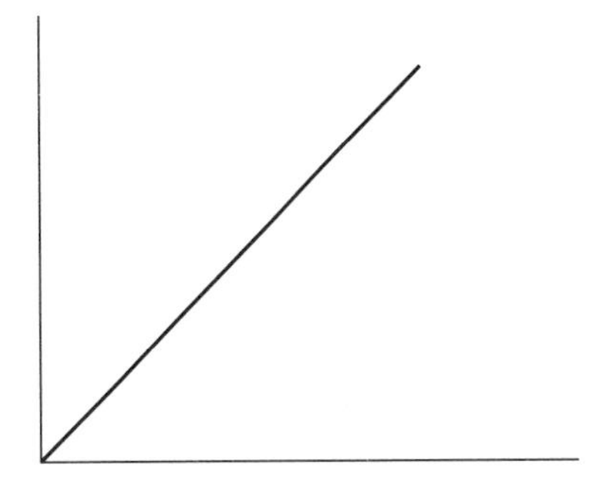

2. A capacitor is charged to 10 V using a charge of 10^{-3} C. How much energy is stored in the capacitor?

3. A capacitor is charged to 50 V with a charge of $0{\cdot}5 \times 10^{-3}$ C.

(a) How much energy is stored in the capacitor?

(b) What is the capacitance of the capacitor?

4. The charge held by a 2 μF capacitor is 4×10^{-4} C.

(a) How much energy has it taken to charge the capacitor?

(b) What is the voltage across the capacitor?

5. A parallel plate capacitor has a capacitance of 1 μF.

(a) How much energy does it take to charge it to 12 V?

(b) How much charge is on the capacitor (at 12 V)?

(c) How much energy does it take to charge it to 6 V?

(d) Explain why the answer to *(c)* is not half of the answer to *(a)*

THE CAPACITOR IN A D.C. CIRCUIT

1.

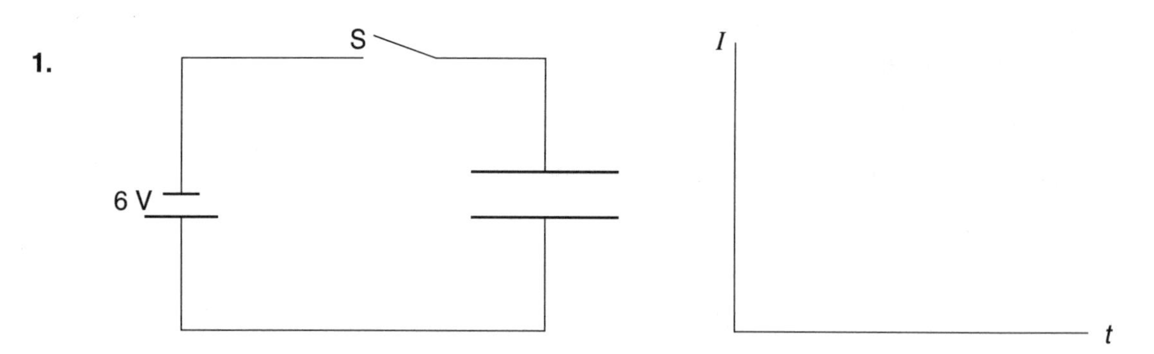

The capacitor in the circuit can be charged from the supply.

(a) Immediately after switch S is closed, is the current high or low?

(b) After a while, what happens to the current?

(c) Copy the axes shown into your jotter and sketch the graph showing how the charging current varies with time.

2. Relating to the circuit in question 1.

(a) What is the voltage across the capacitor immediately the switch is closed?

(b) What is the voltage across the capacitor when fully charged?

(c) Copy the axes shown and sketch a graph of voltage across the capacitor against time while charging.

(d) How does the time axis of the graph in question 1 compare with the time axis in question 2?

3. A charged capacitor (p.d. 6 V) is allowed to discharge through a resistor by closing switch S.

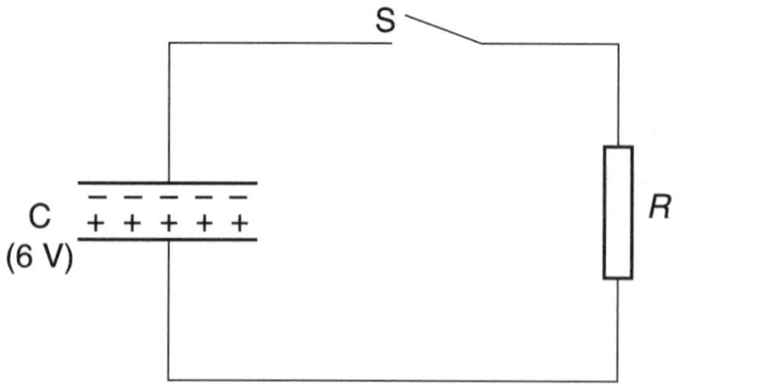

(a) Immediately after switch S is closed, is the current high or low?

(b) After a while, what happens to the current?

(c) Copy the axes shown and sketch a graph of discharge current against time.

4. Relating to the circuit in question 3.

(a) What is the voltage across the capacitor immediately the switch is closed?

(b) What is the voltage across the capacitor when completely discharged?

(c) Copy the axes shown and sketch a graph of voltage across the capacitor against discharging time.

(d) How does the time axis of the graph in question 3 compare with the time axis in question 4?

5. A capacitor can be charged and then discharged by using a two-pole switch as shown in the circuit below.

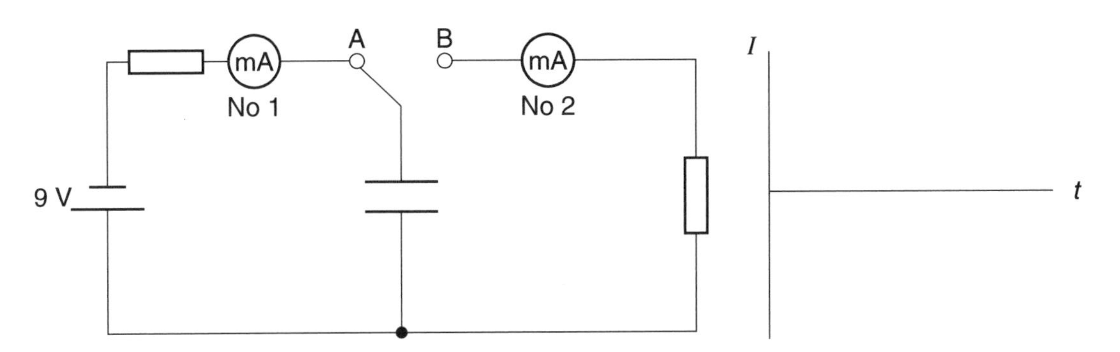

With the switch in position A, the capacitor charges up.

(a) How do we know when the capacitor is fully charged?

The switch is now moved to B and the capacitor discharges.

(b) How do we know when the capacitor is fully discharged?

(c) Sketch a graph of **both** charging and discharging current on the same axes (see above) and **explain** clearly the need for a negative scale.

6. Relating to the circuit in question 5, sketch a graph of voltage against time showing how the voltage across the capacitor varies in both the charging and discharging of the capacitor.

7. Let the switch in the following circuit be closed at $t = 0$.

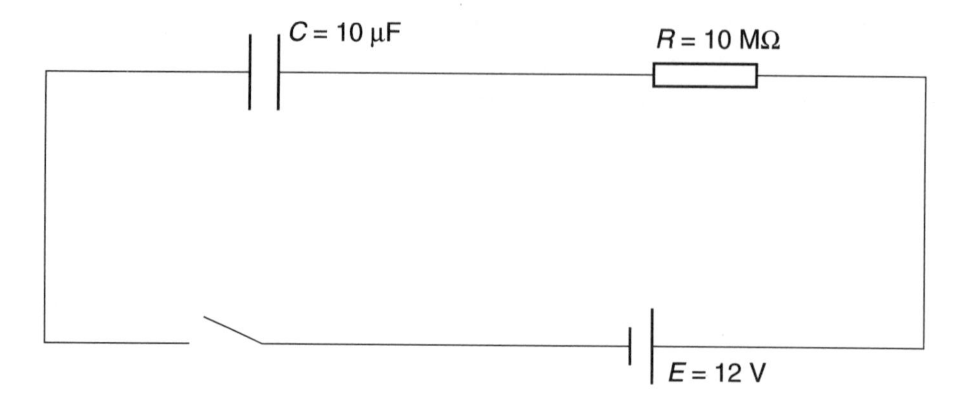

Immediately after the switch is closed.

(a) What is the charge on C?

(b) What is the p.d. across C?

(c) What is the p.d. across R?

(d) What is the current?

8. Relating to the circuit in question 7, after the capacitor is fully charged.

(a) What is the current?

(b) What is the final value of V, the p.d. across C?

(c) What happens to the current while V is building up?

(d) Why does V increase more and more slowly as time goes on?

9. A capacitor is charged and discharged once every second using the circuit below.

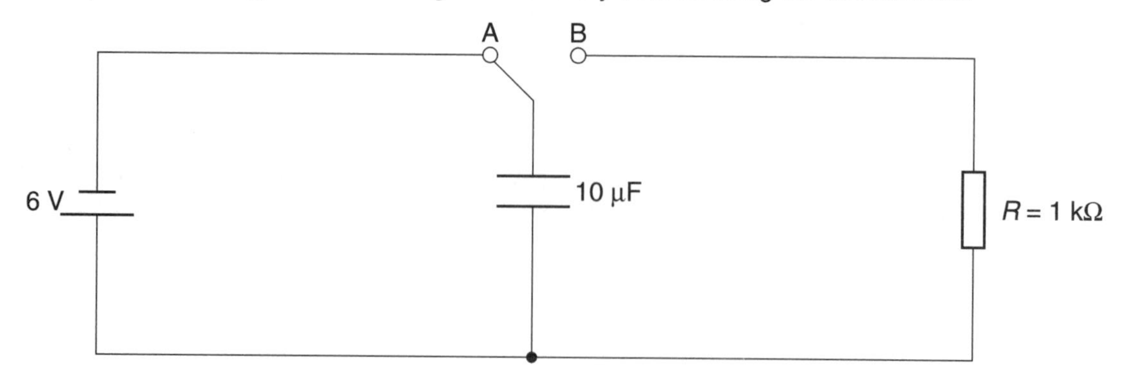

(a) What is the maximum charge the capacitor can hold (at 6 V)?

(b) What is the initial discharge current through the resistor R?

10. When the switch S in the circuit below is closed, the capacitor charges up.

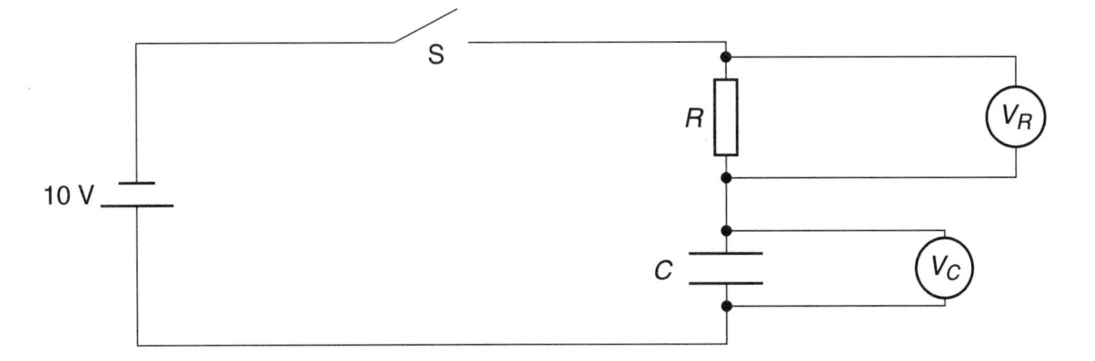

(a) When V_C reads zero, what is the reading on V_R?

(b) When V_C reads 2 V, what is the reading on V_R?

(c) When V_C reads 4 V, what is the reading on V_R?

(d) When V_C reads 6 V, what is the reading on V_R?

(e) When V_C reads 8 V, what is the reading on V_R?

(f) When V_C reads 10 V, what is the reading on V_R?

(g) Sketch a graph of V_C against time (numbers are required at the y-axis only).

(h) On the same graph paper, sketch a graph of V_R against time (numbers are required at the y-axis only).

THE CAPACITOR IN AN A.C. CIRCUIT

1. The effect of frequency of an a.c. supply on current in a resistor was investigated using the circuit below.

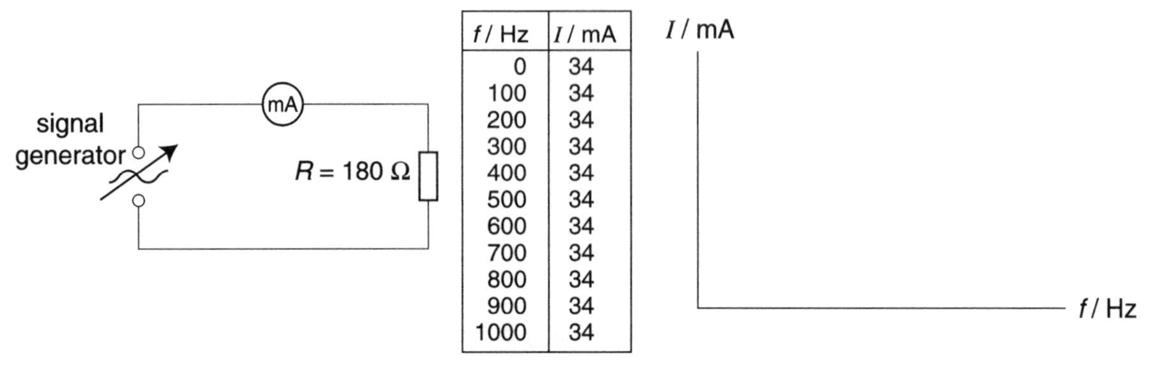

f / Hz	I / mA
0	34
100	34
200	34
300	34
400	34
500	34
600	34
700	34
800	34
900	34
1000	34

(a) Plot a graph of current against frequency for this resistor.

(b) What conclusion can you draw from the graph?

2. The effect of frequency of an a.c. supply on current in a capacitor was investigated using the circuit below.

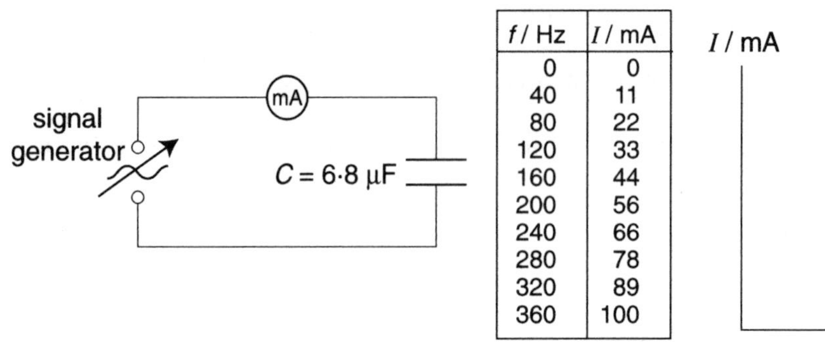

f / Hz	I / mA
0	0
40	11
80	22
120	33
160	44
200	56
240	66
280	78
320	89
360	100

I / mA

f / Hz

(a) Plot a graph of current against frequency for this capacitor.

(b) Why is the current zero when the frequency is zero?

(c) What conclusion can you draw from the graph?

3. Bearing in mind that the supply in the circuit in question 2 has a constant voltage (6 V) throughout the experiment:

(a) find the "resistance" of the capacitor at 120 Hz;

(b) find the "resistance" of the capacitor at 360 Hz;

(c) why does the "resistance" change?

4. A cathode ray oscilloscope is connected across the resistor in each of the three circuits shown below.

In each case, draw the pattern produced on the CRO.

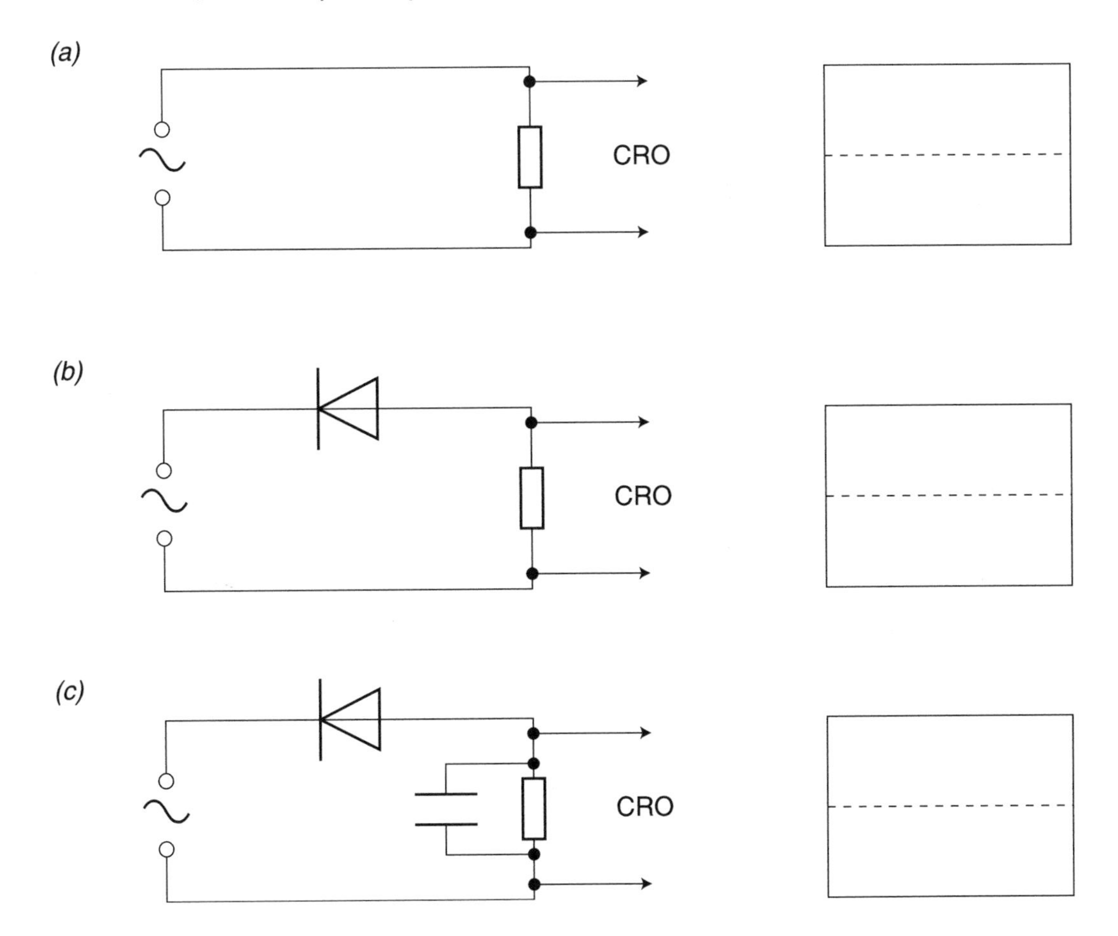

5. In the circuit below, the voltage on the signal generator is kept constant but the frequency is increased.

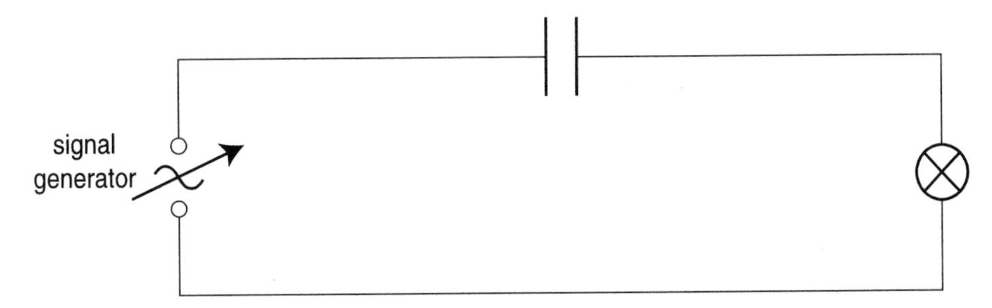

(a) As the frequency increases, the lamp
gets brighter; gets dimmer; stays at the same brightness?

(b) As the frequency increases, the current
increases; decreases; stays the same?

CHAPTER 10

ANALOGUE ELECTRONICS

VOLTAGE DIVISION

1. Find the reading on the voltmeter.

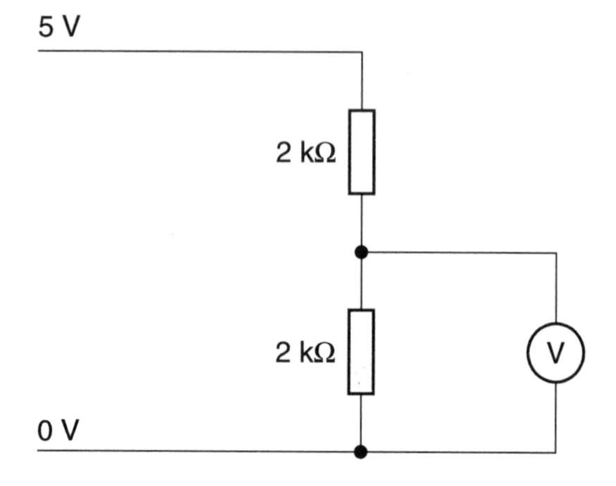

2. Find the reading on the voltmeter.

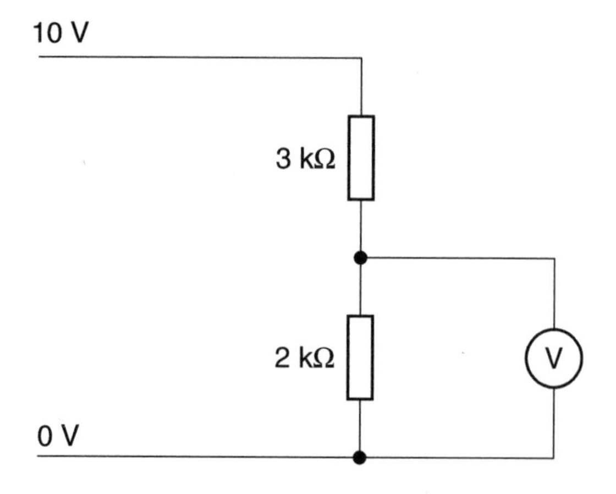

3. Find the reading on the voltmeter.

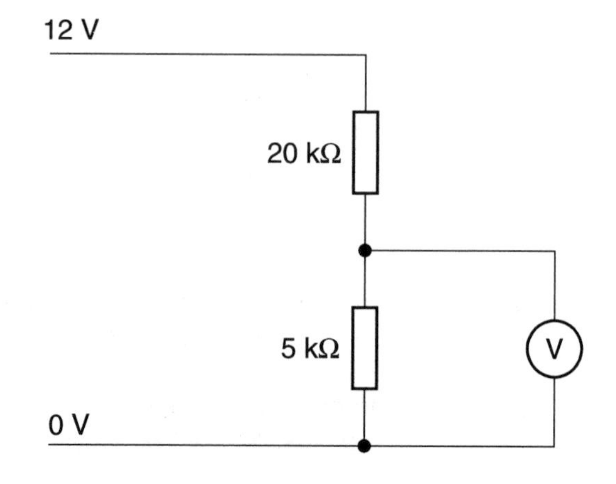

4. Find the reading on the voltmeter.

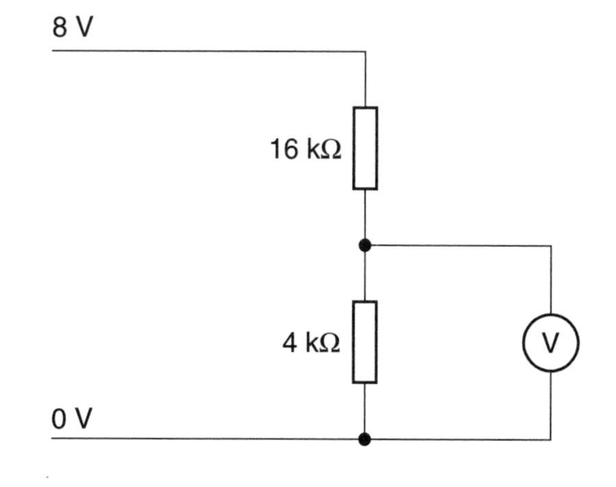

5. Find the reading on the voltmeter.

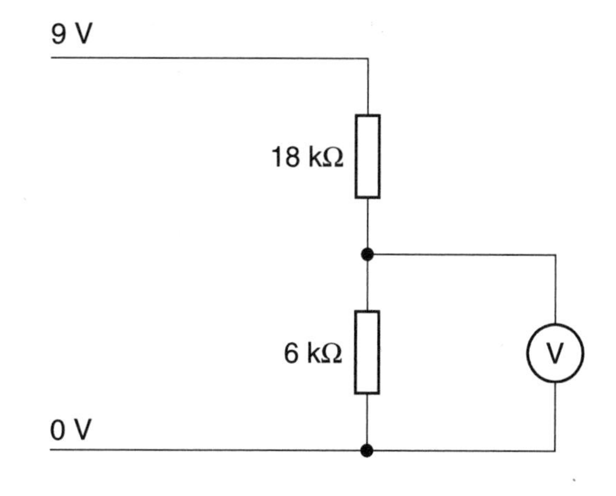

6. A circuit is designed to give an output of 9 V from a 12 V supply.

Calculate *R*.

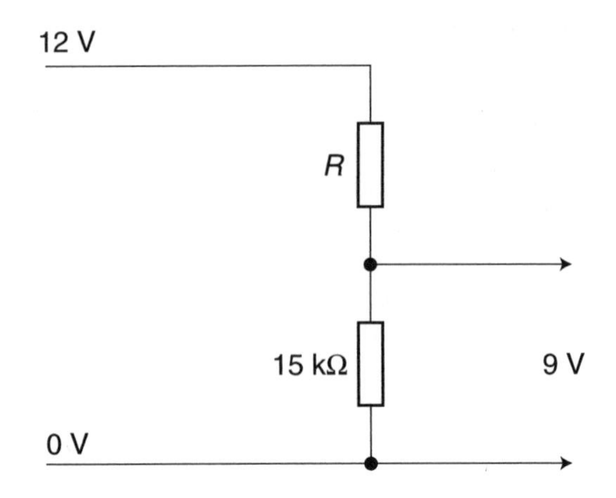

7. A circuit is designed to give an output of 8 V from a 20 V supply.

Calculate *R*.

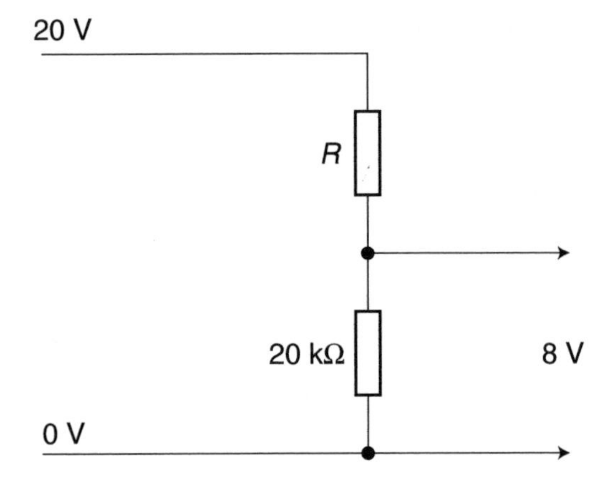

8. A circuit is designed to give an output of 8 V from a 20 V supply.

Calculate *R*.

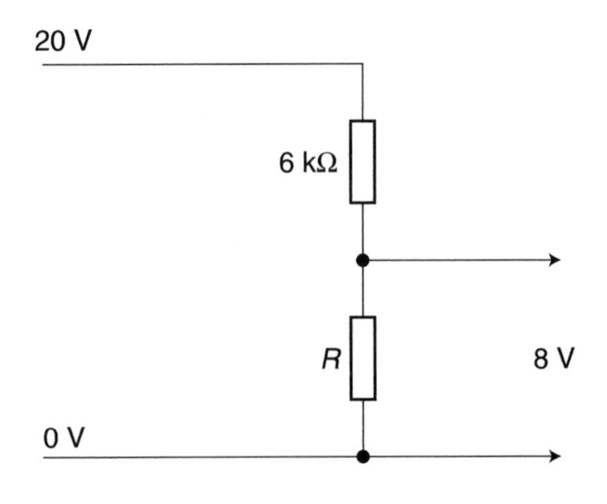

9. This circuit produces an ouput of 6 V.

Calculate the supply voltage.

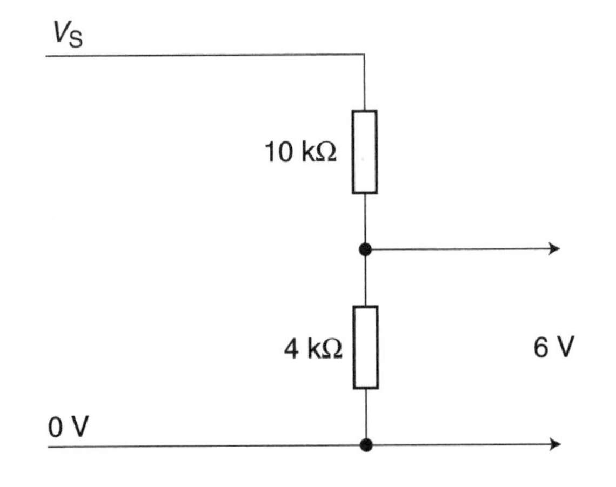

10. The rheostat in the circuit shown can be varied to produce a range of output voltages V_0.

Calculate the range of V_0 permitted by this circuit.

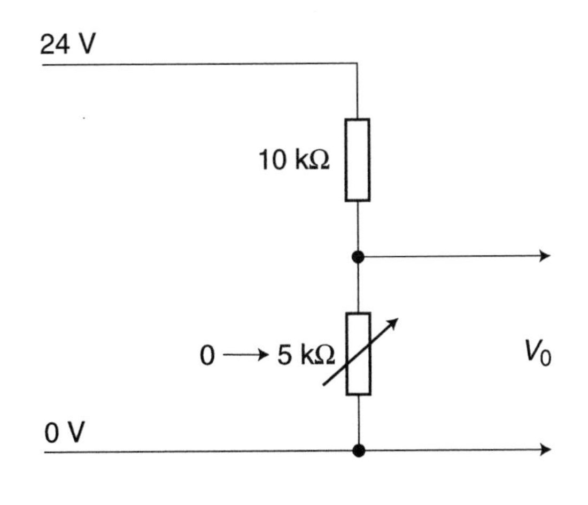

INVERTING MODE

1. Calculate V_0 in the circuit shown if $V_1 = 0{\cdot}5$ V.

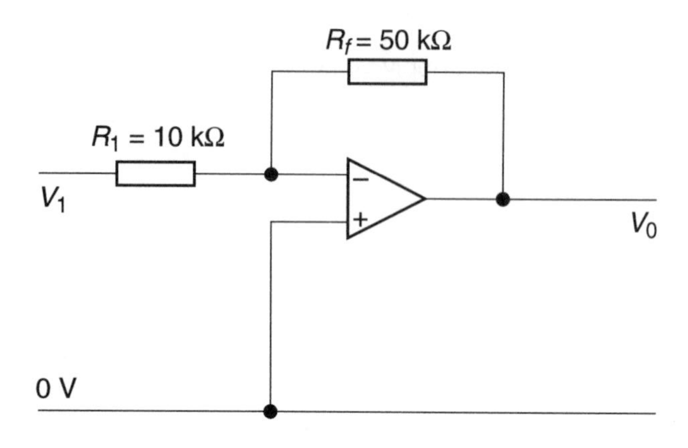

2. Calculate V_0 in the circuit shown when

(a) $V_1 = 0{\cdot}50$ V;

(b) $V_1 = 0{\cdot}75$ V;

(c) $V_1 = 1{\cdot}10$ V.

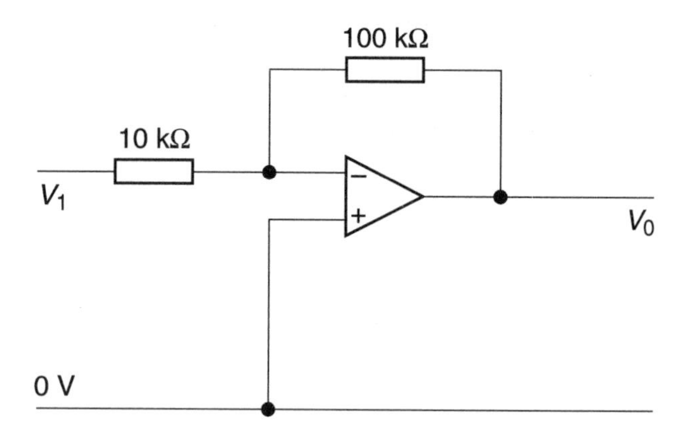

3. Calculate V_1 in the circuit shown when

(a) $V_0 = 10$ V;

(b) $V_0 = 6$ V;

(c) $V_0 = 50$ mV.

4. Calculate R_f in the circuit shown if $V_1 = 50$ mV.

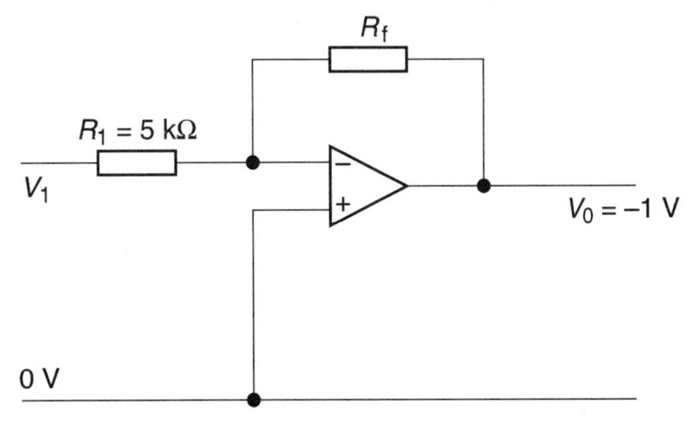

5. Calculate V_0 in the circuit shown when

(a) $V_1 = 0{\cdot}5$ V;

(b) $V_1 = 60$ mV;

(c) $V_1 = 2{\cdot}0$ V.

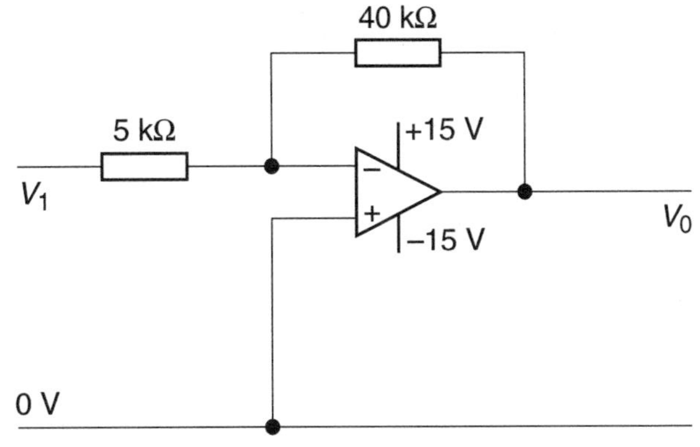

6. In the circuit shown,

(a) calculate V_1;

(b) hence calculate V_0.

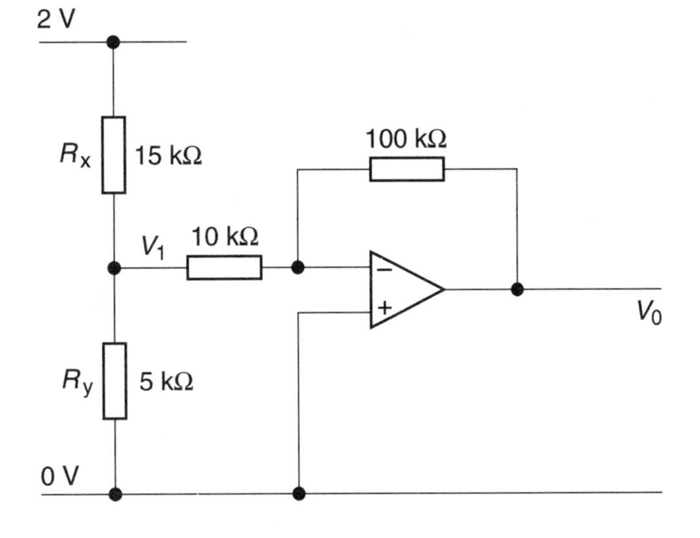

7. In the circuit shown,

(a) calculate V_1;

(b) hence calculate V_0.

8. In the circuit shown,

(a) calculate V_1;

(b) hence calculate V_0.

(c) What is the gain of the operational amplifier?

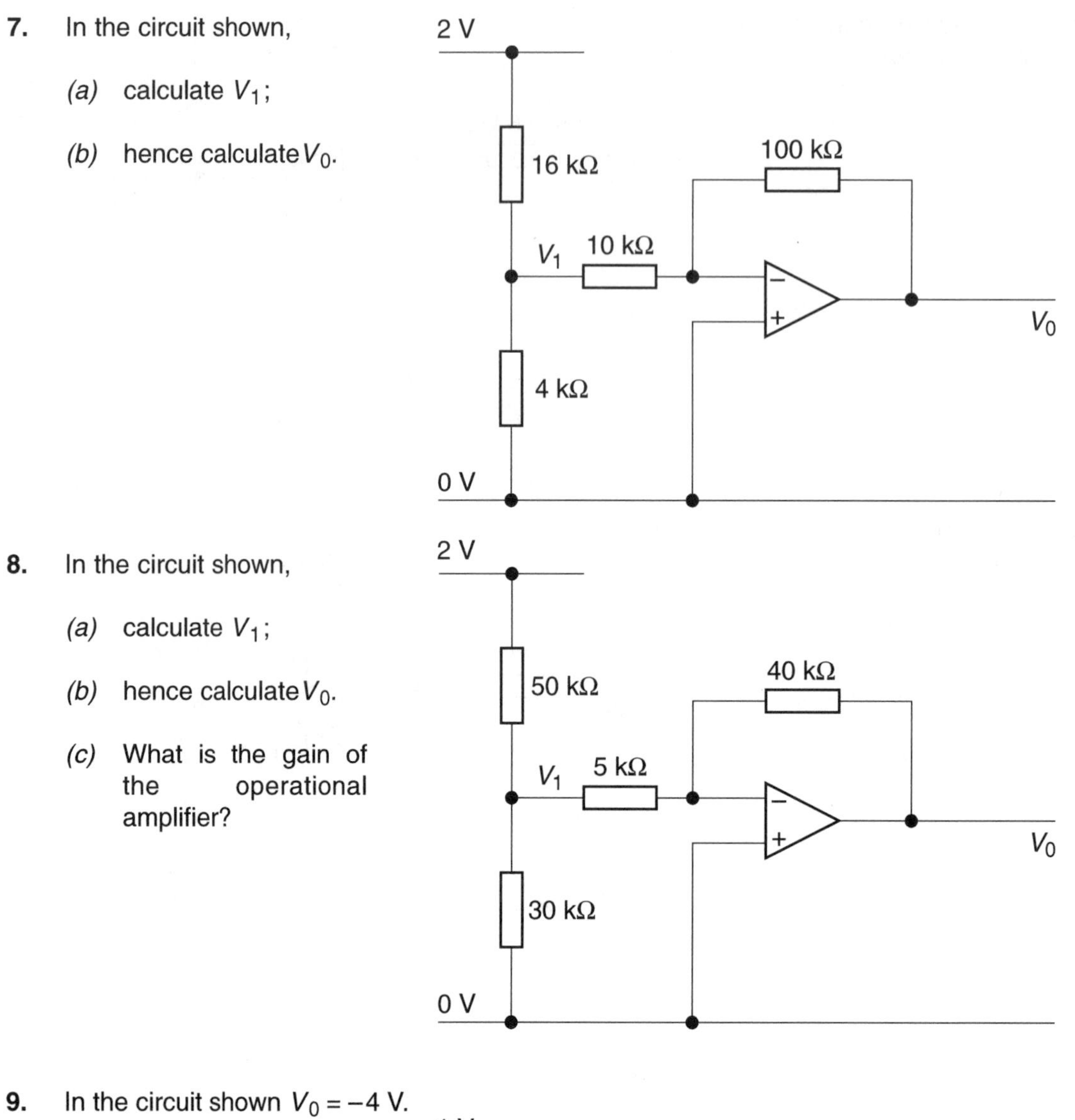

9. In the circuit shown $V_0 = -4$ V.

(a) Calculate V_1.

(b) Hence calculate R_x.

(c) Find the gain of the operational amplifier.

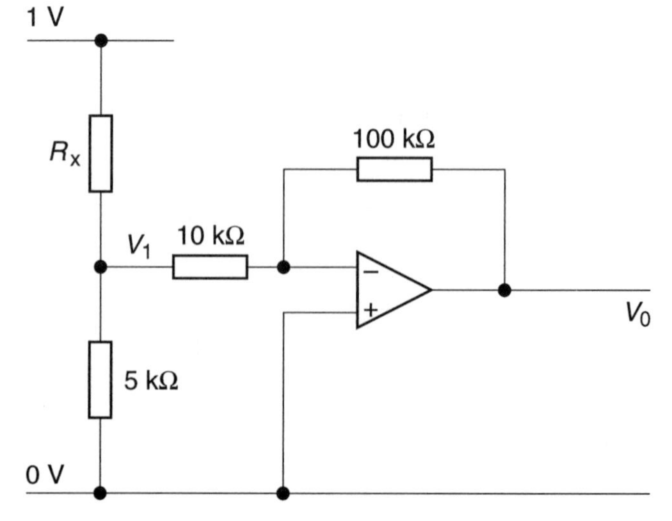

10. In the circuit shown,

- the operational amplifier should have a gain of 8;
- V_0 should be +10 V.

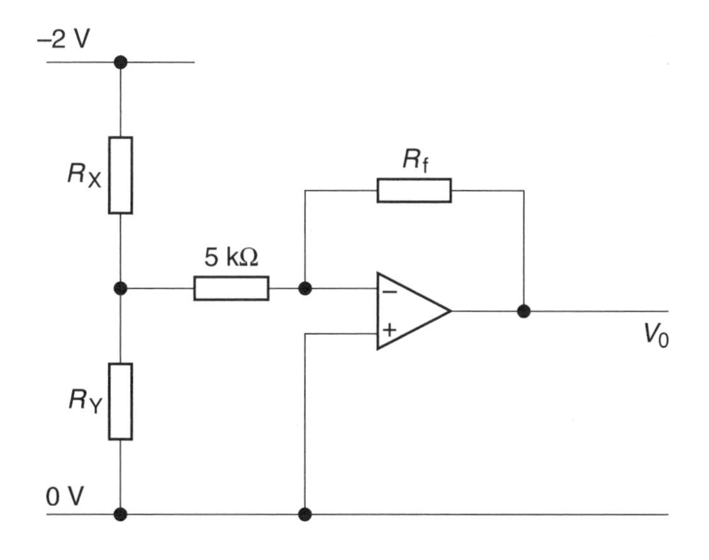

Design the circuit by suggesting suitable values for R_X, R_Y and R_f.

DIFFERENTIAL MODE

1. Calculate V_0 in the circuit shown if

$V_1 = 0{\cdot}5$ V,
$V_2 = 1{\cdot}0$ V,

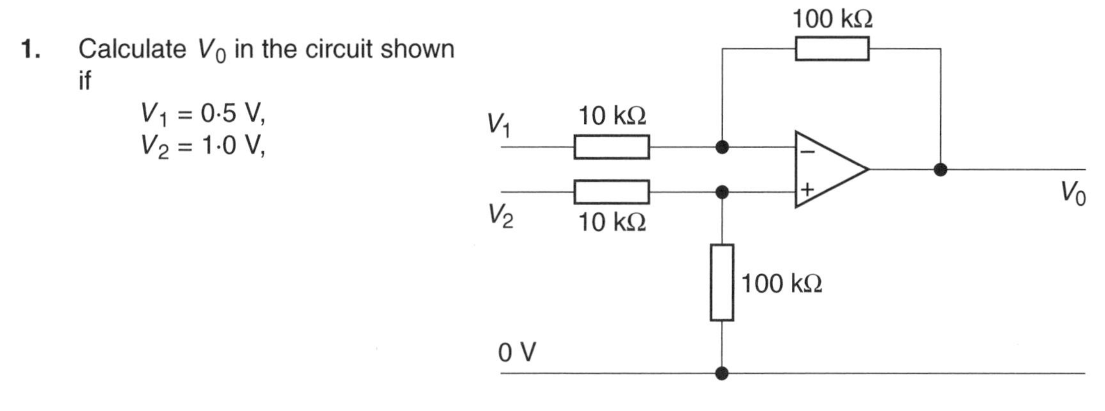

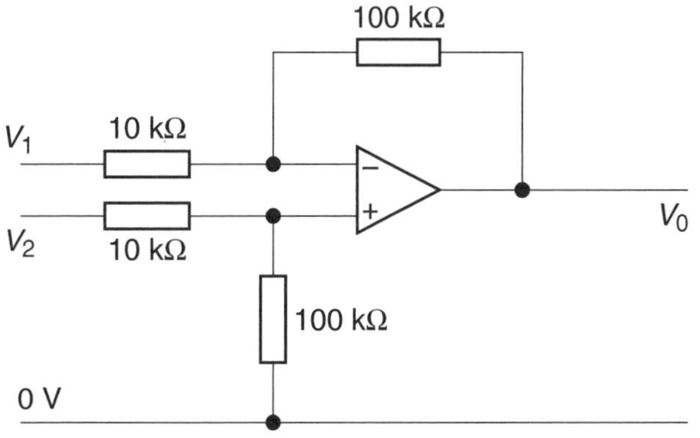

2. Calculate V_0 in the circuit shown when

(a) $V_1 = 5{\cdot}1$ V and $V_2 = 6{\cdot}0$ V;

(b) $V_1 = 2{\cdot}8$ V and $V_2 = 3{\cdot}0$ V;

(c) $V_1 = 150$ mV and $V_2 = 200$ mV.

3. Calculate V_0 in the circuit shown when

(a) $V_1 = 3{\cdot}9$ V and $V_2 = 4{\cdot}0$ V;

(b) $V_1 = 4{\cdot}0$ V and $V_2 = 3{\cdot}9$ V;

(c) $V_1 = 5{\cdot}0$ V and $V_2 = 4{\cdot}6$ V.

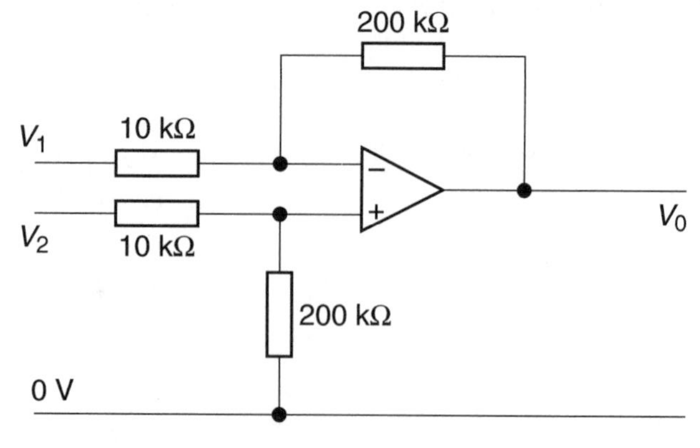

4. Calculate V_2 in the circuit shown when

(a) $V_0 = 10{\cdot}0$ V and $V_1 = 1{\cdot}0$ V;

(b) $V_0 = -8{\cdot}0$ V and $V_1 = 8{\cdot}0$ V;

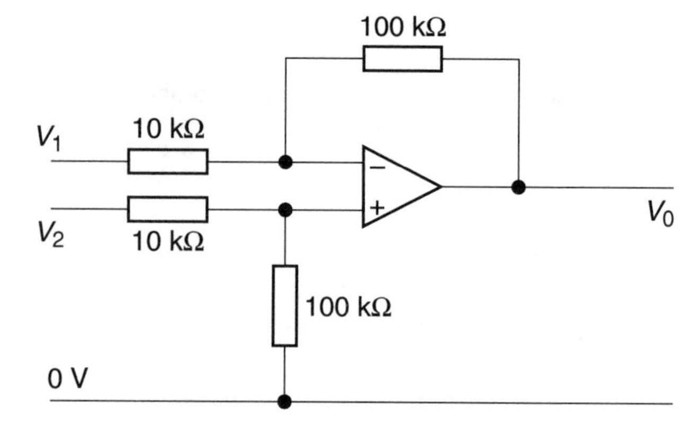

5. Calculate R_f in the circuit shown if

$V_0 = 7{\cdot}2$ V
and $V_1 = 2{\cdot}6$ V
and $V_2 = 3{\cdot}5$V.

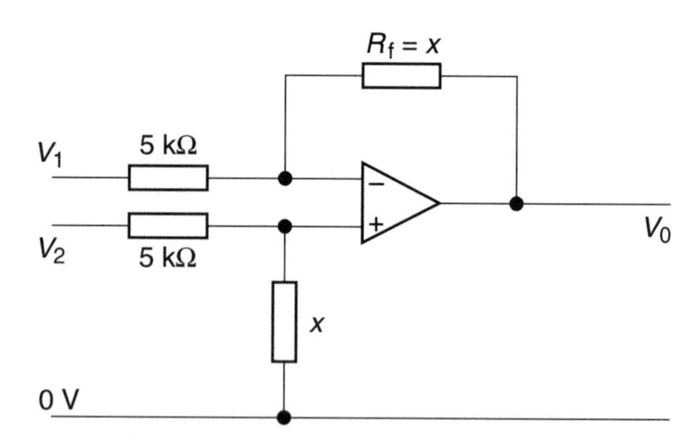

6. In the circuit shown,

(a) calculate V_2.

(b) If $V_1 = 0{\cdot}8$ V, calculate V_0.

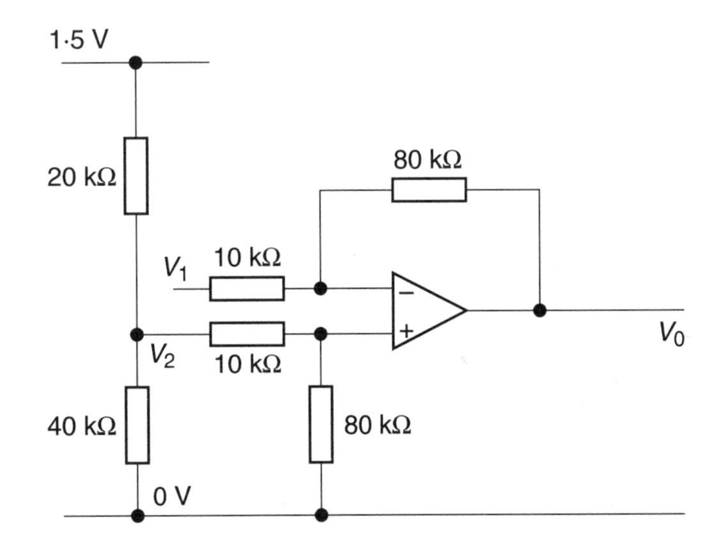

7. In the circuit shown,

(a) calculate V_1.

(b) If $V_2 = 150$ mV, calculate V_0.

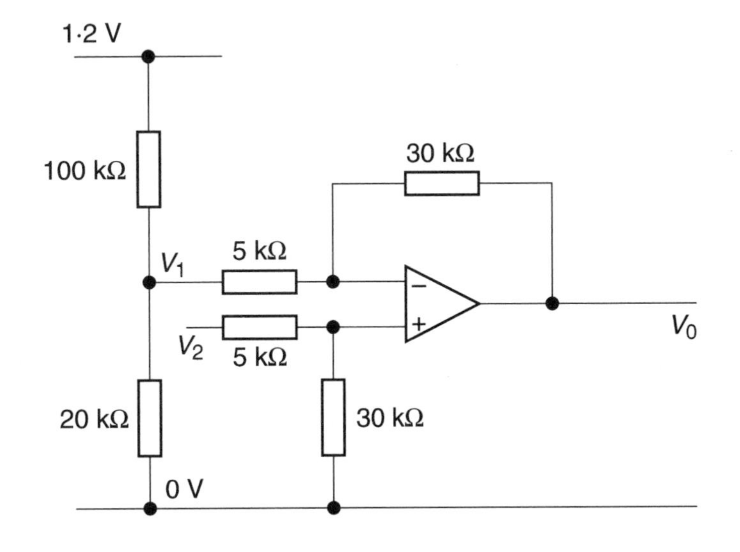

8. In the circuit shown,

(a) calculate V_1;

(b) calculate V_2;

(c) calculate V_0.

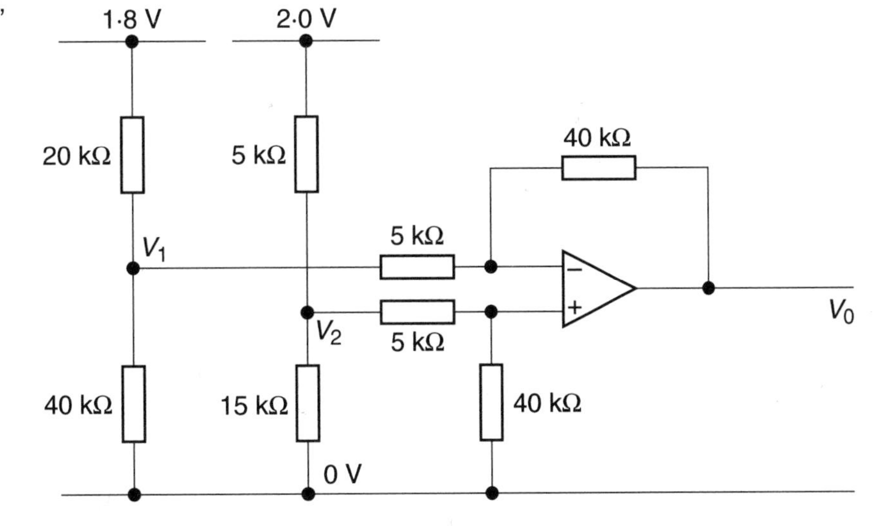

9. In the circuit shown,

(a) calculate V_1.

(b) If $V_0 = 0$, what is V_2?

(c) Calculate the value of R_X in this situation.

(d) If R_X was changed to 15 kΩ, calculate the new value of V_0.

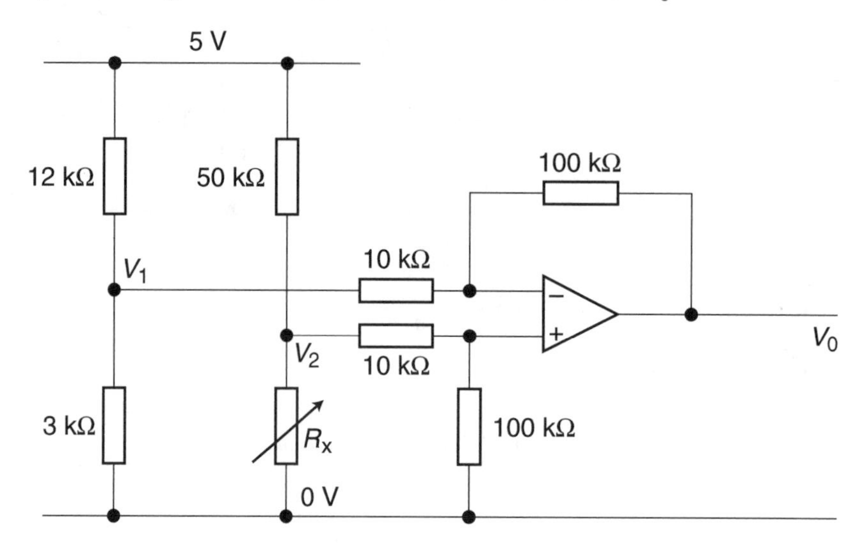

10. Given the two inputs illustrated for the circuit shown,

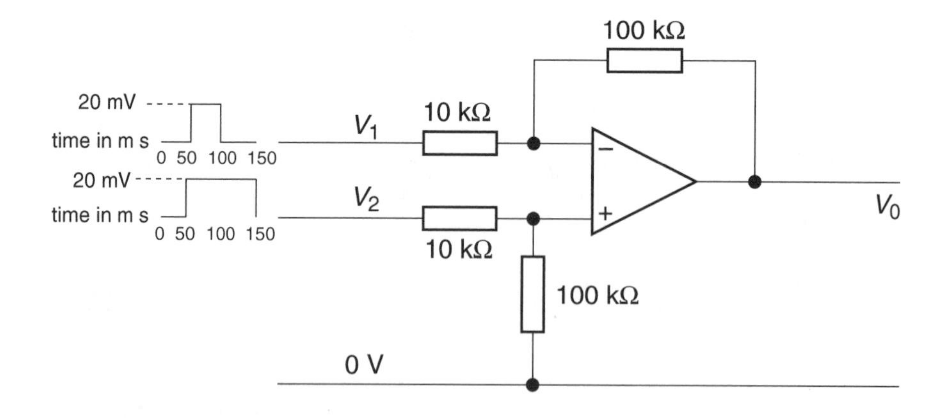

draw the equivalent output for the same 150 ms.

UNIT 3

RADIATION AND MATTER

CHAPTER 11

WAVES

INTERFERENCE

1. Plane water waves diffract through two slits in a barrier in a ripple tank. The diffracted waves overlap to produce an interference pattern (shown below).

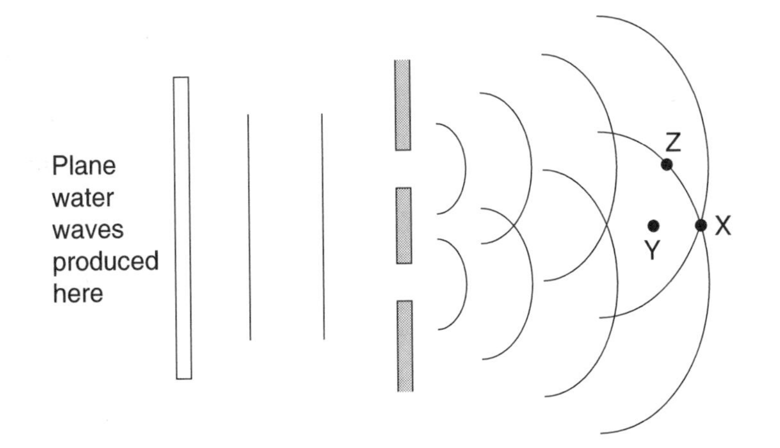

(a) Are two crests meeting at X?

(b) What type of interference is produced at X?

(c) Are two troughs meeting at Y?

(d) What type of interference is produced at Y?

(e) What is meeting at Z?

(f) What type of interference is produced at Z?

2. Two sources in phase produce water waves. The diagram below shows lines of constructive (C) interference.

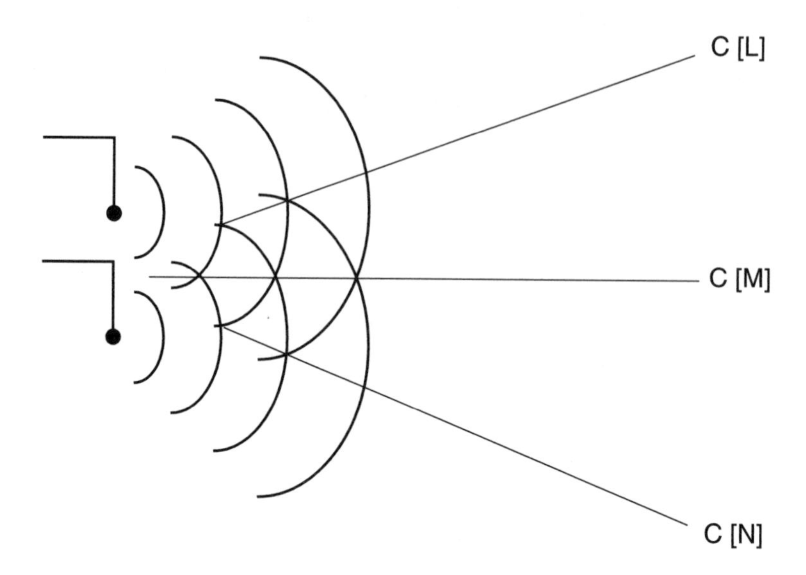

(a) Which is the zero order maximum (L, M or N)?

(b) Which two (from L, M, N) have the same strength of constructive interference?

3. Two loudspeakers connected to the same signal generator (S.G.) emit the same note in phase.

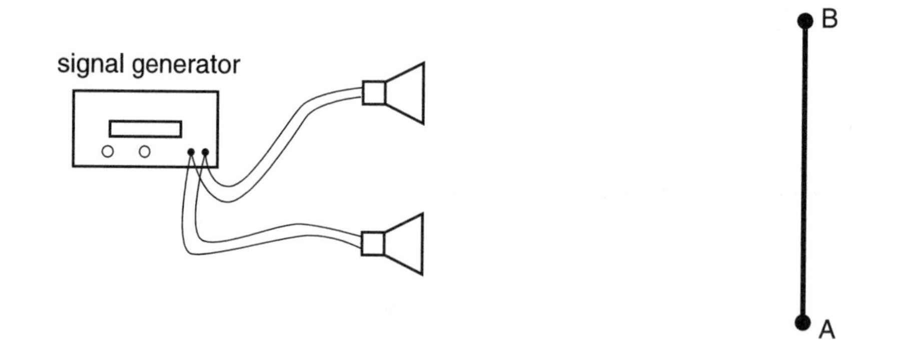

A boy covers his right ear, so that he only hears sounds from his left, and then walks from A to B (see diagram above).

(a) Describe what he hears.

(b) Relate this to constructive and destructive interference.

(c) Where is the loudest point?

4. The diagram shows the plan view of apparatus set up to investigate interference of microwaves.

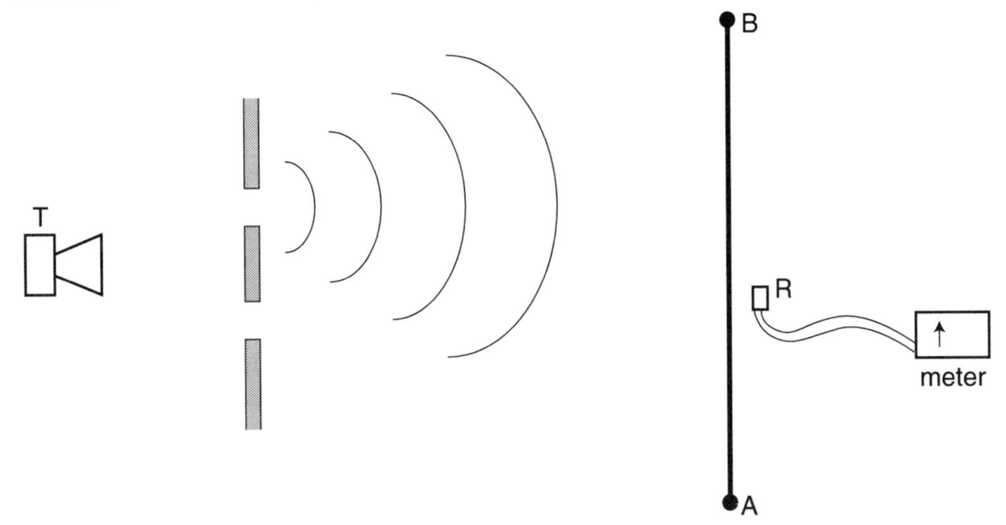

The wave from transmitter T is diffracted at each gap in the metal barrier. The receiver R detects the sigal which is fed into the meter.

(a) Copy and complete the diagram by drawing the second diffracted wave.

(b) On your diagram show:
(i) two crests meeting;
(ii) two troughs meeting
(iii) a crest and a trough meeting.

(c) Describe the reading on the meter as the detector is moved from A to B.

(d) Where is the reading a maximum?

5. Young's Slits are used to show interference of light. An observer sees bright and dark bands (or fringes) on a screen.

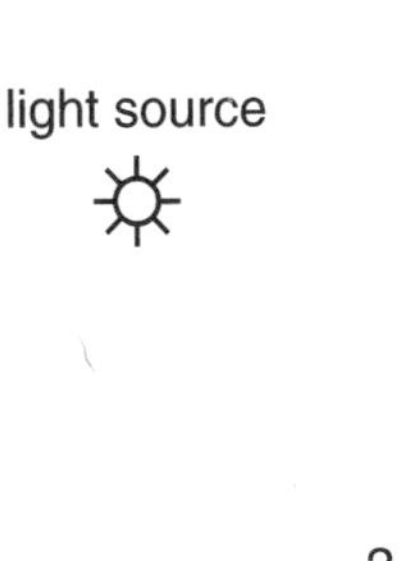

2 slits

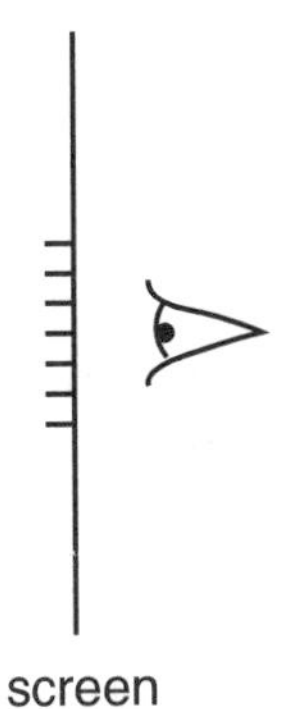

(a) What causes the bright bands?

(b) What causes the dark bands?

(c) Is there an odd number or an even number of bright fringes?

(d) Where is the brightest fringe?

6. The diagram below shows how the first order maximum is produced in an interference pattern using monochromatic light.

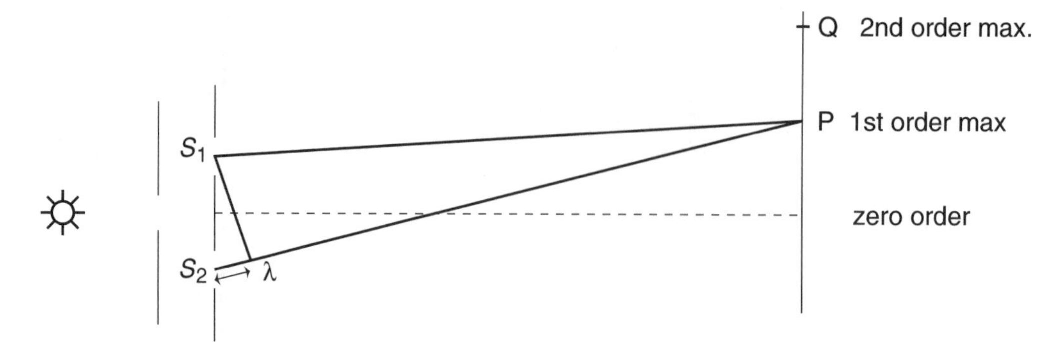

The first order maximum occurs the first time (from zero order) light from S_1 and S_2 are in phase, i.e., $S_2P - S_1P = \lambda$.

(a) (i) How is the second order maximum produced?
(ii) What is the path difference $S_2Q - S_1Q$?

(b) (i) How is the third order maximum produced?
(ii) What is the path difference this time?

7. The diagram below shows how the first order minimum is produced in an interference pattern using monochromatic light

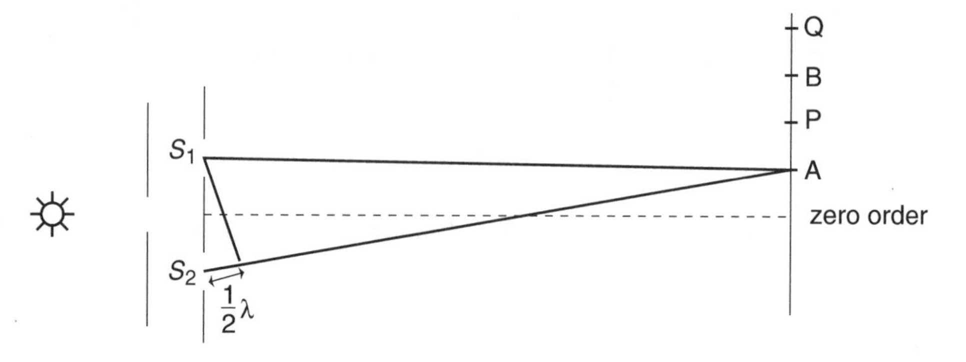

The first order minimum occurs the first time (from zero order) light from S_1 and S_2 are exactly out of phase, i.e., $S_2A - S_1A = \frac{1}{2}\lambda$.

(a) (i) How is the second order minimum produced?
(ii) What is the path difference for the second order minimum?

(b) (i) How is the third order minimum produced?
(ii) What is the path difference this time?

8. The diagram shows light from a laser striking a diffraction grating.

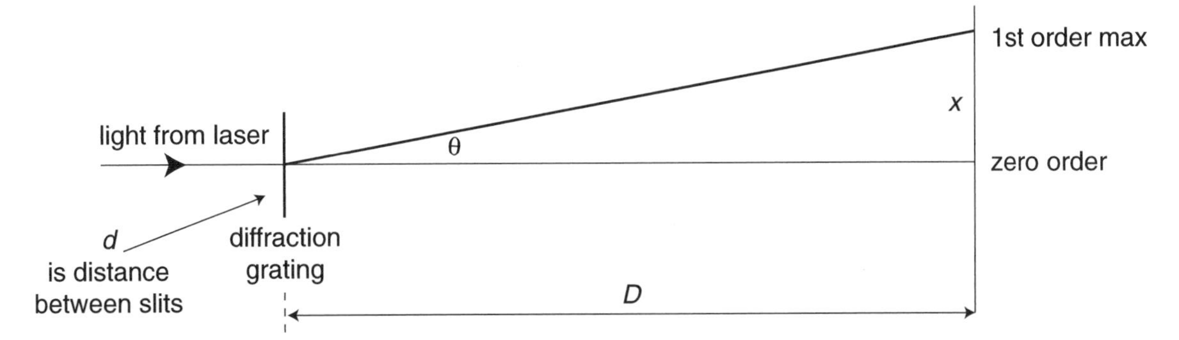

At any order (n) that constructive interference occurs, the grating equation is $n\lambda = d \sin \theta$.

Alternatively $\lambda = \frac{xd}{D}$

Use the diagram to prove that both equations are identical.

9. The diagram shows the interference fringes from a double slit.

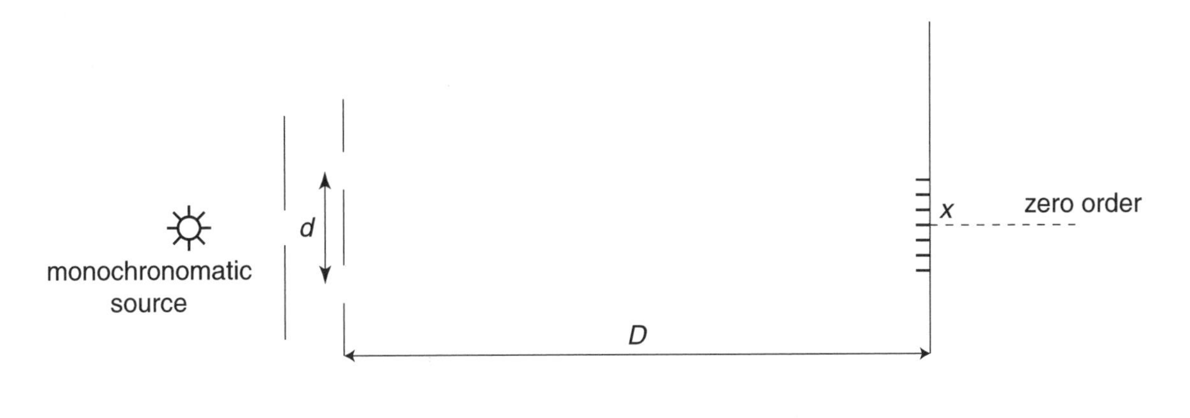

d = slit separation,
x = fringe separation,
D = distance from the slits to the screen.

(a) If the screen is moved farther away, what effect does this have on x, the fringe separation?

(b) If the double slits are replaced with a set which are closer together (i.e., d is less), what effect does this have on x, the fringe separation?

(c) If the source is replaced with a lamp of longer wavelength, what effect does this have on x, the fringe separation?

10. Light from a monochromatic source strikes a diffraction grating of 300 lines per mm.

A first order maximum is produced at an angle of 10·2° (see diagram).

(a) Calculate *d*, the slit separation.

(b) Calculate the wavelength of the light.

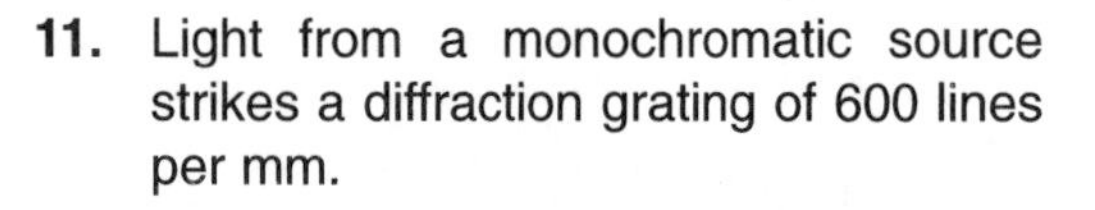

11. Light from a monochromatic source strikes a diffraction grating of 600 lines per mm.

A second order maximum is produced at an angle of 49·1° (see diagram).

(a) Calculate *d*, the slit separation.

(b) Calculate the wavelength of the light.

12. Light of wavelength 633 nm strikes a diffraction grating of 300 lines per mm.

At what angle θ (see diagram) will a third order maximum be produced?

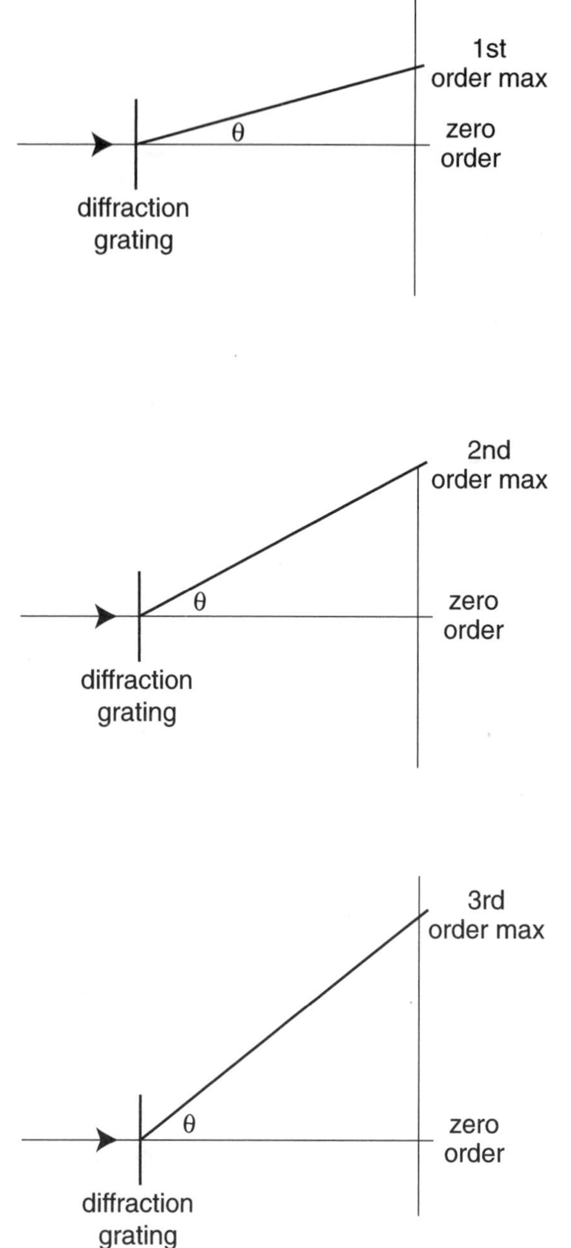

PRISMS AND GRATINGS

1. *(a)* A ray of monochromatic light strikes a glass prism. Copy and complete the diagram by tracing the ray both in the glass and after it emerges from the glass.

prism

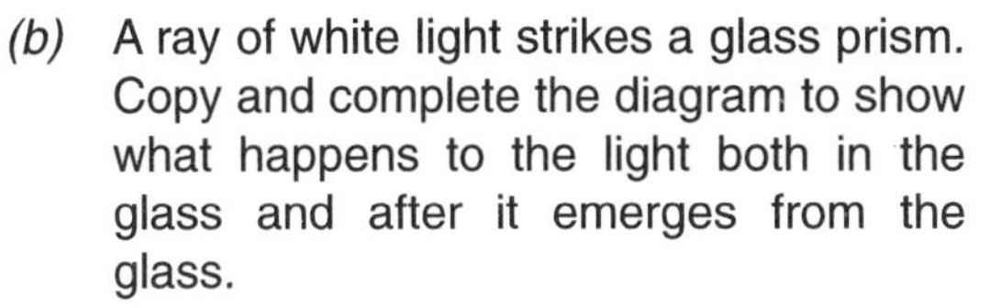

(b) A ray of white light strikes a glass prism. Copy and complete the diagram to show what happens to the light both in the glass and after it emerges from the glass.

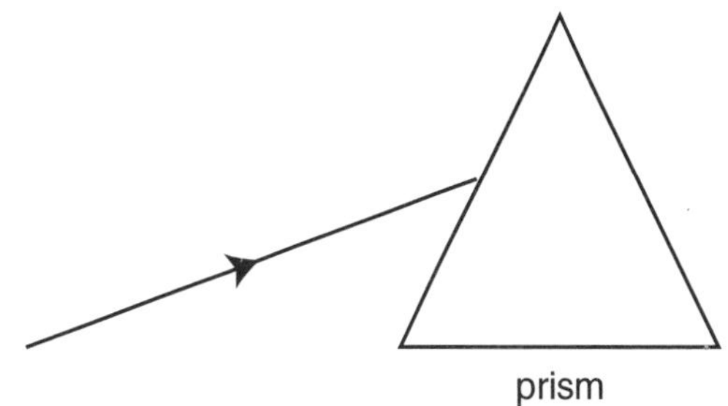

2. Monochromatic (red) light strikes a diffraction grating and produces a fringe pattern on a distant screen.

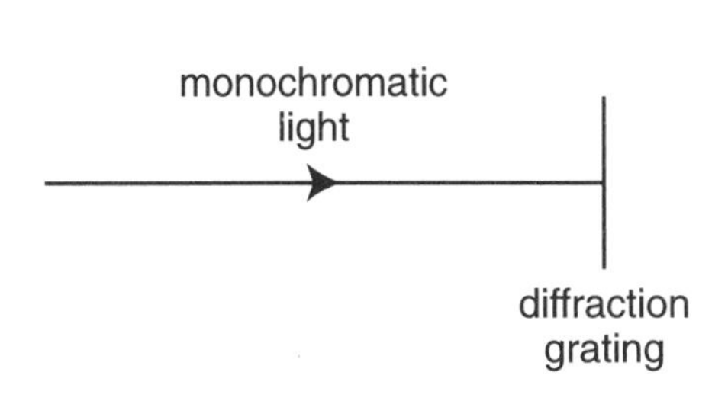

screen

(a) Copy and complete the diagram above by marking the paths of the light between the diffraction grating and the screen.

(b) (i) What colour is the zero order fringe?
(ii) What colour is the first order fringe?
(iii) What colour is the second order fringe?

(c) Which fringe is brightest?

3. White light strikes a diffraction grating and produces fringes on a distant screen.

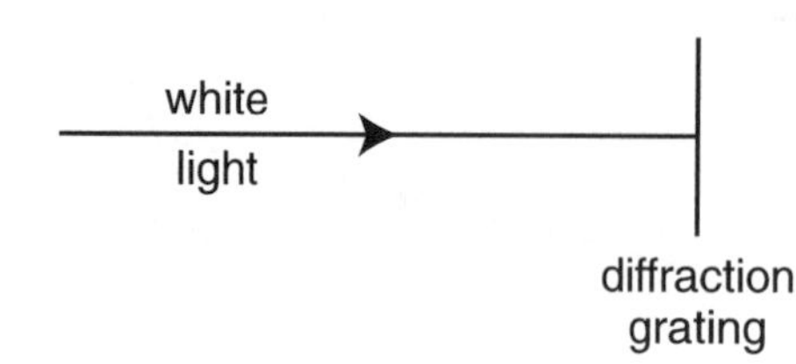

screen

(a) Copy and complete the diagram above by marking the paths of the light between the diffraction grating and the screen.

(b) (i) What colour is the zero order fringe?
(ii) What happens at the first order fringe?

4. *(a)* Is red light refracted more than violet or is violet refracted more than red?

(b) Red or violet — which has the longer wavelength?

(c) Is red light diffracted more than violet or is violet diffracted more than red?

(d) Give a reason for your answer to *(c)* — merely stating a wavelength difference is not enough.

5. The diffraction grating in question 2 (see diagram) is replaced with a set of double slits which were made in the school.

Comment on the effect this has on:

(a) the brightness of the fringes;

(b) the sharpness of the fringes;

(c) the fringe separation.

CHAPTER 12

REFRACTION OF LIGHT

REFRACTIVE INDEX

1. Calculate the refractive index of water from the angles shown.

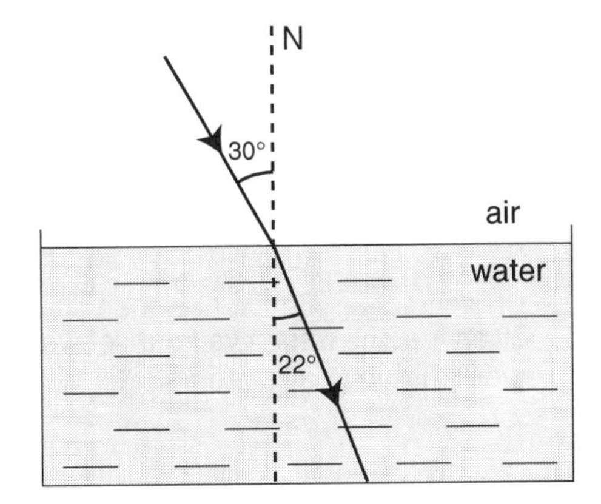

2. Calculate the refractive index of glass from the angles shown.

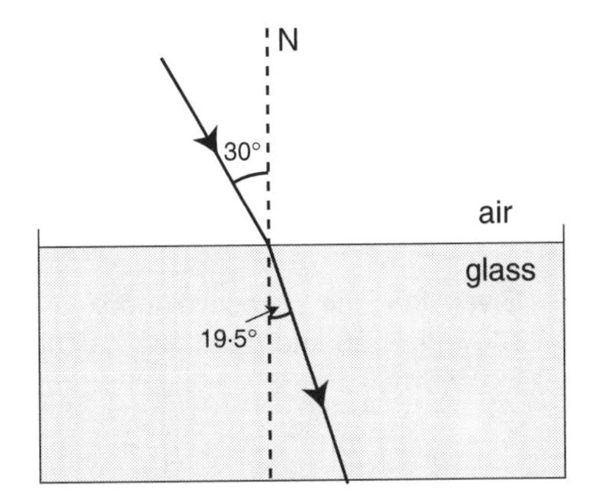

3. Given that the refractive index of water is 1·33 and θ_1 is 25°, calculate θ_2.

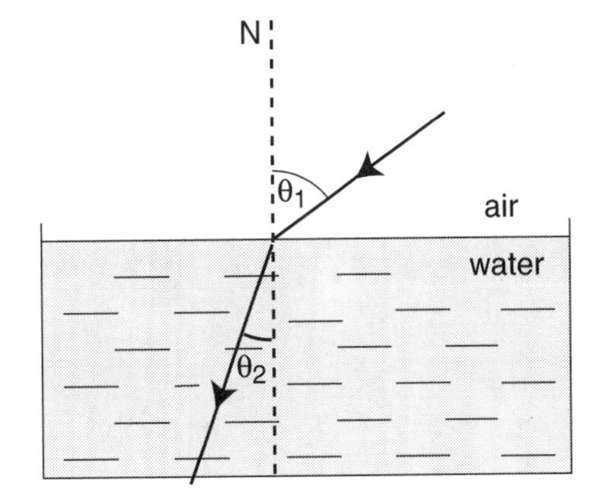

4. Given that the refractive index of the glass shown is 1·50 and θ_1 is 25°, calculate θ_2.

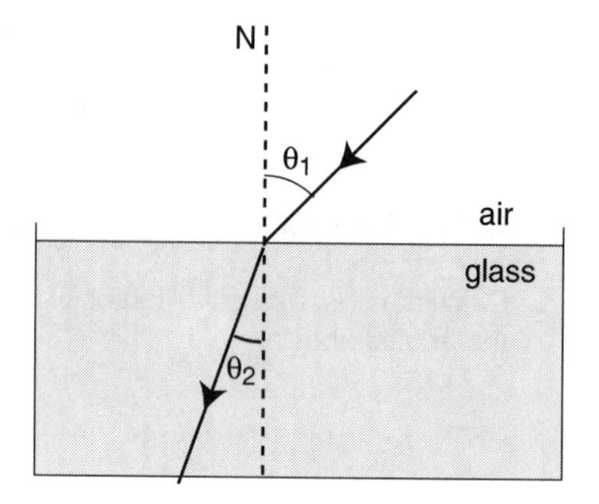

5. Given that the refractive index of water is 1·33 and θ_2 is 18°, calculate θ_1.

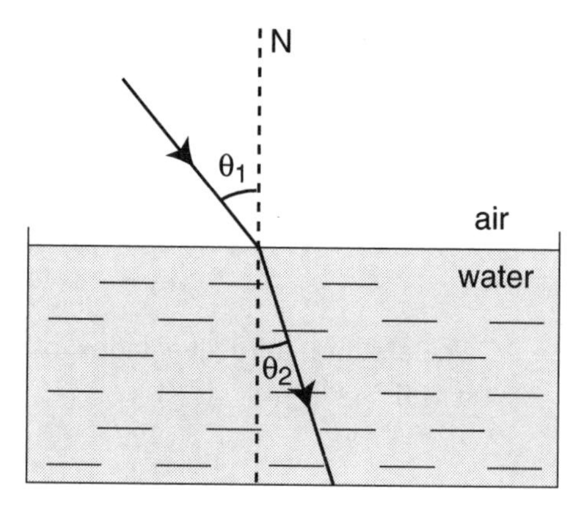

6. Given that the refractive index of the glass shown is 1·50 and θ_2 is 18°, calculate θ_1.

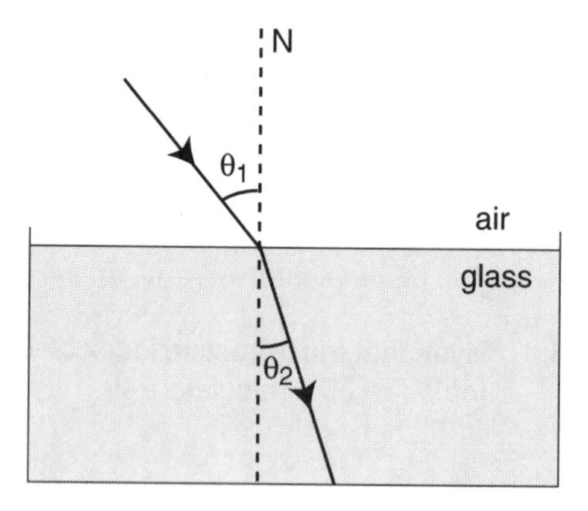

7. A ray of light travels from water to air. Given the refractive index of water is 1·33 and the angle θ_w is 35°, calculate θ_a.

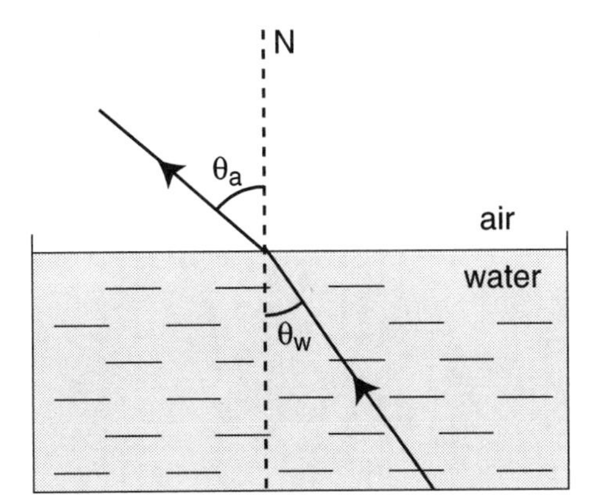

8. A ray of light travels from glass to air. Given the refractive index of this glass is 1·50 and the angle θ_g is 35°, calculate θ_a.

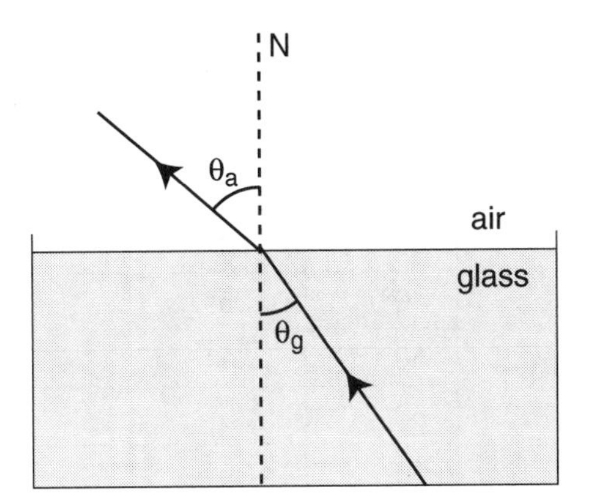

9. The diagram shows a glass block of refractive index 1·50. A ray of light strikes the block at N_1, travels through the glass and emerges at N_2.

(a) Given that $\theta_a = 40°$, calculate θ_g.

(b) Hence find *x*.

(c) Hence find *y*.

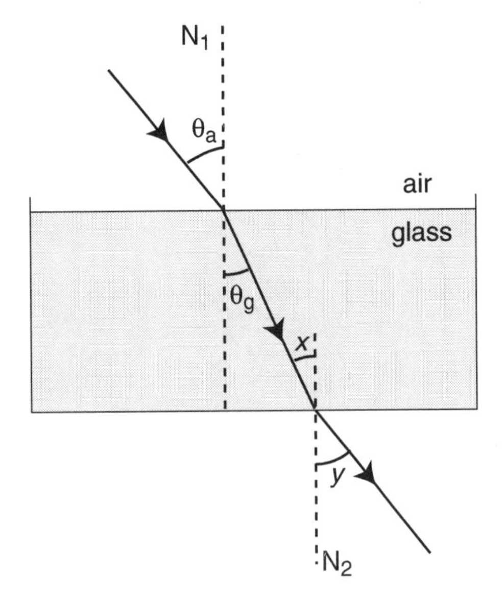

10. In an experiment to find the relationship between the angle of incidence and the angle of refraction, the following table of results was obtained.

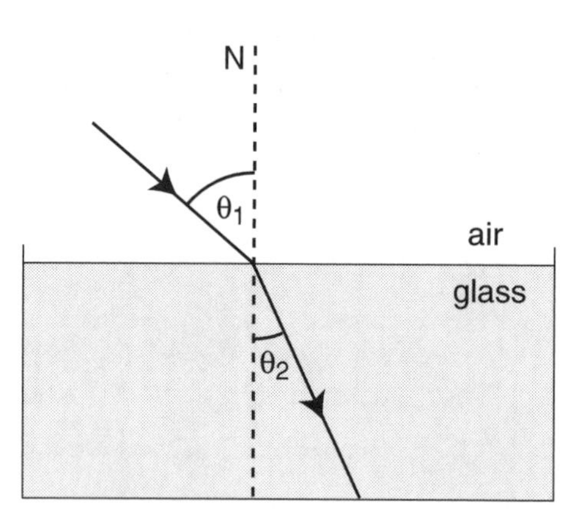

θ_1	θ_2	$\sin\theta_1$	$\sin\theta_2$	$\frac{\sin\theta_1}{\sin\theta_2}$
10°	6°			
20°	13°			
30°	20°			
40°	25°			
50°	31°			
60°	35°			
70°	39°			
80°	41°			

(a) Copy and complete the empty three columns in the table.

(b) Plot a graph of $\sin\theta_1$ against $\sin\theta_2$.

(c) What conclusion can you come to about the ratio $\frac{\sin\theta_1}{\sin\theta_2}$?

REFRACTIVE INDEX AND VELOCITY

1. The velocity of light in air is 3×10^8 m s^{-1}. Calculate the velocity of light in

(a) glass ($n = 1{\cdot}50$),

(b) water ($n = 1{\cdot}33$).

2. The velocity of light in air is 3×10^8 m s^{-1}. Calculate the velocity of light in

(a) glycerol ($n = 1{\cdot}47$),

(b) diamond ($n = 2{\cdot}42$).

3. The denser the material, the slower the light. True or false.

4. A ray of light shines into a salt solution as shown.

(a) Calculate the refractive index of the salt solution.

(b) Calculate the velocity of light in the salt solution.

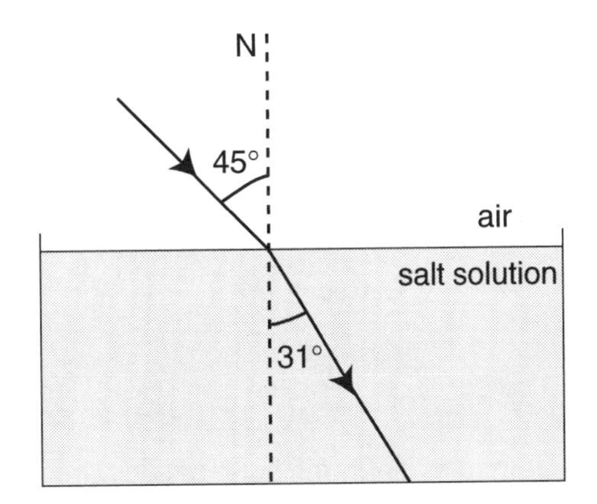

5. A ray of light shines into a dense solution as shown.

(a) Calculate the refractive index of the dense solution.

(b) Calculate the velocity of light in the dense solution.

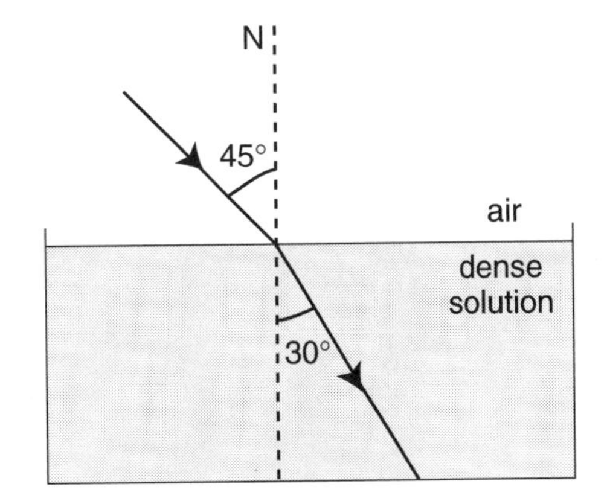

6. Laser light of wavelength 633 nm in air strikes glass (n = 1·50). Calculate the wavelength of light in the glass.

7. Monochromatic light has a wavelength of 500 nm in air. Calculate the wavelength of this light in:

(a) water (n = 1·33);

(b) glass (n = 1·50).

8. A ray of laser light shines from air to water (n = 1·33) as shown.

(a) Given that θ_1 is 25°, calculate θ_2.

(b) If the wavelength of the laser light in air is 633 nm, find the wavelength in water.

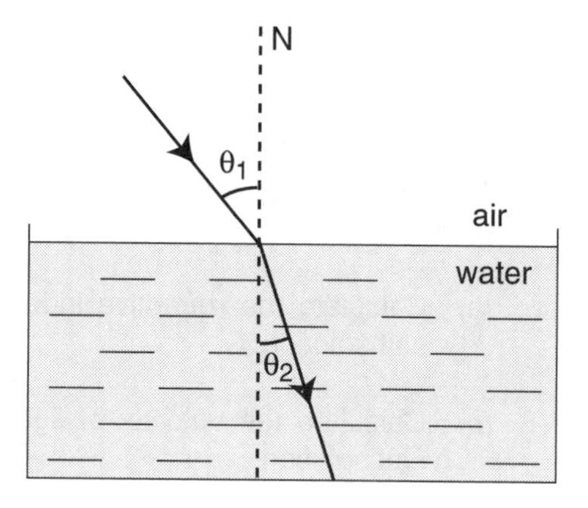

9. In the diagram, light passes from glass A (n = 1·55) into glass B (n = 1·65). If monochromatic light of wavelength 600 nm (in air) was directed at glass A, calculate:

(a) the wavelength of the light in glass A;

(b) the wavelength of the light in glass B;

(c) the frequency of the light in glass A;

(d) the frequency of the light in glass B.

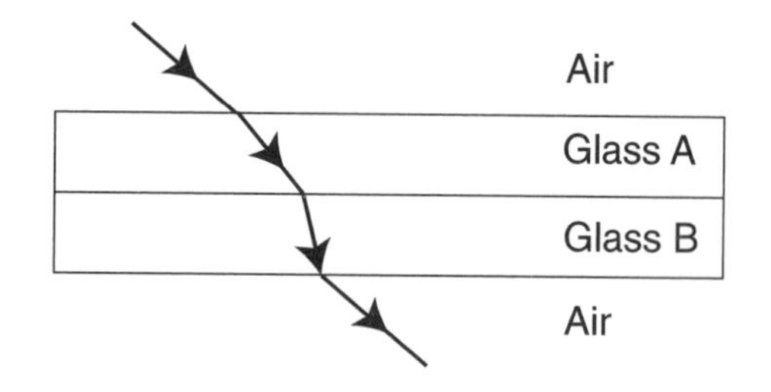

10. White light travelling at 3×10^8 m s^{-1} in air strikes a prism and splits up into the colours of the visible spectrum.

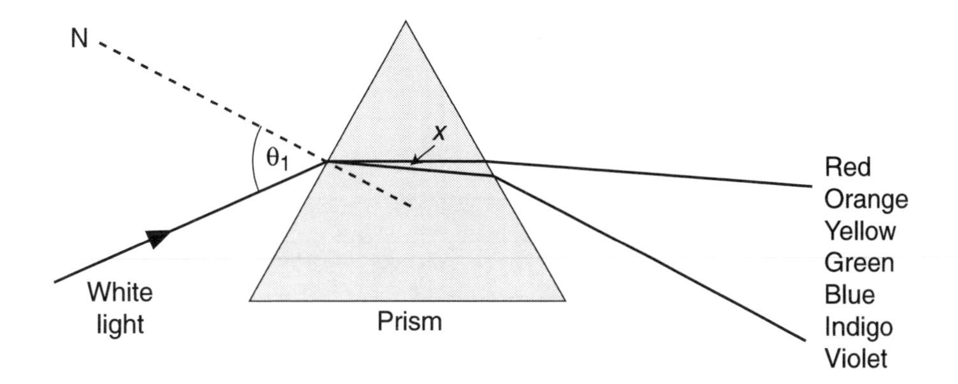

(a) The refractive index for red light in the glass is 1·51. Calculate the velocity of the red light in the glass.

(b) The refractive index for violet light in the glass is 1·53. Calculate the velocity of the violet light in the glass.

(c) Given that $\theta_1 = 40°$, find x, the angle of spread of the beam in the prism.

CRITICAL ANGLE AND TOTAL INTERNAL REFLECTION

1. Light is directed from a piece of perspex (refractive index 1·50) into air. The incident angle is increased until it reaches the critical angle as shown in the diagram.

This means that the angle of refraction is 90°.

Calculate the critical angle for perspex.

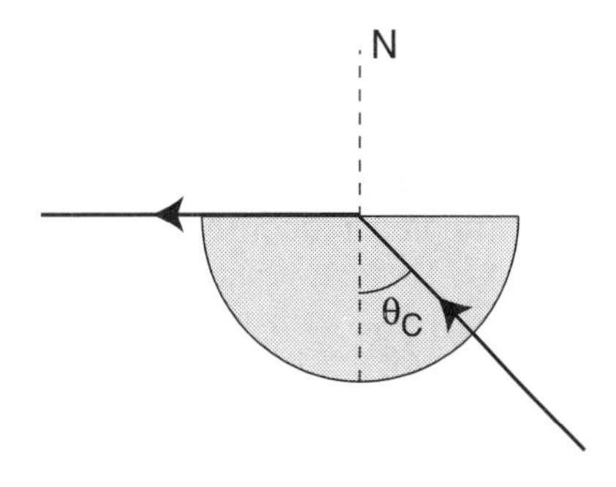

2. The refractive index of water is 1·33, calculate the critical angle for water.

3. The refractive index of diamond is 2·42, calculate the critical angle for diamond.

4. Light is directed into a 45° prism as shown below, i.e., parallel to the bottom edge of the prism.

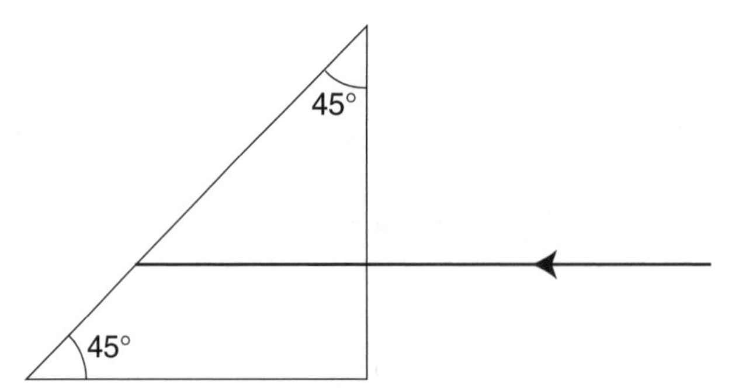

(a) Prove that total internal reflection occurs. (Refractive index of glass is 1·50.)

(b) In which optical instrument is this arrangement found?

5. A ray of light is incident on a glass–air boundary as shown in the diagrams. The refractive index of the glass is 1·50.

(a) Given that light strikes the boundary at 45°, copy and complete the diagram by drawing in the ray after it strikes the boundary. Mark all angles in degrees.

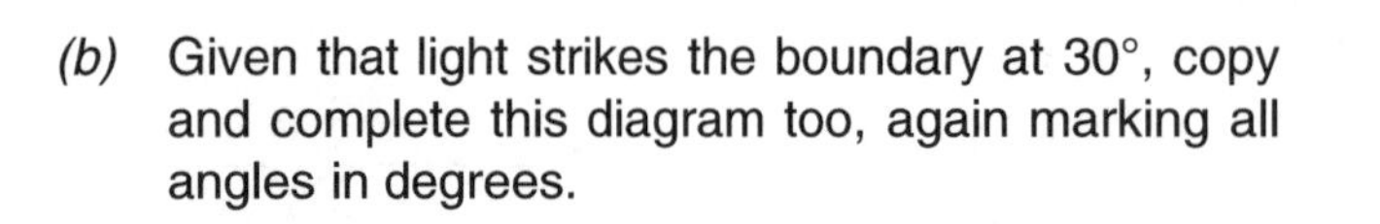

(b) Given that light strikes the boundary at 30°, copy and complete this diagram too, again marking all angles in degrees.

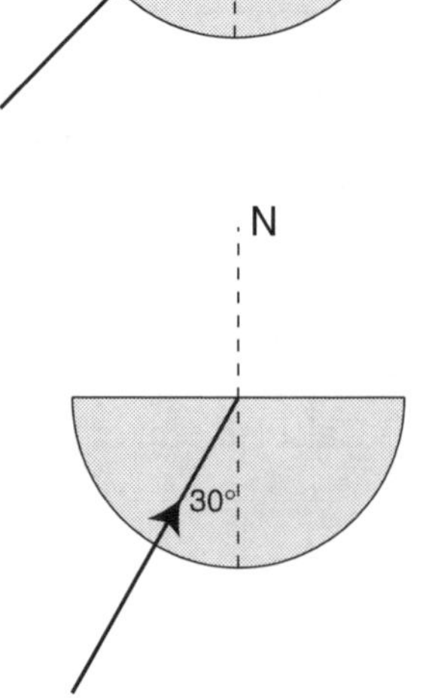

6. A laser beam strikes the edge of a rectangular block of glass of refractive index 1·50 as shown below.

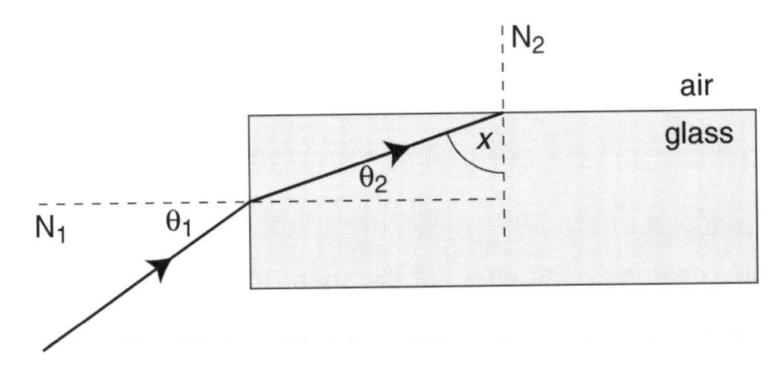

(a) Calculate θ_2 if θ_1 is 45°.

(b) Hence find *x*.

(c) Find the critical angle for this glass.

(d) Does the laser beam escape from the glass at N_2?
You must justify your answer

CHAPTER 13

OPTOELECTRONICS AND SEMICONDUCTORS

INTENSITY OF LIGHT

1. In an experiment to measure the effect of distance (d) from a light source on intensity (I), the following results were obtained.

d / m	I / units	$\frac{1}{d^2}$ / m^{-2}	
0·5	200		
1·0	52		
1·5	24		
2·0	13		
2·5	10		
3·0	7		

(a) Copy and complete the third column.

(b) Plot a graph of I against $\frac{1}{d^2}$.

(c) What is the relationship proved by the graph?

(d) The final column shows a constant (within the limits of experimental error). What is the heading of the final column?

2. A beam of light from a bulb shines through a square window in a black box.

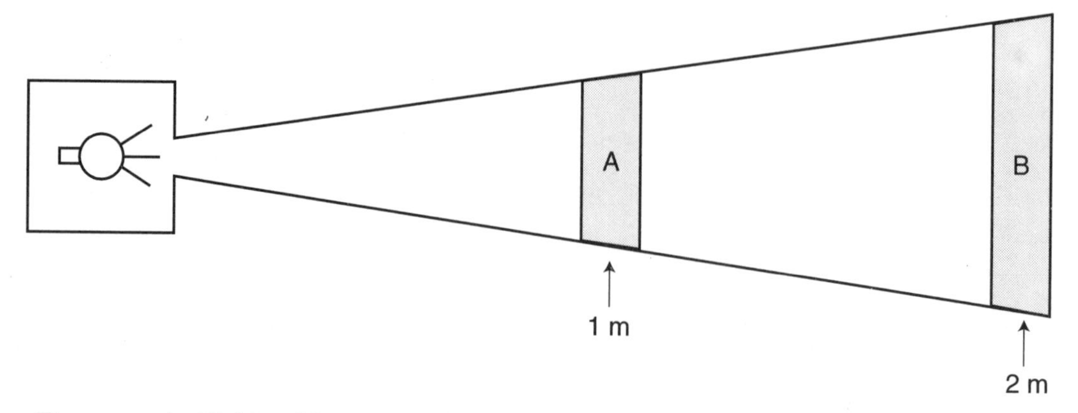

The amount of light striking area A (1 m from the source) is the same as that striking area B (2 m from the source).

What is the numerical relationship between area A and area B?

3. A light source hangs from the ceiling.

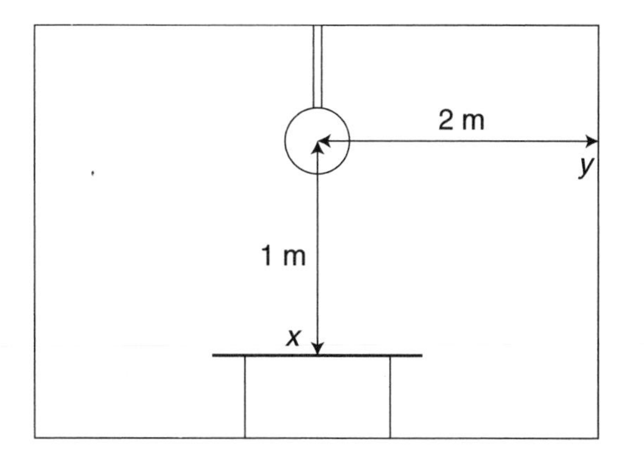

The intensity of light on the table (X) is 8 Wm^{-2}. Find the intensity of light in the wall (Y)?

4. A bulb is the only source of light in a dark room.

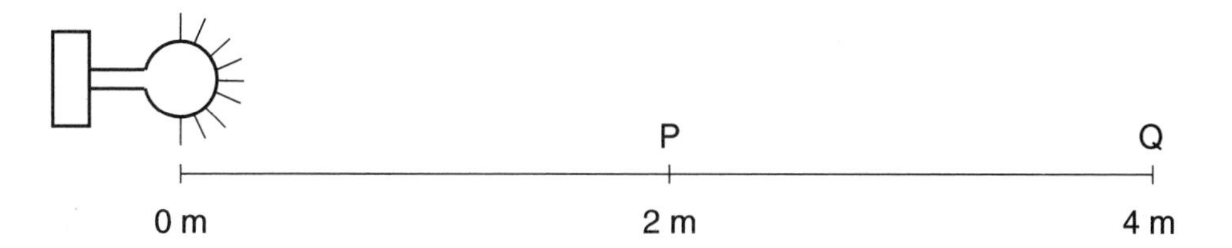

The intensity of light at point Q is 60 units on the light meter. Find the intensity of light at point P.

5. A bulb is the only source of light in a dark room.

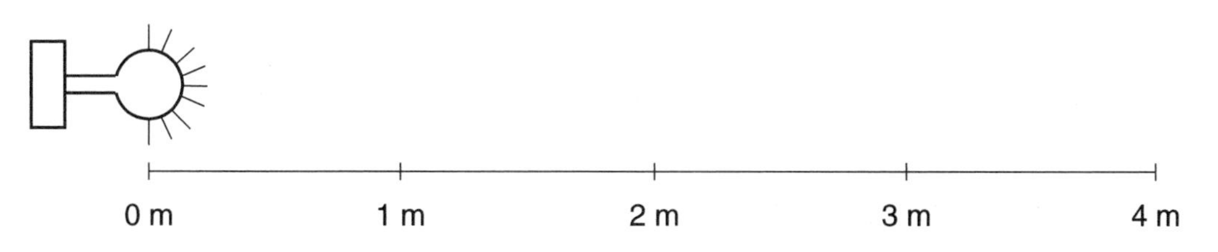

The intensity of light 4 m from the bulb is measured as 30 units on a light meter. Find the intensity of light 3 m from the bulb..

6. Given that intensity is measured in watts per square meter, form an equation for intensity.

THE PHOTOELECTRIC EFFECT

1. In an experiment to examine the effect of ultraviolet light on a charged gold leaf electroscope, an ultraviolet lamp was clamped in position above the clean plate of a charged gold leaf electroscope.

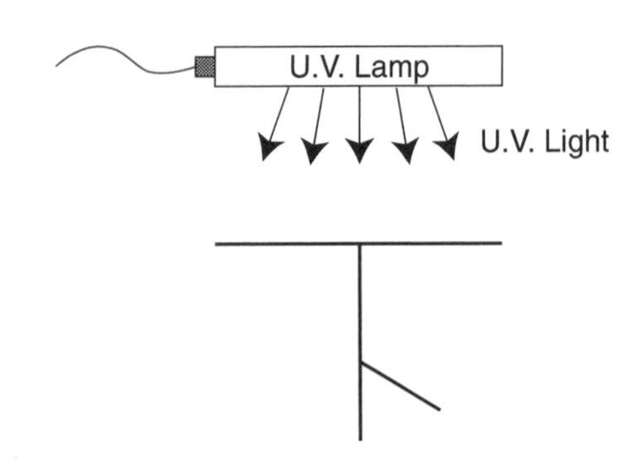

A clean brass plate was used and then a clean zinc plate was used. In each case the experiment was repeated for a positively charged and a negatively charged electroscope.

(a) Copy and complete the final column in the table below by filling in the effect of the ultraviolet light on the leaf of the electroscope.

Clean plate	*Charge on electroscope*	*Effect of U.V. light on leaf*
brass	+	
brass	–	
zinc	+	
zinc	–	

(b) If the experiment was repeated with a white light source, nothing would happen. How does
(i) the frequency and
(ii) the energy
of the white light compare with that of the ultraviolet radiation?

(c) Under what conditions does the photoelectric effect occur?

(d) How could the electroscope leaf in the ultraviolet lamp experiment be made to fall faster?

2. Thermionic emission occurs when electrons are heated at the cathode of (say) a diode valve.

(a) What happens to the reading on the milliammeter when the heater is switched on?

(b) What happens to the reading on the milliammeter when the heater is switched off?

(c) What happens to an individual electron in a shell in an atom when it is heated?

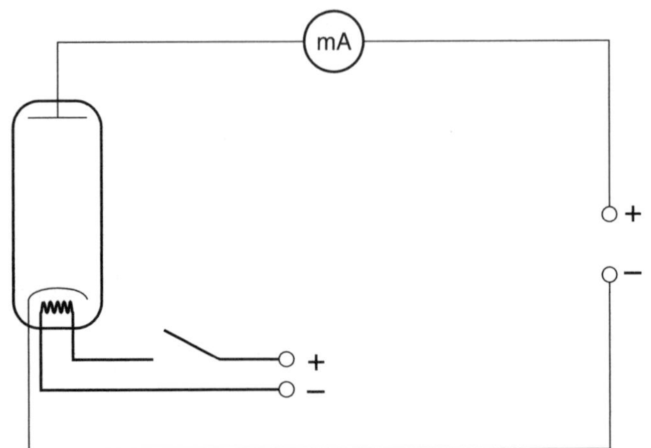

3. Instead of using heat we could use ultraviolet light as an energy source to free electrons from a zinc cathode

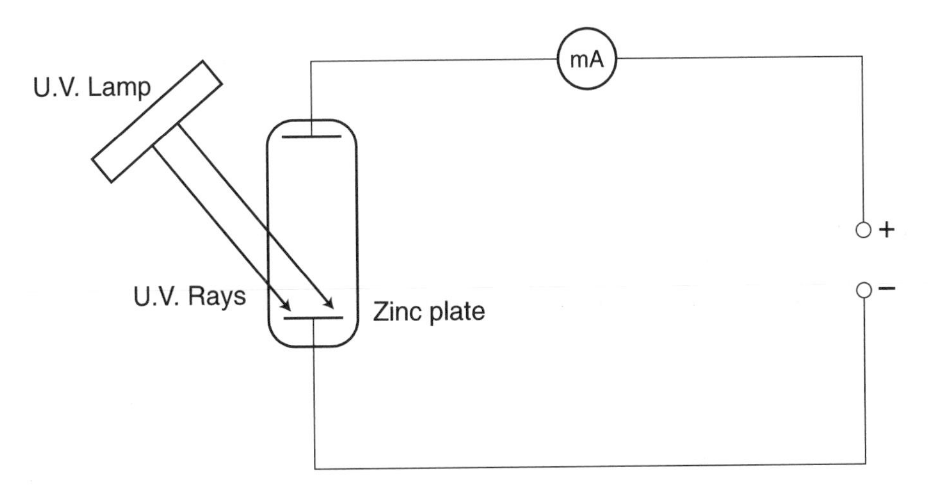

(a) What happens to the reading on the milliammeter when the ultraviolet lamp is switched on?

(b) What happens to the reading on the milliammeter when the ultraviolet lamp is switched off?

(c) What happens to an individual electron in a shell of zinc when an ultraviolet wave strikes it?

Questions 4, 5 and 6 refer to the circuit in Question 3.

4. A graph of the photoelectric current against frequency is shown below.

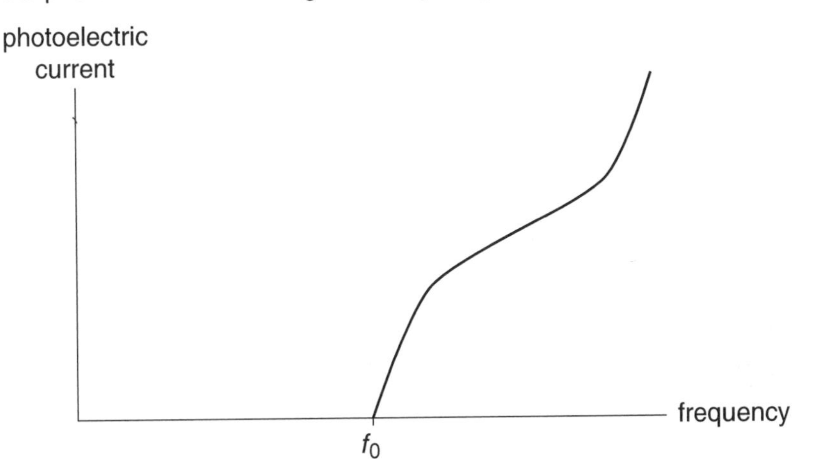

(a) Explain why there is no current below a certain “threshold” frequency f_0.

(b) State the relationship between photoelectric current and frequency.

(c) Suggest why the photoelectric current does this when frequency increases (answer must include reference to individual electrons).

5. *(a)* What happens to the photoelectric current when the intensity is increased?

(b) Sketch a graph of photoelectric current against intensity (no scales required).

(c) What effect would high intensity light of low frequency (i.e., below threshold frequency) have on the photoelectric current?

6. A graph showing how photoelectric current varies with applied potential difference between the plates is shown below.

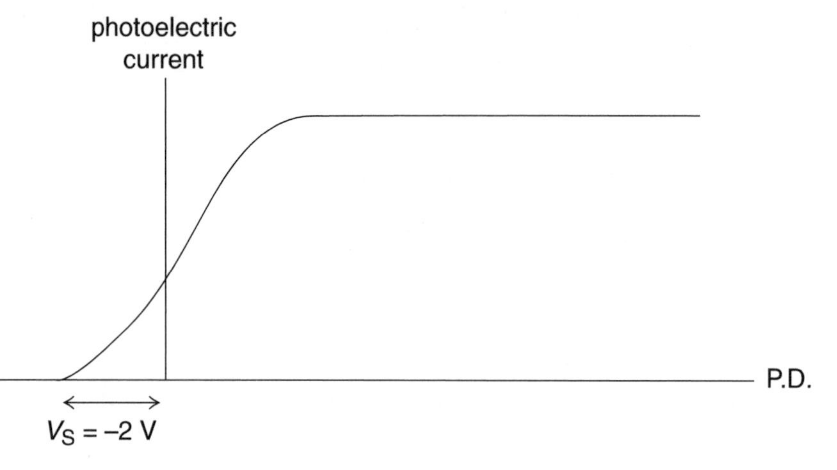

(a) Is it true to say that an increase in applied P.D. produces an increase in the photocurrent?

(b) Explain the plateau achieved by the photocurrent.

(c) What is meant by V_S, the so-called "stopping voltage"?

(d) Is there a photocurrent when the voltage is zero?

7. A photon of orange light has a wavelength of 600 nm.

(a) Calculate the frequency of orange light ($c = 3 \times 10^8$ m s^{-1}).

(b) Calculate the energy of the photon ($h = 6{\cdot}63 \times 10^{-34}$ Js).

8. Calculate the energy of two photons of light of wavelength 589·0 nm and 589·6 nm.

9. The table below lists the minimum energy required to free an electron from the surface of four different metals.

Metal	potassium	sodium	aluminium	copper
Energy / J	$3{\cdot}5 \times 10^{-19}$	$3{\cdot}6 \times 10^{-19}$	$6{\cdot}7 \times 10^{-19}$	$7{\cdot}1 \times 10^{-19}$
Frequency / Hz				

(a) Copy and complete the third row of the table by calculating the minimum frequency (threshold frequency) of light required to free an electron from each metal.

(b) Comment on the connection between the minimum energy required to free an electron and the chemical activity of these four metals.

10. The threshold wavelength for the emission of electrons from a zinc surface is 293 nm.

(a) Calculate the minimum energy required to free an electron from the surface of zinc.

(b) If a photon of wavelength 200 nm strikes an electron on the surface, calculate the kinetic energy of the photoelectron emitted.

SPECTRA

1. Draw a diagram to show how white light can be split into its constituent colours with a prism.

(a) Mark in the positions of longest and shortest wavelengths.

(b) Is this a continuous spectrum?

2. A narrow beam of light from a discharge tube is incident on a prism. A line spectrum is formed.

(a) Draw a sketch of the experimental arrangement.

(b) Is this an emission or absorption spectrum?

(c) How does this line spectrum compare with a continuous spectrum?

3. In order to explain spectral lines in atoms, Bohr put forward the idea that electrons exist in individual shells and orbit the nucleus.

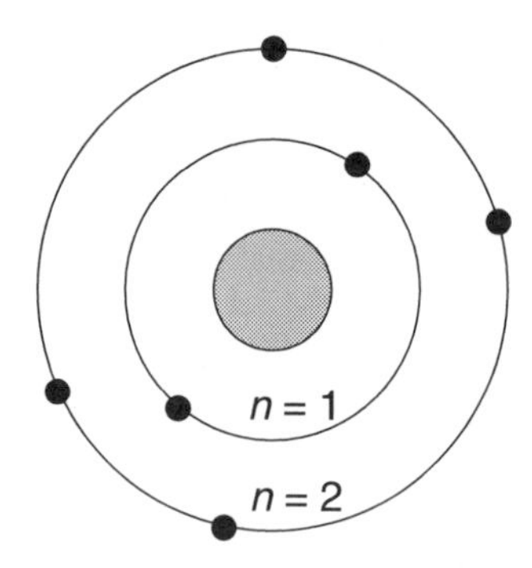

(a) This clashed with the classical theory of planetary motion. What did the classical theory predict would happen to the orbiting electrons?

(b) Bohr talked about transitions between shells to produce spectral lines. What is a transition?

4. The diagram shows four energy levels corresponding to four shells in an atom. When an electron "jumps" from an outer shell to an inner shell, it emits energy in the form of a wave.

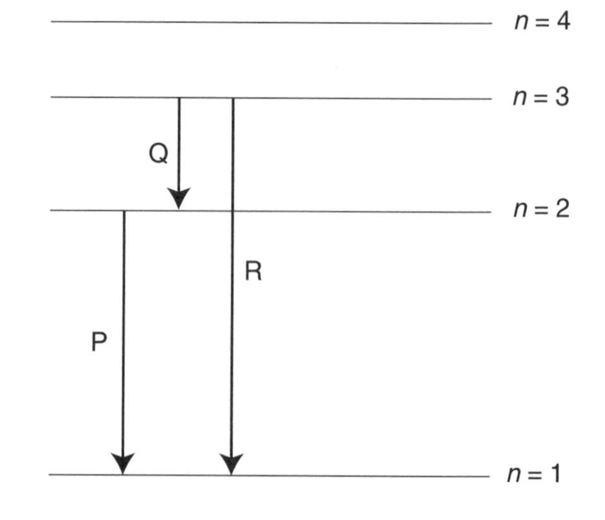

(a) Of the three transitions shown, which one has:
- (i) the highest energy;
- (ii) the lowest energy;
- (iii) the highest frequency;
- (iv) the lowest frequency;
- (v) the longest wavelength;
- (vi) the shortest wavelength?

(b) Copy and complete the diagram by marking in **all** other possible emission transitions.

5. The diagram shows a transition from the first energy level to the second energy level for hydrogen.

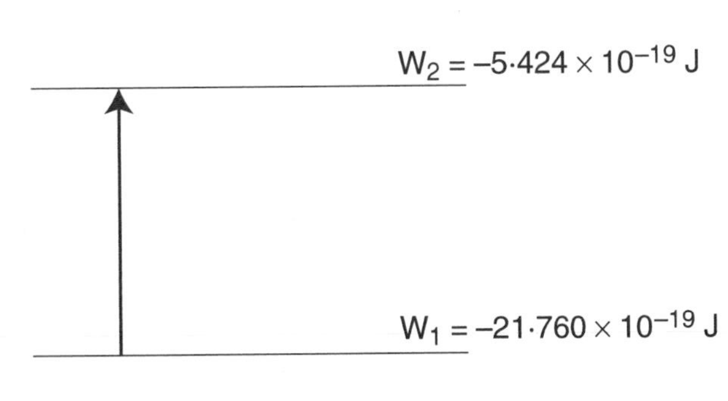

(a) Explain how the electron has an initial energy of $-21{\cdot}760 \times 10^{-19}$ J.

(b) How much energy has the electron absorbed in the transition?

(c) Now that it has reached the second shell, how much more energy does it need to be free of the atom?

6. The diagram shows how an electron in the first shell of hydrogen escapes from the atom.

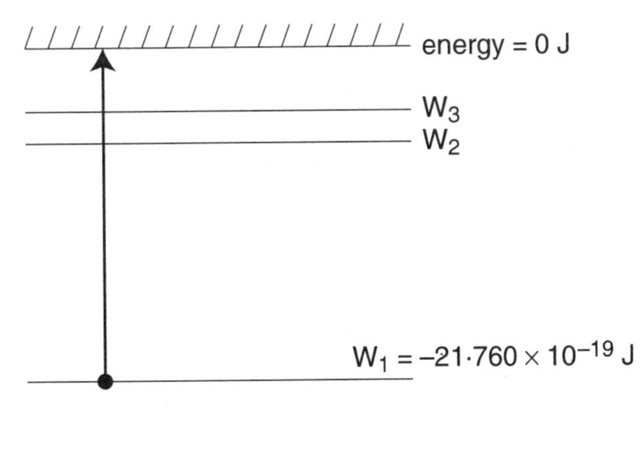

(a) How much energy does the electron need to absorb to be free?

(b) What is the minimum frequency of radiation required to free the electron?

(c) If radiation of higher frequency (than the minimum) were to strike an electron in the first shell of hydrogen, explain what would happen to the electron.

7. An electron can be considered to be either a wave or a particle.

(a) Calculate the momentum of an electron (mass $9{\cdot}11 \times 10^{-31}$ kg) moving at 2×10^8 m s^{-1}.

(b) Given the equation $\lambda = \frac{h}{mv}$ where *h* is Planck's Constant ($6{\cdot}63 \times 10^{-34}$ J s), find the wavelength of the electron moving at 2×10^8 m s^{-1}.

LASERS

1. A laser works on the principle of stimulated emission. What do the letters L A S E R stand for?

2. One photon stimulates an electron in energy level E_X above the ground state.

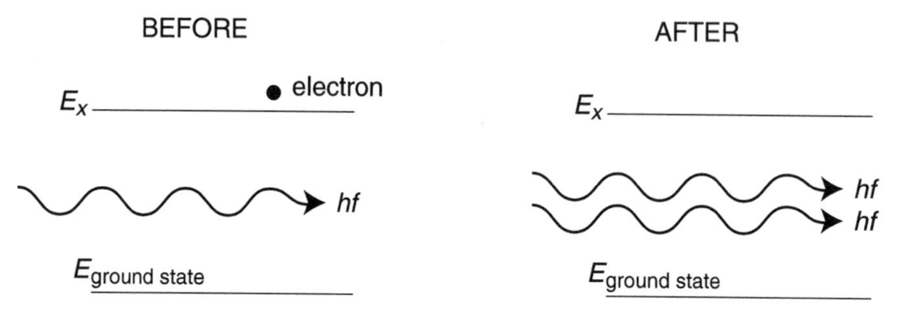

After stimulation, two photons are emitted.

Copy and complete the diagram titled "AFTER" showing clearly what has happened to the electron.

3. Answer true or false to the following statements which refer to the two photons in question 2.

   (a) The two photons have the same frequency.

   (b) The two photons have the same energy.

   (c) The two photons have the same wavelength.

   (d) The two photons are in phase.

4. A helium-neon laser uses two mirrors M_1 and M_2 as shown.

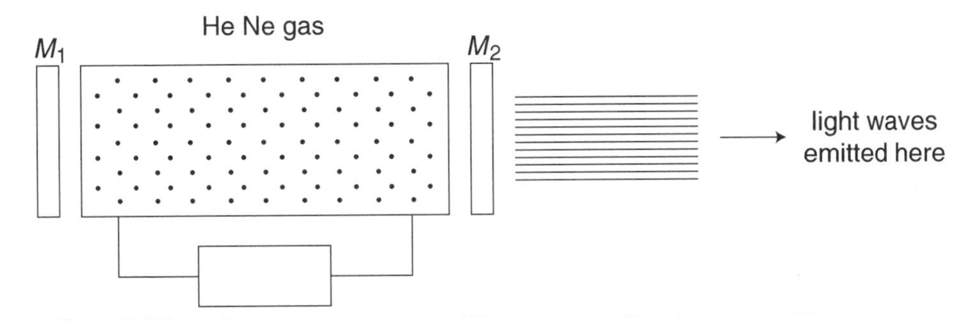

(a) What is the purpose of the mirrors?

(b) Are M_1 and M_2 identical?

5. The wavelength of a school laser is 633 nm. Calculate the energy of a single photon of light emitted from this laser.

6. A laser beam covers an area of a circle of diameter $d = 1 \times 10^{-3}$ m on the laboratory wall.

If the power of the laser is 0·2 mW, calculate the intensity of the beam on the wall.

7. A technician switches on a laser of power 0·2 mW and then switches on a bulb of power 100 W.

John asks the technician, "The bulb is more dangerous than the laser because it has a higher power unit, isn't it?"

Write the technician's reply.

SEMICONDUCTORS

1. Give examples of:

(a) two conductors;

(b) two insulators;

(c) two semiconductors.

2. Silicon has four electrons in its outer shell.
Arsenic has five electrons in its outer shell.
Pure (intrinsic) silicon is doped with arsenic.

(a) Explain how this decreases the resistance of the intrinsic semiconductor.

(b) Is the doped semiconductor *p*-type or *n*-type?

3. Silicon has four electrons in its outer shell.
Indium has three electrons in its outer shell.
Pure (intrinsic) silicon is doped with indium.

(a) Explain how this decreases the resistance of the intrinsic semiconductor.

(b) Is the doped semiconductor *p*-type or *n*-type?

4. In a *p—n* junction diode, electrons from the *n*-type fill holes in the *p*-type. This creates a depletion layer.

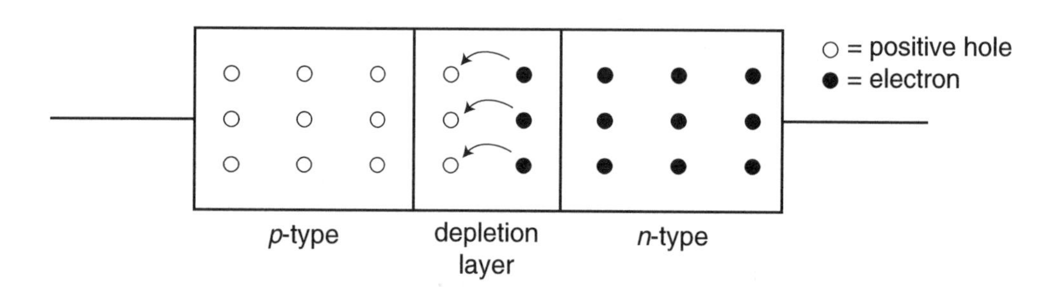

(a) Draw the *p—n* junction above in a circuit showing forward bias.

(b) Do electrons flow across the depletion layer?

(c) Draw the *p—n* junction above in a circuit showing reverse bias.

(d) Do electrons flow across the depletion layer?

5. A particular L.E.D. emits red light when a current passes through it.

(a) Is the junction forward or reversed biased?

(b) What causes this red light?

6. An L.E.D. emits red light of wavelength 650 nm.

Use this to calculate the recombination energy of the L.E.D. (Additional information can be found in the data page.)

7. A diode is rated at 1·2 V, 20 mA (maximum), so it needs a protective resistor in the circuit shown.

Calculate the size of R required to protect the diode.

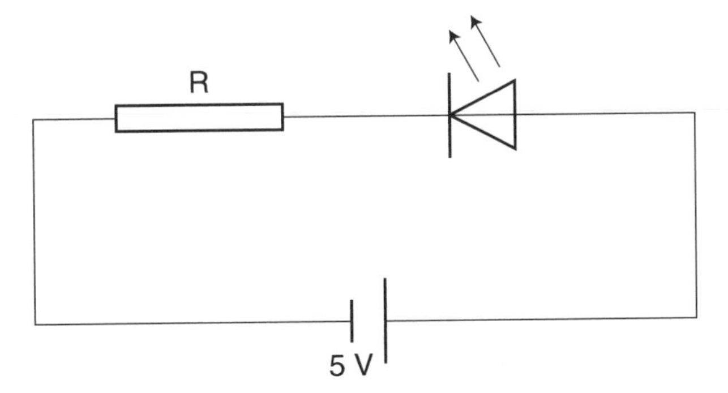

8. A photodiode is connected in the circuit below.

When the light level increases, the resistance of the photodiode decreases.

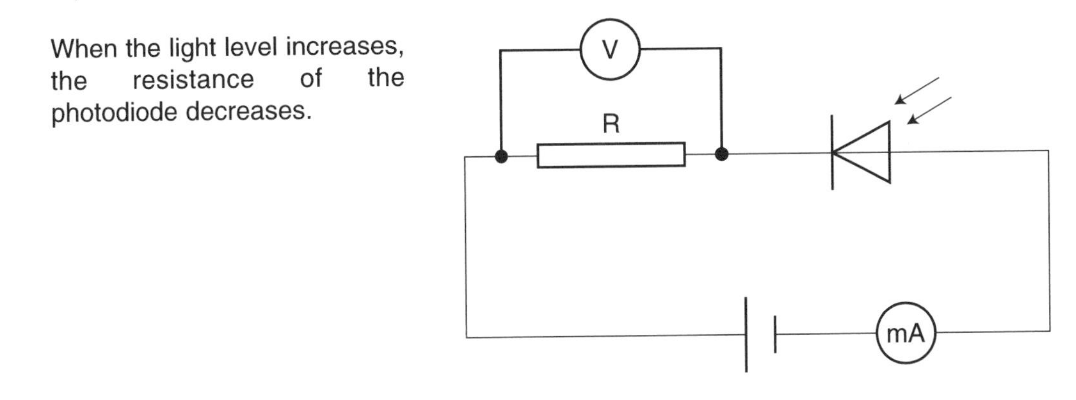

(a) Is the diode connected in photovoltaic mode or photoconductive mode?

(b) What happens to the reading on the milliammeter?

(c) What happens to the reading on the voltmeter?

(d) What (inside the photodiode) causes the decrease in resistance?

9. This is the circuit symbol for an *n*-channel enhancement MOSFET.

Copy the symbol and mark in the gate, the source and the drain.

10. Given the circuit shown.

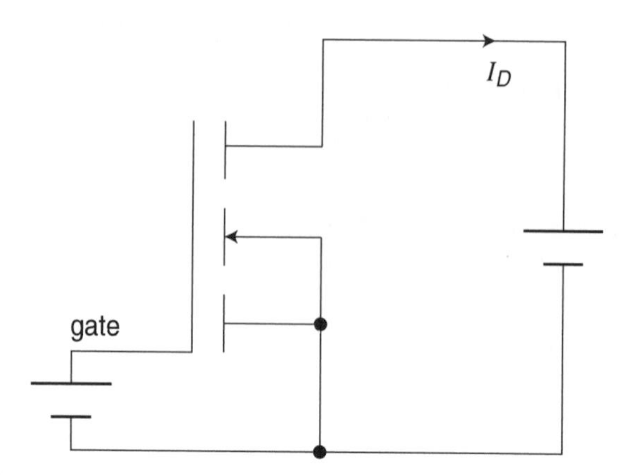

(a) Initially the gate voltage is below the threshold voltage for the MOSFET. What is I_D?

(b) If the gate voltage is increased to 2 V (the threshold for the MOSFET), what happens to I_D?

(c) If the gate voltage is increased to 3 V, what happens to I_D?

11. Given the circuit shown.

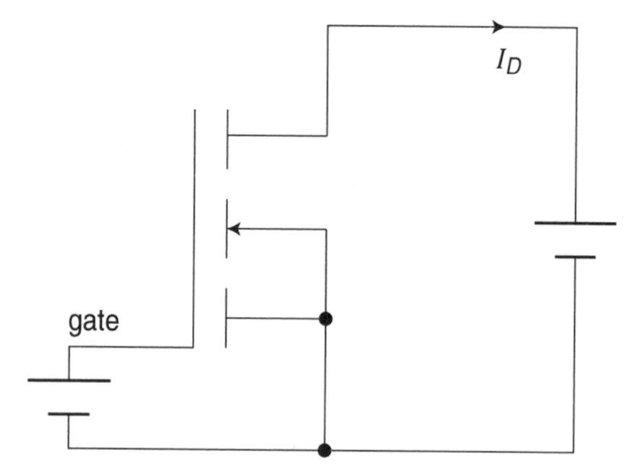

The gate voltage is set at 2·5 V (i.e., above the threshold) and **not** changed.

How could I_D be increased?

12. Given the circuit shown.

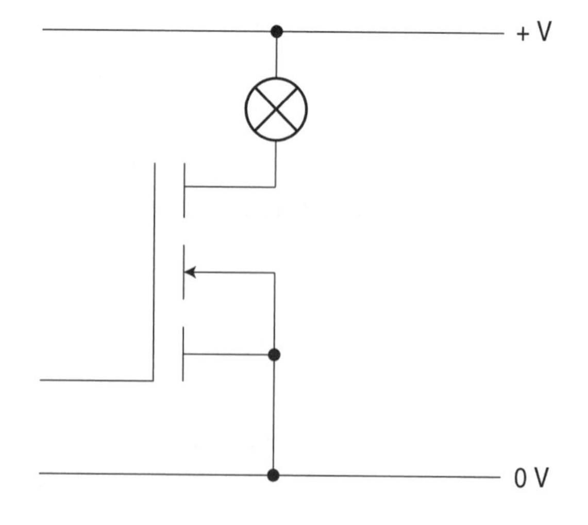

The threshold voltage of this MOSFET is 2 V.

Explain how to use the circuit as a switch to switch on the bulb.

CHAPTER 14

NUCLEAR REACTIONS

THE NUCLEUS

1. The Thomson model of the atom puts electrons on the outside, stuck on to a solid positive mass. This model was based on the results of his thermionic emission experiments.

(a) Draw a diagram of the apparatus Thomson used.

(b) Why did Thomson believe electrons were lighter than protons?

2. The Rutherford model of the atom is based on an experiment by Geiger and Marsden in which alpha particles are fired at a thin gold leaf.

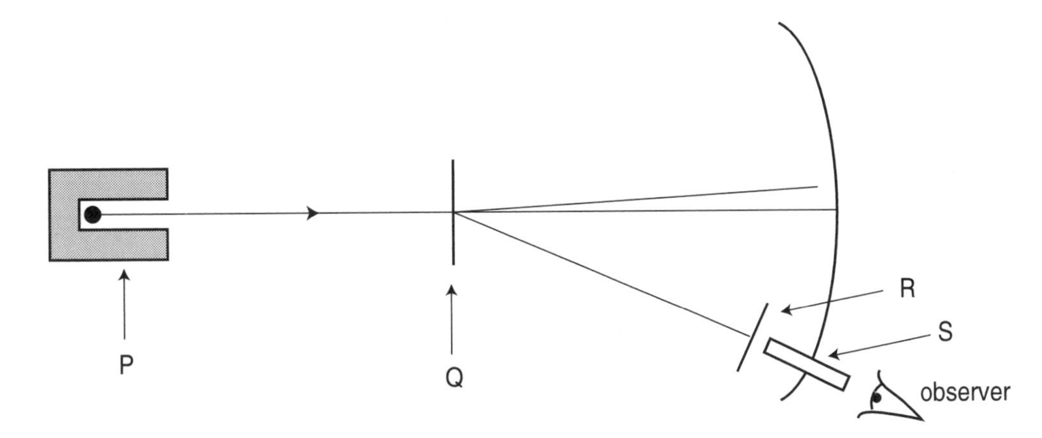

(a) Copy the diagram above and mark in the names of P, Q, R and S.

(b) Rutherford expected most of the alpha particles to go straight through. Is this what happened?

(c) He saw large angle scattering of the alpha particles. How did he explain this scattering?

(d) What experimental evidence led Rutherford to think that most of the atom is space?

(e) Where were the electrons in the Rutherford model of the atom?

3. Rutherford was the first person to put forward the idea of a nucleus.

(a) In a head-on collision, would the alpha particle actually touch the nucleus?

(b) In a "collision" where the alpha particle is deflected by, e.g., 30° from its original horizontal path, the alpha particle did not touch the nucleus. Explain.

(c) What experimental evidence did Rutherford have to back up his claim that the nucleus had a very large mass?

4. Identify the type of radiation (α, β or γ) appropriate to each property.

(a) Undeflected in magnetic field.

(b) Charged negatively.

(c) Can penetrate lead.

(d) Mass of 4 a.m.u.

(e) Charge of $3{\cdot}2 \times 10^{-19}$ C.

(f) Stopped by 2 mm of aluminium.

5. Identify the type of radiation appropriate to each property.

(a) A helium nucleus.

(b) Travels at 90% of the speed of light.

(c) Produces heavy ionisation in air.

(d) Mass of 1 a.m.u. and undeflected by electric field.

6. There are three isotopes of hydrogen:

$$^{1}_{1}H, \quad ^{2}_{1}H \quad \text{and} \quad ^{3}_{1}H.$$

By taking each isotope in turn.

(a) How many protons does each nucleus have?

(b) How many neutrons does each nucleus have?

7. The equation below is an example of beta emission.

$$^{228}_{88}Ra \longrightarrow \, ^{228}_{89}Ac \quad + \quad ^{0}_{-1}e.$$

(a) How many protons are in radium?

(b) How many neutrons are in radium?

(c) How many protons are in actinium?

(d) How many neutrons are in actinium?

(e) Explain how the nucleus gained a proton and yet the mass number remained constant.

8. In the following reactions, fill in the missing mass and atomic numbers.

$$^{14}_{7}\text{N} + ^{1}_{0}n \longrightarrow \text{X} + ^{1}_{1}\text{H}$$

$$^{232}_{90}\text{Th} \longrightarrow \text{Y} + ^{4}_{2}\text{He}$$

$$^{234}_{91}\text{Pa} \longrightarrow \text{Z} + ^{0}_{-1}\text{e}.$$

9. *(a)* Which particles are emitted at each stage in the following decay series?

$$^{216}_{84}\text{Po} \longrightarrow ^{212}_{82}\text{Pb} \longrightarrow ^{212}_{83}\text{Bi} \longrightarrow ^{212}_{84}\text{Po} \longrightarrow ^{208}_{82}\text{Pb}$$

(b) What is the difference between ^{216}Po and ^{212}Po?

10. When $^{235}_{92}\text{U}$ is bombarded with a neutron, it produces the two fission fragments $^{141}_{56}\text{Ba}$ and $^{92}_{36}\text{Kr}$ plus energy.

(a) By writing the equation for the reaction, explain what else is emitted.

(b) How can this type of reaction be controlled in a nuclear reactor?

FISSION AND FUSION

1. Mass can be changed into energy. How much energy can be produced from 1 kg of material?

2. How much energy is formed by changing:

(a) 2 kg of material into energy;

(b) 0·1 kg of material into energy;

(c) 1 gm of material into energy;

(d) 4×10^{-6} kg of material into energy?

3. Energy can be changed into mass. How much mass is produced from 1 joule of energy?

4. How much mass is formed by changing:

(a) 2 J of energy into mass;

(b) 0·1 J of energy into mass

(c) 1×10^{-3} J of energy into mass;

(d) 4×10^{-6} J of energy into mass?

5. When a large nucleus spontaneously breaks down into two smaller nuclei . . .

(a) is it more stable or less stable?

(b) does the large nucleus have a greater or smaller mass than the mass of the two nuclei formed?

6. Distinguish between spontaneous fission and induced fission.

7. In the fission of uranium 235, a neutron strikes the nucleus of U235 and forms two smaller nuclei and two neutrons:

$$ {}^{1}_{0}n + {}^{235}_{92}\mathrm{U} \longrightarrow {}^{137}_{56}\mathrm{Ba} + {}^{97}_{42}\mathrm{Mo} + 2\,{}^{1}_{0}\mathrm{n} + 6\,{}^{0}_{-1}\beta + \text{energy} $$

1·009   235·044   136·917   96·905   1·009 each

Using the masses shown (in a.m.u.) and treating the mass of the electrons as negligible, find:

(a) the total mass before the collision (in a.m.u.);

(b) the total mass after the collision (in a.m.u.);

(c) the mass defect (in a.m.u.);

(d) the mass defect (in kg) [1 a.m.u. = $1{\cdot}66 \times 10^{-27}$ kg];

(e) the energy released in this fission.

8. In the fission of uranium 235, a neutron strikes the nucleus of U235 and forms two smaller nuclei and two neutrons:

$$ {}^{1}_{0}n + {}^{235}_{92}\mathrm{U} \longrightarrow {}^{144}_{56}\mathrm{Ba} + {}^{90}_{36}\mathrm{Kr} + 2\,{}^{1}_{0}\mathrm{n} + \text{energy} $$

$0{\cdot}017 \times 10^{-25}$ $3{\cdot}901 \times 10^{-25}$ $2{\cdot}388 \times 10^{-25}$ $1{\cdot}492 \times 10^{-25}$ $0{\cdot}017 \times 10^{-25}$ each

Using the masses shown (in kg), find:

(a) the total mass before the collision (in kg);

(b) the total mass after the collision (in kg);

(c) the mass defect (in kg);

(d) the energy released in this fission.

9. *(a)* What is meant by a chain reaction?

(b) Explain how neutrons liberated in the fission of uranium 235 make a chain reaction possible.

(c) How are the number of "free" neutrons controlled in a nuclear reactor?

The data table below relates to questions 10, 11 and 12.

Particle	*Mass / kg*
proton	$1{\cdot}672 \times 10^{-27}$
neutron	$1{\cdot}674 \times 10^{-27}$
deuteron ($^{2}_{1}H$)	$3{\cdot}342 \times 10^{-27}$
triton ($^{3}_{1}H$)	$5{\cdot}005 \times 10^{-27}$
helium 3	$5{\cdot}004 \times 10^{-27}$
helium 4	$6{\cdot}642 \times 10^{-27}$

10. One possible fusion reaction is shown below.

$$^{2}_{1}H \quad + \quad ^{2}_{1}H \longrightarrow \ ^{3}_{1}H \quad + \quad ^{1}_{1}p$$

By making reference to the table shown, find:

(a) the total mass before fusion;

(b) the total mass after fusion;

(c) the mass defect;

(d) the energy released in this fusion.

11. One possible fusion reaction is shown below.

$$^{2}_{1}H \quad + \quad ^{2}_{1}H \longrightarrow \ ^{3}_{2}He \quad + \quad ^{1}_{0}n$$

Use the table to find:

(a) the mass defect;

(b) the energy released in this fusion.

12. One possible fusion reaction is shown below.

$$^{2}_{1}H \quad + \quad ^{3}_{1}H \longrightarrow \ ^{4}_{2}He \quad + \quad ^{1}_{0}n$$

Find the energy released in this fusion.

CHAPTER 15

DOSIMETRY AND SAFETY

DOSIMETRY EQUATIONS

Solve problems 1–4 using the equation $A = \frac{N}{t}$

1. A radioactive source produces 100 disintegrations per second. Calculate the activity in becquerels.

2. A radioactive source produces 1000 disintegrations in one minute. Calculate the activity in becquerels.

3. Lyndsey measures background radiation at 30 counts per minute using a Geiger Counter. Convert this to becquerels.

4. The activity of a radioactive source is 1 MBq. How many disintegrations would there be in one minute?

Solve problems 5–8 using the equation $D = \frac{E}{m}$

5. Calculate the absorbed dose when a 2 kg mass absorbs 0·1 J.

6. Calculate the absorbed dose to a radiation worker, mass 80 kg, who absorbs 0·2 J of energy.

7. Calculate the absorbed dose to a radiation worker, mass 60 kg, who absorbs 0·2 J of energy.

8. A radiation worker receives an absorbed dose of 100 μ Gy of γ-radiation and an absorbed dose of 50 μ Gy of fast neutrons.

   Explain why it makes no sense to say the total absorbed dose is 150 μ Gy.

Solve problems 9–12 using the equation $H = DQ$

9. A radiation worker receives an absorbed dose of 50 μ Gy of fast neutrons. Calculate the dose equivalent.

10. A radiation worker receives an absorbed dose of 100 μ Gy of γ-radiation. Calculate the dose equivalent.

11. A radiation worker receives an absorbed dose of 120 μ Gy of fast neutrons and an absorbed dose of 60 μ Gy of β-particles.

Calculate the total dose equivalent.

12. A radiation worker receives the following absorbed doses:
90 μ Gy of β-particles;
130 μ Gy of γ-radiation;
50 μ Gy of α-particles; [N.B. use Q = 20 for α-particles].

Calculate the total dose equivalent.

Solve problems 13–16 using the equation $\dot{H} = \frac{H}{t}$

13. The average annual dose equivalent for members of the public is 2·0 mSv. Calculate the dose equivalent rate in $\mu Sv\ h^{-1}$.

14. A radiation detector on an aircraft gives a reading of 12 $\mu Sv\ h^{-1}$ during a 3-hour flight. Calculate the dose equivalent received by the passengers.

15. The radiation detector in question 14 reads 12 $\mu Sv\ h^{-1}$ during the flight. What happens to the reading when the plane comes in to land?

16. For workers in the radiation industry, the maximum dose equivalent is 50 mSv in a year.

(a) Calculate the dose equivalent rate in $\mu Sv\ h^{-1}$.

(b) Monitoring radiation shields would show if a worker was receiving too much radiation. After three months, what would be the maximum permissible dose equivalent?

17. Name three sources of background radiation.

18. For members of the public, the annual dose equivalent limit is

2 mSv per year / 5 mSv per year / 10 mSv per year?

19. For radiation workers, the annual dose equivalent limit is

10 mSv per year / 50 mSv per year / 100 mSv per year?

20. The dose equivalent rate is reduced by shielding the source.

How else could a safety officer reduce the dose equivalent rate?

HALF-LIFE

1. In an experiment to measure half-life, the table of results below was obtained. Readings were taken every two days.

Time / days	*Corrected count rate / min*
start	130
2	85
4	55
6	38
8	24

Plot a graph of corrected count rate against time and hence find the half-life of the source.

2. After 24 days, a radioactive source shows a count rate of 9 counts per minute (excluding background count rate).

If the half-life of the source is 6 days, what was the original count rate at the start of timing?

3. A source initially has an activity of 160 kBq (corrected) and this drops to 20 kBq (corrected) in 1 hour.

What is the half-life of the source?

HALF-VALUE THICKNESS

1. John tells his teacher that gamma radiation cannot get through 2 cm of lead. John's teacher says, "The lead stops most of the gamma radiation but some will still get through. We measure the half-value thickness for lead."

What is meant by the half-value thickness of lead?

2. Explain the following statements.

(a) The half-value thickness of lead (for γ-rays) is 12 mm.

(b) The half-value thickness of concrete (for γ-rays) is 25 mm.

3. The results below show the measurements made by a geiger counter measuring the activity of a γ-source after it has passed through various thicknesses of lead. Background count rate is 2 Bq.

Thickness of lead / mm	*Count rate recorded / Bq*	*Corrected count rate / Bq*
0	82	
3	69	
6	59	
9	50	
12	42	
15	35	
18	29	
21	25	
24	22	

(a) Copy the final column from the table and fill it in.

(b) Draw a graph of corrected count rate against thickness of lead.

(c) Find the half-value thickness of lead for γ-rays.

UNCERTAINTIES

UNCERTAINTIES

1. Convert the following errors into percentage errors:

(a) 5·0 ± 0·5;

(b) 6·2 ± 0·2;

(c) 6·5 ± 0·5;

(d) 540 ± 5.

2. John measures the height of his little sister Alice four times.

Results
1·30 m
1·31 m
1·30 m
1·29 m

(a) Calculate the average value for Alice's height.

(b) Why did John repeat his measurement to take four readings? Isn't one enough?

3. Paul has five stones. He drops each one down a well and times how long it takes to fall.

Results
1·87 s
1·77 s
1·84 s
1·79 s
1·82 s

(a) Calculate the average time.

(b) Find the approximate random error in the mean.

(c) Express Paul's answer in the form mean ±.

4. Paul's friend Stephen tells him if he repeats his experiment (Question 3) and gets some extra readings the result will be more accurate.

Extra results / s	1·85	1·82	1·80	1·79	1·84

Using all ten results:

(a) calculate the average time;

(b) find the approximate random error in the mean;

(c) express Paul's new answer in the form mean ±.

(d) Was Stephen right?

5. The two diagrams below show the same voltmeter used in two different circuits. The scale error is estimated at ± half a scale division.

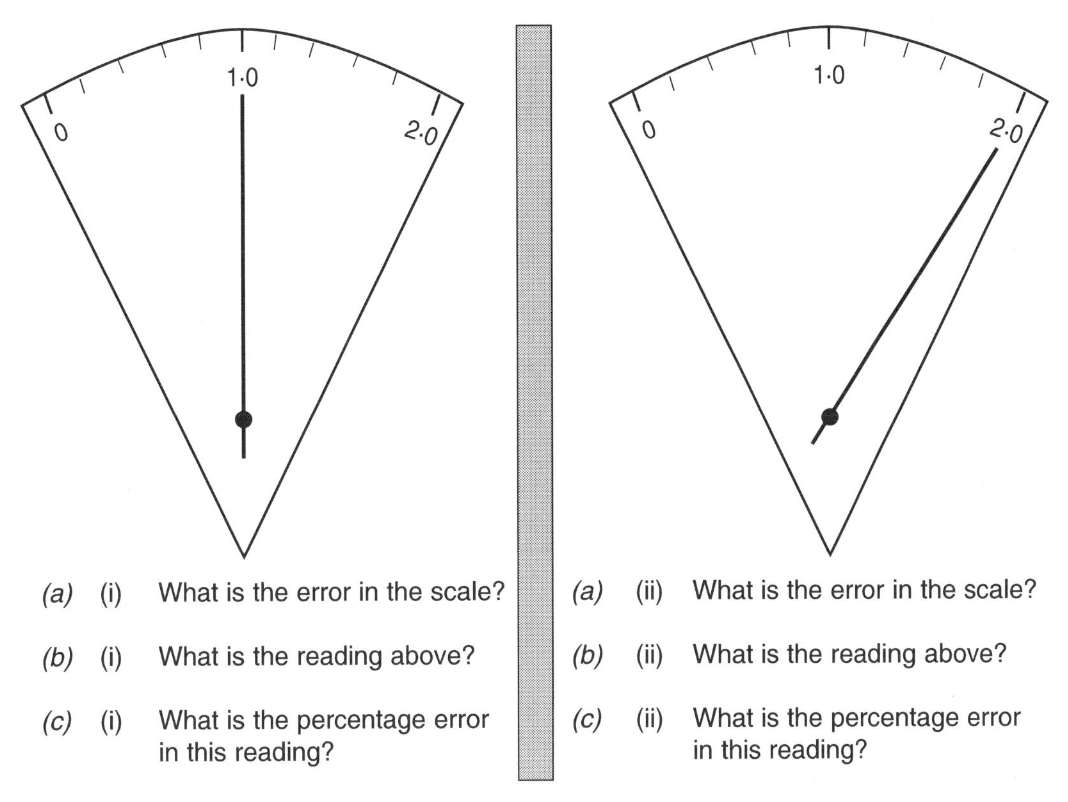

(a) (i) What is the error in the scale?

(b) (i) What is the reading above?

(c) (i) What is the percentage error in this reading?

(a) (ii) What is the error in the scale?

(b) (ii) What is the reading above?

(c) (ii) What is the percentage error in this reading?

6. In an experiment to measure the wavelength of monochromatic light the following equation is used with three measurements.

$$\lambda = \frac{xd}{D} \qquad \begin{aligned} x &= 6 \times 10^{-3}\ \text{m} \pm 1 \times 10^{-3}\ \text{m} \\ d &= 0{\cdot}20\ \text{mm} \pm 0{\cdot}01\ \text{mm} \\ D &= 2{\cdot}00\ \text{m} \pm 0{\cdot}01\ \text{m} \end{aligned}$$

(a) Find the percentage error in x.

(b) Find the percentage error in d.

(c) Find the percentage error in D.

(d) Which of the three errors has the greatest effect on the accuracy of λ?

ANSWERS

UNIT 1 — MECHANICS AND PROPERTIES OF MATTER

CHAPTER 1

Vectors (page 7)

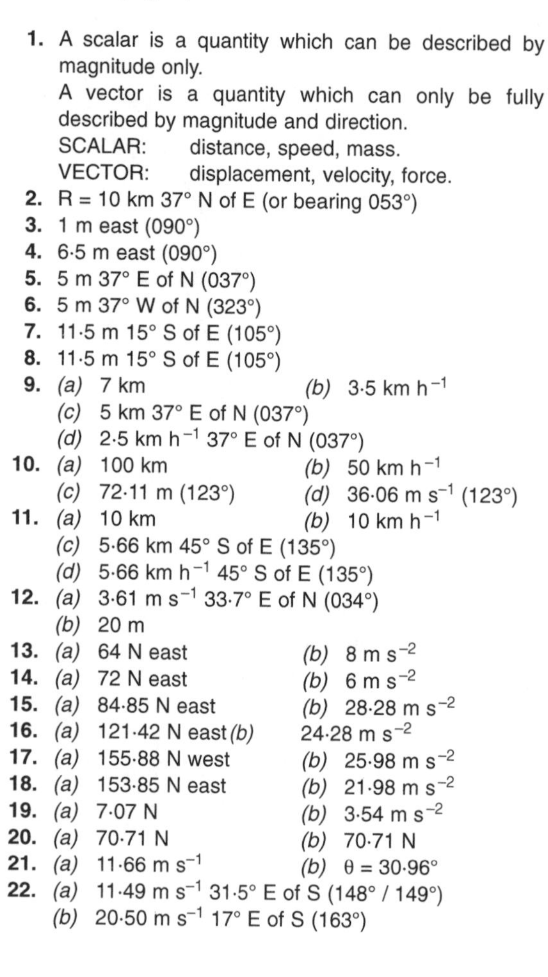

1. A scalar is a quantity which can be described by magnitude only.
   A vector is a quantity which can only be fully described by magnitude and direction.
   SCALAR: distance, speed, mass.
   VECTOR: displacement, velocity, force.
2. R = 10 km 37° N of E (or bearing 053°)
3. 1 m east (090°)
4. 6·5 m east (090°)
5. 5 m 37° E of N (037°)
6. 5 m 37° W of N (323°)
7. 11·5 m 15° S of E (105°)
8. 11·5 m 15° S of E (105°)
9. *(a)* 7 km *(b)* 3·5 km h^{-1}
   (c) 5 km 37° E of N (037°)
   (d) 2·5 km h^{-1} 37° E of N (037°)
10. *(a)* 100 km *(b)* 50 km h^{-1}
    (c) 72·11 m (123°) *(d)* 36·06 m s^{-1} (123°)
11. *(a)* 10 km *(b)* 10 km h^{-1}
    (c) 5·66 km 45° S of E (135°)
    (d) 5·66 km h^{-1} 45° S of E (135°)
12. *(a)* 3·61 m s^{-1} 33·7° E of N (034°)
    (b) 20 m
13. *(a)* 64 N east *(b)* 8 m s^{-2}
14. *(a)* 72 N east *(b)* 6 m s^{-2}
15. *(a)* 84·85 N east *(b)* 28·28 m s^{-2}
16. *(a)* 121·42 N east *(b)* 24·28 m s^{-2}
17. *(a)* 155·88 N west *(b)* 25·98 m s^{-2}
18. *(a)* 153·85 N east *(b)* 21·98 m s^{-2}
19. *(a)* 7·07 N *(b)* 3·54 m s^{-2}
20. *(a)* 70·71 N *(b)* 70·71 N
21. *(a)* 11·66 m s^{-1} *(b)* θ = 30·96°
22. *(a)* 11·49 m s^{-1} 31·5° E of S (148° / 149°)
    (b) 20·50 m s^{-1} 17° E of S (163°)

CHAPTER 2

Graphs of Motion (page 12)

1.

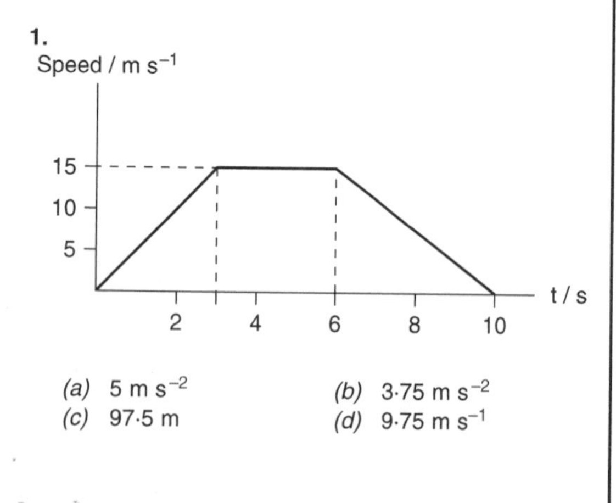

(a) 5 m s^{-2} *(b)* 3·75 m s^{-2}
(c) 97·5 m *(d)* 9·75 m s^{-1}

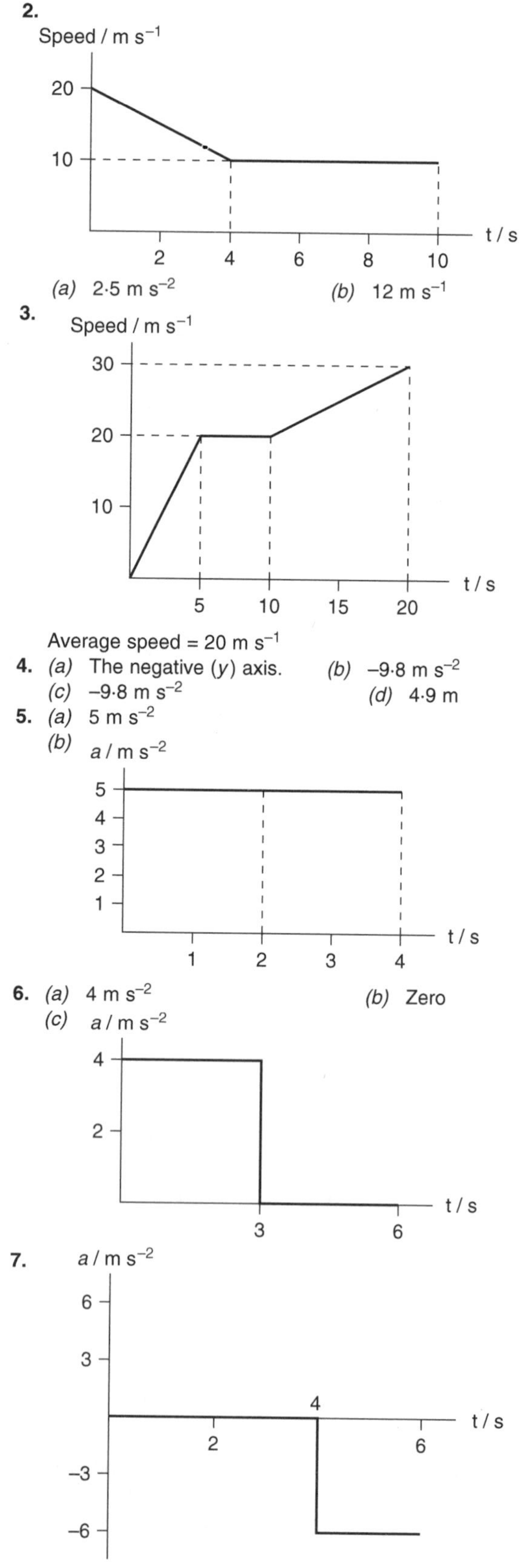

2.

(a) 2·5 m s^{-2} *(b)* 12 m s^{-1}

3.

Average speed = 20 m s^{-1}

4. *(a)* The negative (*y*) axis. *(b)* –9·8 m s^{-2}
   (c) –9·8 m s^{-2} *(d)* 4·9 m
5. *(a)* 5 m s^{-2}
   (b)

6. *(a)* 4 m s^{-2} *(b)* Zero
   (c)

7.

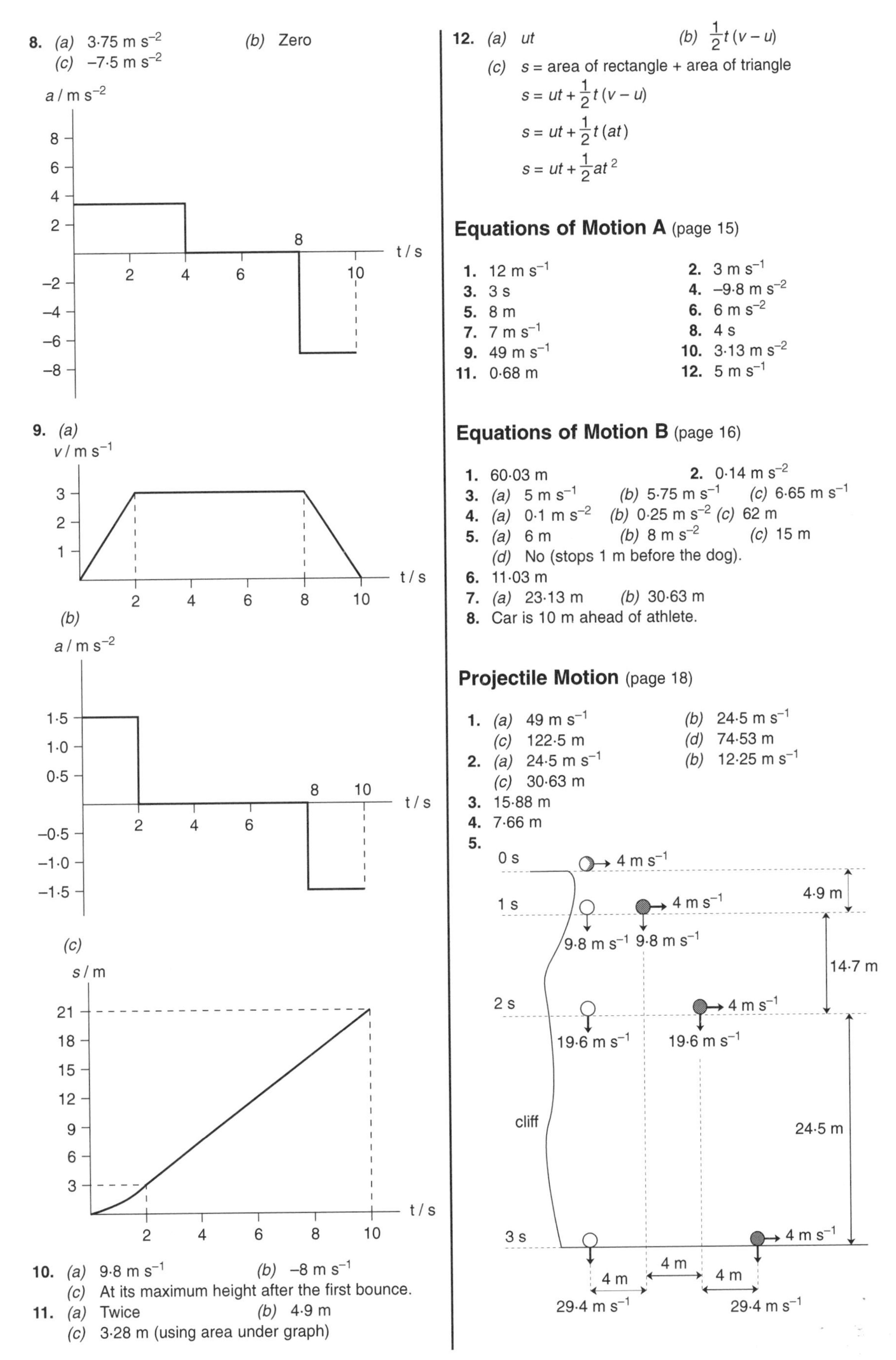

8. *(a)* $3{\cdot}75\ m\ s^{-2}$ *(b)* Zero
(c) $-7{\cdot}5\ m\ s^{-2}$

9. *(a)* *(b)* *(c)*

10. *(a)* $9{\cdot}8\ m\ s^{-1}$ *(b)* $-8\ m\ s^{-1}$
(c) At its maximum height after the first bounce.

11. *(a)* Twice *(b)* 4·9 m
(c) 3·28 m (using area under graph)

12. *(a)* ut *(b)* $\frac{1}{2}t(v-u)$
(c) s = area of rectangle + area of triangle

$$s = ut + \frac{1}{2}t(v-u)$$
$$s = ut + \frac{1}{2}t(at)$$
$$s = ut + \frac{1}{2}at^2$$

Equations of Motion A (page 15)

1. $12\ m\ s^{-1}$
2. $3\ m\ s^{-1}$
3. 3 s
4. $-9{\cdot}8\ m\ s^{-2}$
5. 8 m
6. $6\ m\ s^{-2}$
7. $7\ m\ s^{-1}$
8. 4 s
9. $49\ m\ s^{-1}$
10. $3{\cdot}13\ m\ s^{-2}$
11. 0·68 m
12. $5\ m\ s^{-1}$

Equations of Motion B (page 16)

1. 60·03 m
2. $0{\cdot}14\ m\ s^{-2}$
3. *(a)* $5\ m\ s^{-1}$ *(b)* $5{\cdot}75\ m\ s^{-1}$ *(c)* $6{\cdot}65\ m\ s^{-1}$
4. *(a)* $0{\cdot}1\ m\ s^{-2}$ *(b)* $0{\cdot}25\ m\ s^{-2}$ *(c)* 62 m
5. *(a)* 6 m *(b)* $8\ m\ s^{-2}$ *(c)* 15 m
   (d) No (stops 1 m before the dog).
6. 11·03 m
7. *(a)* 23·13 m *(b)* 30·63 m
8. Car is 10 m ahead of athlete.

Projectile Motion (page 18)

1. *(a)* $49\ m\ s^{-1}$ *(b)* $24{\cdot}5\ m\ s^{-1}$
   (c) 122·5 m *(d)* 74·53 m
2. *(a)* $24{\cdot}5\ m\ s^{-1}$ *(b)* $12{\cdot}25\ m\ s^{-1}$
   (c) 30·63 m
3. 15·88 m
4. 7·66 m
5.

6. *(a)* 19·6 m s^{-1} *(b)* 10 m
7. *(a)* 800 m *(b)* 78·4 m
8. *(a)* 5 s *(b)* 122·5 m
(c) Over the factory.
9. *(a)* 4 s *(b)* 78·4 m
(c) Horizontally 1600 m from the tank.
10. *(a)* 2 s *(b)* 4·9 m
(c) 120 m
11. 2·5 kg
12. 0·31 m
13. *(a)* 2·04 s *(b)* 20·39 m
(c) 4·08 s *(d)* 326·4 m
(e) 82·46 m s^{-1} at 14° above the horizontal (or N of E) (076°)
14. *(a)* 60 m s^{-1} *(b)* 103·92 m s^{-1}
(c) 183·67 m
(d) Based on 6·12 s up and 6·12 s down.
Horizontal range = 1272 m (to nearest meter)
15. *(a)* 843·25 m *(b)* 4020 m (to nearest meter)
16. 4·31°

CHAPTER 3

Newton's Second Law (page 25)

1. 12 N
2. 8 m s^{-2}
3. *(a)* 6 N to the right *(b)* 4 m s^{-2}
(c) 14 m s^{-1}
4. *(a)* 4 m s^{-2} *(b)* 3·6 N
5. *(a)* 4 m s^{-2}
(b)

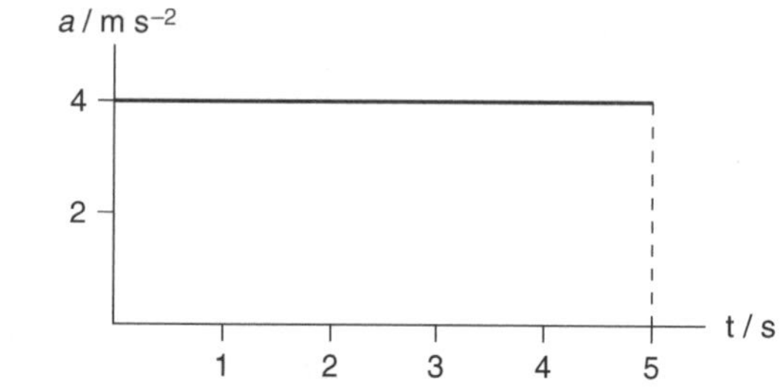

(c)

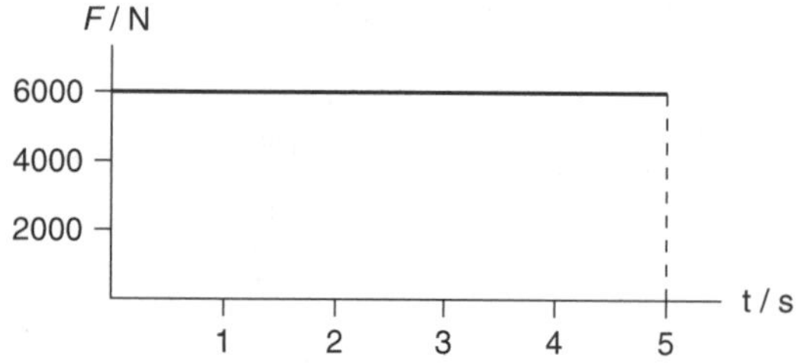

6. *(a)* 4 m s^{-2}
(b)

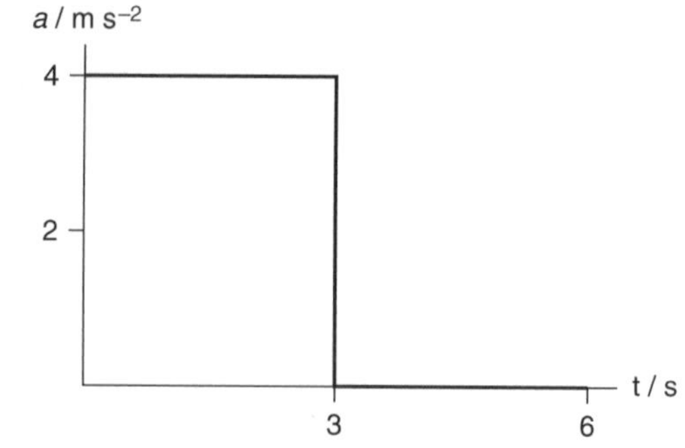

(c)

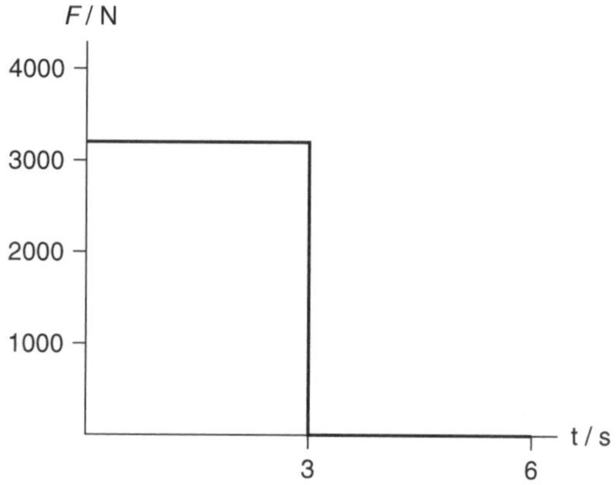

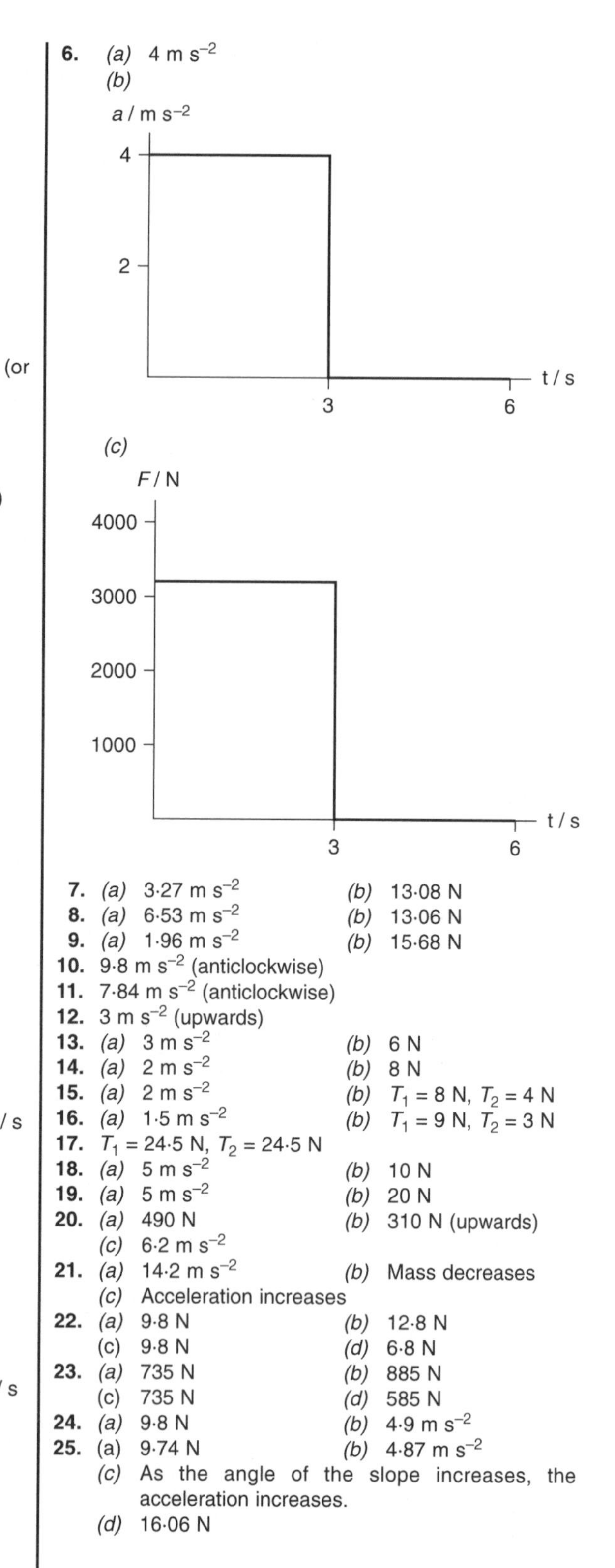

7. *(a)* 3·27 m s^{-2} *(b)* 13·08 N
8. *(a)* 6·53 m s^{-2} *(b)* 13·06 N
9. *(a)* 1·96 m s^{-2} *(b)* 15·68 N
10. 9·8 m s^{-2} (anticlockwise)
11. 7·84 m s^{-2} (anticlockwise)
12. 3 m s^{-2} (upwards)
13. *(a)* 3 m s^{-2} *(b)* 6 N
14. *(a)* 2 m s^{-2} *(b)* 8 N
15. *(a)* 2 m s^{-2} *(b)* T_1 = 8 N, T_2 = 4 N
16. *(a)* 1·5 m s^{-2} *(b)* T_1 = 9 N, T_2 = 3 N
17. T_1 = 24·5 N, T_2 = 24·5 N
18. *(a)* 5 m s^{-2} *(b)* 10 N
19. *(a)* 5 m s^{-2} *(b)* 20 N
20. *(a)* 490 N *(b)* 310 N (upwards)
(c) 6·2 m s^{-2}
21. *(a)* 14·2 m s^{-2} *(b)* Mass decreases
(c) Acceleration increases
22. *(a)* 9·8 N *(b)* 12·8 N
(c) 9·8 N *(d)* 6·8 N
23. *(a)* 735 N *(b)* 885 N
(c) 735 N *(d)* 585 N
24. *(a)* 9·8 N *(b)* 4·9 m s^{-2}
25. (a) 9·74 N *(b)* 4·87 m s^{-2}
(c) As the angle of the slope increases, the acceleration increases.
(d) 16·06 N

E_P, E_K, Work Done and Power (page 33)

1.

E_P			E_K
313·6 J	16 m	2kg	0 J
235·2 J	12 m		78·4 J
156·8 J	8 m		156·8 J
78·4 J	4 m		235·2 J
0 J	ground level		313·6 J

2. 20 m s^{-1}
3. E_K at Y = E_P at X

$$\frac{1}{2}mv^2 = mgh$$
$$v^2 = 2gh$$
$$v = \sqrt{2gh}$$

4. *(a)* 0·98 J *(b)* 0·98 J
   (c) 1·98 m s^{-1}
5. 589·96 W
6. 4·85 m s^{-1}
7. *(a)* 9·8 J *(b)* 7·22 J
   (c) Some potential energy is "lost", i.e., converted into heat and sound due to friction with the slope.
   (d) 1·29 N
8. 39·6 m s^{-1}
9 *(a)* 2·97 m s^{-1} *(b)* 1·49 m
   (c) 1·23 m

CHAPTER 4

Momentum A (page 37)

1. *(a)* 240 kg m s^{-1} *(b)* 160 kg m s^{-1}
   (c) 40 kg m s^{-1} *(d)* 24 kg m s^{-1}
   (e) 60 kg m s^{-1}
2. 7 m s^{-1}
3. 6·2 m s^{-1}
4. 59 kg
5. 0·75 kg
6. 2 m s^{-1}
7. 3·6 m s^{-1}
8. 2 m s^{-1}
9. 3 m s^{-1}
10. 2 m s^{-1}
11. 1·5 m s^{-1}
12. 4 m s^{-1}
13. *(a)* Mom before = 2×6 = 12 kg m s^{-1}; Mom after = 4×3 = 12 kg m s^{-1} } same
    (b) 36 J *(c)* 18 J
14. *(a)* 2·4 m s^{-1} *(b)* 36 J
    (c) 14·4 J *(d)* Inelastic
15. 23·3 m s^{-1}
16. YES by 3 m s^{-1} (33 m s^{-1})
17. *(a)* 39·2 kg m s^{-1} *(b)* 98·0 kg m s^{-1}
    (c) 152·88 kg m s^{-1}
18. *(a)* To the left *(b)* 5 m s^{-1} (to the left)
    (c) 5000 N acting (to the right)
19. *(a)* 15 m s^{-1} (to the right)
    (b) 2550 N acting against the cars.
20. *(a)* 19·6 m s^{-1} *(b)* 4·9 m s^{-1}
    (c) 0·20 s
21. 0·4 m s^{-1}
22. *(a)* Card, light gate + timer.
    (b) List

Length of card
Time on timer
Mass of bullet
Mass of trolley + wood

Fix a card to the wooden block. Fire the bullet horizontally at the wooden block. Trolley moves off and card cuts the light beam.

(c) 100 m s^{-1}

Momentum B (page 42)

1. Momentum — Kinetic energy
2. *(a)* 4 m s^{-1} *(b)* 1·6 J
   (c) 1·6 J *(d)* Elastic
3. *(a)* 0·02 kg m s^{-1} *(b)* –0·002 kg m s^{-1}
   (c) 0·55 m s^{-1}
   (d) E_K before = 0·01 J
   E_K after = $6{\cdot}15 \times 10^{-3}$ J
   i.e., E_K is not conserved.
   ∴ Inelastic

Momentum C (page 43)

1. 6 m s^{-1}
2. 3 m s^{-1}
3. 2 m s^{-1}
4. 3 m s^{-1}
5. 1 m s^{-1}
6. 0·75 m s^{-1}
7. 2×10^5 m s^{-1}
8. 2·67 m s^{-1}

Impulse (page 44)

1. Increases — Decreases
2. *(a)* (–) 150 kg m s^{-1} *(b)* (–) 600 N
3. 13·33 N
4. 750 m s^{-1}
5. 1·2 m s^{-1}
6. *(a)* To complete the circuit and enable timer 1 to measure the time of contact.
   (b) When the boot makes contact with the ball.
   (c) When the ball leaves the boot.
   (d) The time taken for the diameter of the ball to pass through the light beam.
7. *(a)* 4 m s^{-1} *(b)* 400 N
   (c) 500 m s^{-2}
8. *(a)* (–) 9 kg m s^{-1} *(b)* 180 N
9. *(a)* 3·13 Ns
   (b) 6·25 m s^{-1} (or 6·26 m s^{-1})
   (c) 0·39 m
10. 0·03 s

CHAPTER 5

Density and Pressure (page 47)

1. 1×10^5 Nm^{-2}
2. 1×10^5 Nm^{-2}
3. 29·4 Nm^{-2}
4. $7{\cdot}5 \times 10^3$ Nm^{-2}
5. *(a)* 1×10^5 Nm^{-2} *(b)* $1{\cdot}5 \times 10^6$ N
   (c) Pressure will be less 1000 feet above sea level.
   Reasons
   1. Molecules "colder" moving more slowly fewer collisions per second.
   2. Air density is less higher above sea level.
6. *(a)* 13 720 Nm^{-2} *(b)* 27 440 Nm^{-2}
7. *(a)* $2{\cdot}63 \times 10^4$ Nm^{-2} *(b)* $4{\cdot}8 \times 10^5$ Nm^{-2}
   (c) Same force acting but woman has smaller area ∴ pressure greater.
   (d) Spread force over a large area reduces pressure and stops sinking into snow.
8. 100 N
9. *(a)* 2·5 kg m^{-3} *(b)* 1·25 kg m^{-3}
   (c) 0·625 kg m^{-3} *(d)* 0·125 kg m^{-3}
   (e) $1{\cdot}25 \times 10^{-2}$ kg m^{-3} *(f)* 0·5 kg m^{-3}
   (g) 1·0 kg m^{-3} *(h)* 2·5 kg m^{-3}
   (i) 10 kg m^{-3} *(j)* 5×10^3 kg m^{-3}
10. *(a)* m is mass of container with some air.
    $M - m$ is mass of **extra** air pumped in.
    (b)

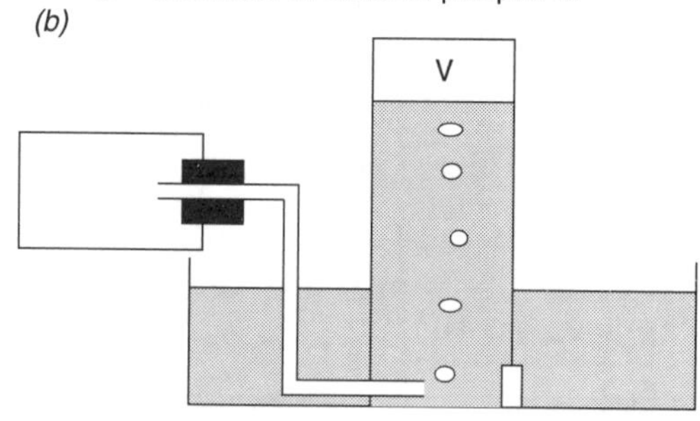

Air flows into the water in the gas jar. Volume of air can be measured inside gas jar.
    (c) Air leaves container until pressure is equalised, i.e., when pressure inside container equals atmospheric pressure.
    (d) Density $= \dfrac{\text{mass}}{\text{volume}} = \dfrac{M - m}{V}$
11. 58 800 Nm^{-2}
12. *(a)* 8820 Nm^{-2} *(b)* 21 560 Nm^{-2}
13. *(a)* 980 Nm^{-2} *(b)* 0·01 m^2
    (c) 9·8 N
14. *(a)* 1372 Nm^{-2} *(b)* 26·89 N
15. *(a)* 1960 Nm^{-2} *(b)* 3920 Nm^{-2}
    (c) 78·4 N *(d)* 156·8 N
    (e) 78·4 N upwards

CHAPTER 6

Boyle's Law (page 51)

1. *(a)*

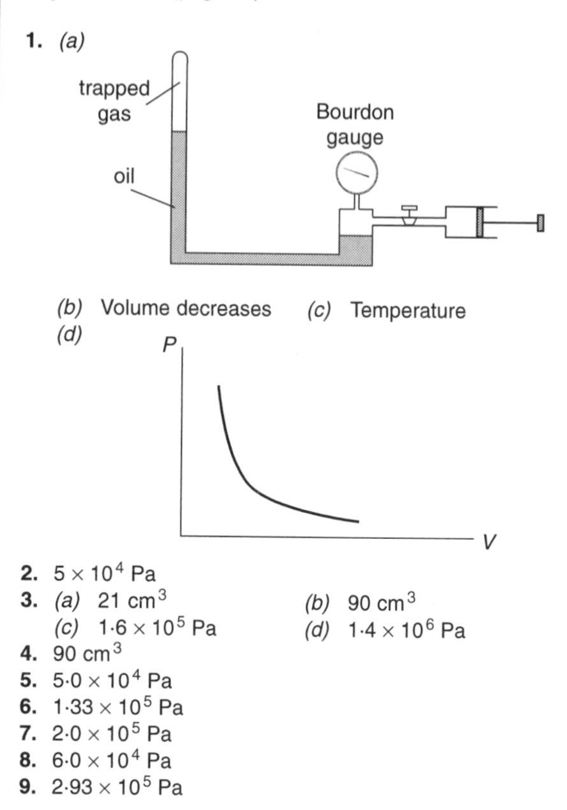

(b) Volume decreases *(c)* Temperature
(d)

2. 5×10^4 Pa
3. *(a)* 21 cm^3 *(b)* 90 cm^3
   (c) $1{\cdot}6 \times 10^5$ Pa *(d)* $1{\cdot}4 \times 10^6$ Pa
4. 90 cm^3
5. $5{\cdot}0 \times 10^4$ Pa
6. $1{\cdot}33 \times 10^5$ Pa
7. $2{\cdot}0 \times 10^5$ Pa
8. $6{\cdot}0 \times 10^4$ Pa
9. $2{\cdot}93 \times 10^5$ Pa

Pressure Law (page 53)

1. *(a)*

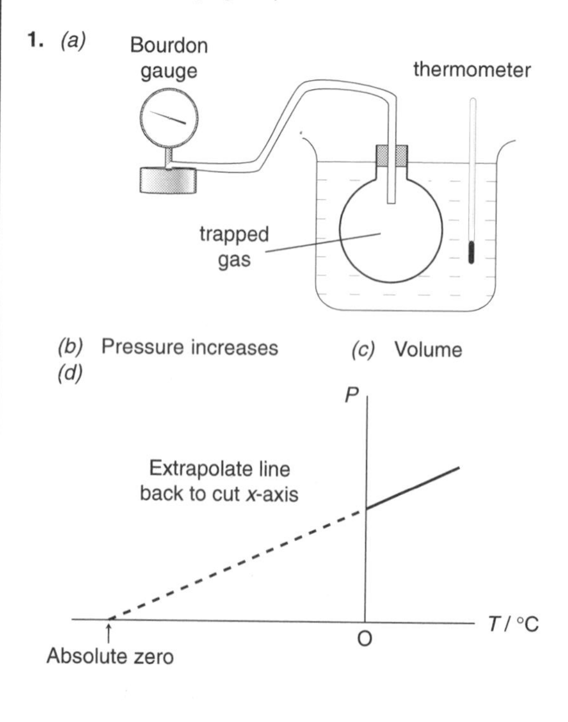

(b) Pressure increases *(c)* Volume
(d)

P
Extrapolate line back to cut x-axis
Absolute zero
O
T / °C

2. $1{\cdot}17 \times 10^5$ Pa
3. *(a)* $1{\cdot}5 \times 10^5$ Pa *(b)* 100 K
   (c) $1{\cdot}33 \times 10^5$ Pa *(d)* 210 K or –63° C
4. *(a)* $\left.\begin{array}{l} \frac{P_1}{T_1} = \frac{1{\cdot}5 \times 10^5}{293} = 341 \\ \frac{P_2}{T_2} = \frac{1{\cdot}20 \times 10^5}{352} = 341 \end{array}\right\}$ same
   (b) This is TRUE — introduces error
   Solution
   1. Very short tube
   or
   2. Fit Bourdon gauge directly on to flask.
   (c) Yes.

Charles' Law (page 54)

1. *(a)*

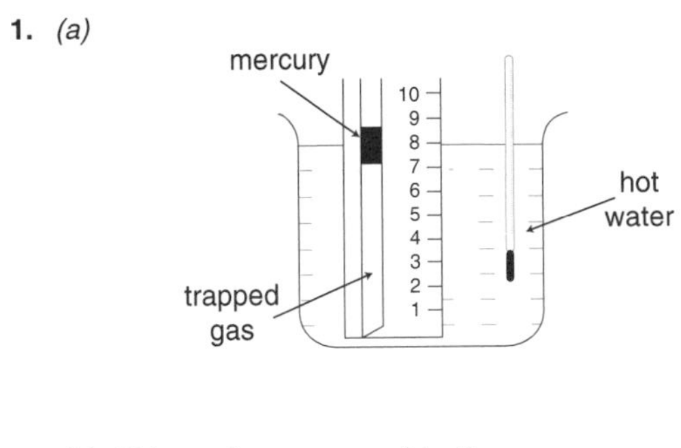

(b) Volume decreases *(c)* Pressure

(d)

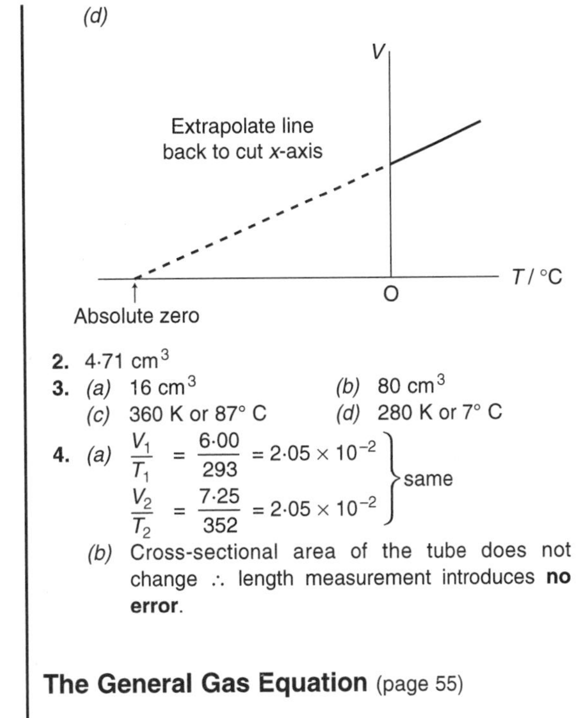

2. $4{\cdot}71$ cm^3
3. *(a)* 16 cm^3 *(b)* 80 cm^3
   (c) 360 K or 87° C *(d)* 280 K or 7° C
4. *(a)* $\left.\begin{array}{l} \frac{V_1}{T_1} = \frac{6{\cdot}00}{293} = 2{\cdot}05 \times 10^{-2} \\ \frac{V_2}{T_2} = \frac{7{\cdot}25}{352} = 2{\cdot}05 \times 10^{-2} \end{array}\right\}$ same
   (b) Cross-sectional area of the tube does not change ∴ length measurement introduces **no error**.

The General Gas Equation (page 55)

1. 160 cm^3
2. $4{\cdot}2 \times 10^5$ Pa
3. 131 °C
4. 1×10^5 Pa
5. $1{\cdot}38 \times 10^6$ Pa

UNIT 2

ELECTRICITY AND ELECTRONICS

CHAPTER 7

Charges Moving in Electric Fields (page 56)

1. $3{\cdot}2 \times 10^{-18}$ J
2. $1{\cdot}02 \times 10^{-17}$ J
3. 20 V
4. *(a)* 8×10^{-17} J *(b)* 8×10^{-17} J
5. *(a)* $1{\cdot}6 \times 10^{-16}$ J *(b)* $1{\cdot}6 \times 10^{-16}$ J
   (c) $1{\cdot}87 \times 10^7$ m s^{-1}
6. *(a)* $4{\cdot}8 \times 10^{-16}$ J *(b)* $4{\cdot}8 \times 10^{-16}$ J
   (c) $3{\cdot}25 \times 10^7$ m s^{-1}
7. *(a)* $6{\cdot}4 \times 10^{-16}$ J *(b)* $6{\cdot}4 \times 10^{-16}$ J
   (c) $3{\cdot}75 \times 10^7$ m s^{-1}
8. *(a)* $7{\cdot}2 \times 10^{-16}$ J *(b)* $7{\cdot}2 \times 10^{-16}$ J
   (c) $3{\cdot}98 \times 10^7$ m s^{-1}
9. *(a)* $2{\cdot}96 \times 10^7$ m s^{-1} *(b)* $4{\cdot}19 \times 10^7$ m s^{-1}
   (c) V is not proportional to velocity $V \propto v^2$
10. 2562 V
11. *(a)* $1{\cdot}6 \times 10^{-15}$ J *(b)* $5{\cdot}93 \times 10^7$ m s^{-1}
12. $1{\cdot}25 \times 10^{16}$ electrons

E.M.F. and Internal Resistance (page 60)

1. *(a)* 10 V *(b)* 2 V *(c)* 1 Ω
2. (a) 7·5 V *(b)* 2·5 V *(c)* 1 Ω
3. (a) 4·8 V *(b)* 1·2 V *(c)* 3 Ω
4. (a) 1·2 V *(b)* 0·3 V *(c)* 1 Ω
5. *(a)* 6 Ω in every circuit.
   (b) As external resistance is increased, the "lost volts" decreases.
6. *(a)* 2 Ω for each circuit.
   (b) (i) $\frac{1}{3}$ (ii) $\frac{1}{5}$ (iii) $\frac{1}{6}$ *(c)* circuit (iii)
7. *(a)* 24 V for each circuit
   (b) circuit (ii) *(c)* circuit (iii) — 36 W
8. 1·5 V
9. *(a)* 1·5 A *(b)* 7 Ω
10. *(a)* 12 V *(b)* 8 V *(c)* 4 V
    (d) 4 Ω *(e)* 2 Ω

11. *(a)*

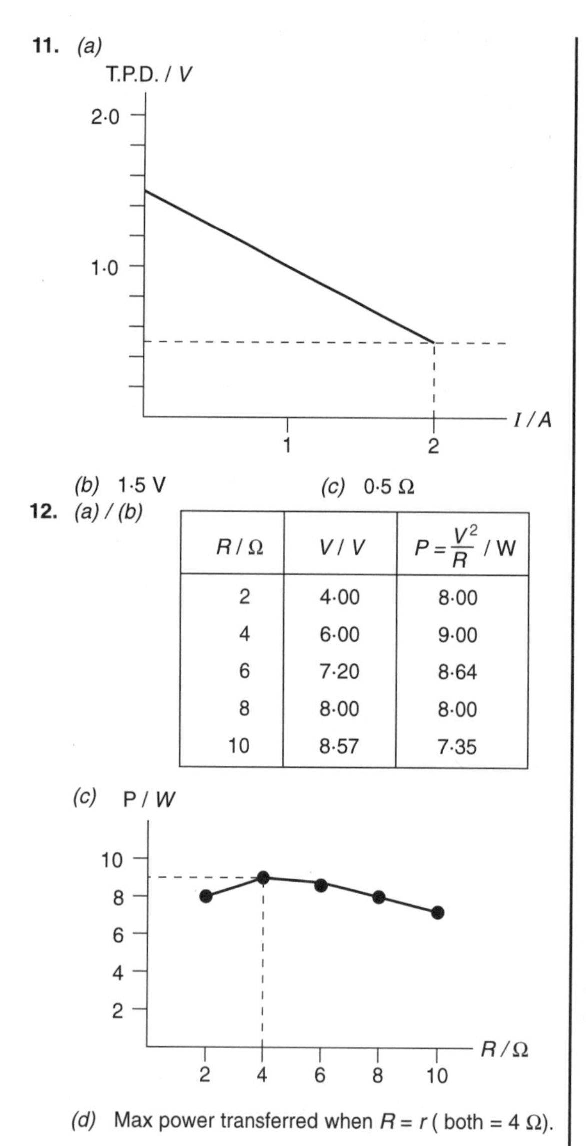

(b) 1·5 V *(c)* 0·5 Ω

12. *(a) / (b)*

R / Ω	V / V	$P = \frac{V^2}{R}$ / W
2	4·00	8·00
4	6·00	9·00
6	7·20	8·64
8	8·00	8·00
10	8·57	7·35

(c) P / W

(d) Max power transferred when $R = r$ (both = 4 Ω).

Resistors in Circuits (page 67)

1. 16 Ω
2. 21 Ω
3. *(a)* 60 Ω *(b)* 28 Ω
4. *(a)* 150 Ω *(b)* 90 Ω
5. *(a)* 9 Ω *(b)* 21 Ω *(c)* 24 Ω
6. 2 Ω
7. 12 Ω
8. 16 Ω
9. *(a)* 12 Ω *(b)* 1 A
10. *(a)* 0·75 A *(b)* 1 A
11. *(a)* 0·5 A *(b)* 0·33 A
12. *(a)* 5 V *(b)* 10 V
13. *(a)* 15 V *(b)* 20 V
14. *(a)* 3 V *(b)* 4·8 V

Ohm's Law and Power (page 71)

1. *(a)* 6 Ω
   (b) $A_1 = 2$ A, $A_2 = 1$ A, $A_3 = 1$ A
2. *(a)* 9 Ω *(b)* 12 V
3. *(a)* 10 Ω *(b)* 9·6 V
   (c) $A_1 = 2{\cdot}4$ A, $A_2 = 0{\cdot}8$ A, $A_3 = 1{\cdot}6$ A
4. *(a)* 15 Ω
   (b) $A_1 = 2$ A, $A_2 = 0{\cdot}5$ A
   (c) 24 V
5. *(a)* $V_1 = 6$ V, $V_2 = 10$ V
   (b) 5 Ω *(c)* 8 Ω
6. 24 Ω
7. *(a)* 2 A *(b)* 6 V *(c)* 3 Ω
8. *(a)* 1 A *(b)* 2 A *(c)* 4 Ω
9. 18 W
10. 18 Ω ⟶ 18 W
    18 Ω ⟶ 18 W
    9 Ω ⟶ 36 W
    4 Ω ⟶ 36 W
    12 Ω ⟶ 12 W

Wheatstone and Meter Bridges (page 74)

1. *(a)* 0 V *(b)* 18 000 Ω
2. *(a)* 0 V *(b)* 5000 Ω
3. *(a)* 0 V *(b)* 750 Ω
4. *(a)* 0 V *(b)* 40 000 Ω
5. *(a)* 40 Ω *(b)* Increased
6. *(a)* 3 V *(b)* 3 V *(c)* 3 V
   (d) 3 V *(e)* 3 V *(f)* 3 V
   (g) 0 V
7. *(a)* 0 V *(b)* 40 Ω
8. *(a)* 0 V *(b)* 300 Ω
9. *(a)* 0 V *(b)* 9414 Ω
10. *(a)* 0 μA *(b)* 1500 Ω
    (c) To protect the galvanometer from large currents.
11. $l_1 = 30$ cm
12. *(a)* $l_1 = 40$ cm *(b)* $l_1 = 25$ cm
    (c) After G reads ZERO, switch S is closed to remove r from the circuit before any final adjustment is made.

Unbalanced Wheatstone Bridge (page 78)

1. *(a)*

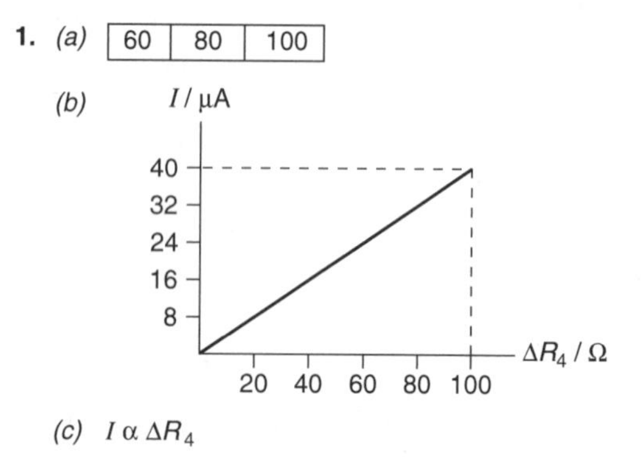

(b)

(c) $I \propto \Delta R_4$

2. *(a)*

−16	−24	−32	−40
−40	−60	−80	−100

(b)

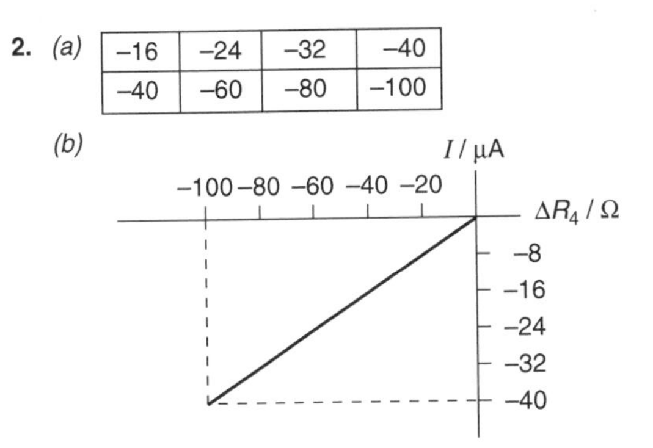

(c) $I \propto \Delta R_4$

3. No. Because the graph is only a straight line near the origin (i.e., for small charges in R_4).

4. *(a)* 6 V *(b)* 2 V *(c)* 4 V
 (d) 1·5 V *(e)* 4·5 V *(f)* 4·5 V
 (g) 4 V *(h)* 0·5 V

5. *(a)* 4 V *(b)* 3·75 V *(c)* 0·25 V
 (d) No

CHAPTER 8

Oscilloscopes and Voltage (page 80)

1. *(a)* *(b)*

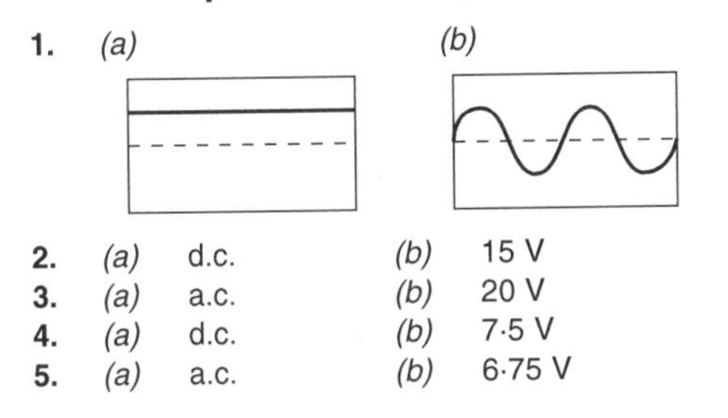

2. *(a)* d.c. *(b)* 15 V
3. *(a)* a.c. *(b)* 20 V
4. *(a)* d.c. *(b)* 7·5 V
5. *(a)* a.c. *(b)* 6·75 V

Oscilloscopes and Frequency (page 81)

1. *(a)* 12 waves *(b)* 3 waves

2. *(a)* 50 m s = 0·05 s *(b)* 20 Hz
3. *(a)* 4 m s = 0·004 s *(b)* 250 Hz
4. *(a)* 20 m s = 0·02 s *(b)* 50 Hz
5. *(a)* 0·67 s *(b)* 1·5 Hz

Peak and R.M.S. Voltage (page 82)

1. 7·07 V
2. 33·94 V
3.

R.M.S. Voltage
10·61 V
35·36 V
53·03 V
169·71 V

4.

Peak Voltage
8·48 V
28·28 V
141·42 V
325·27 V

CHAPTER 9

Capacitance, Charge, Voltage, Current, Time (page 83)

1. *(a)*

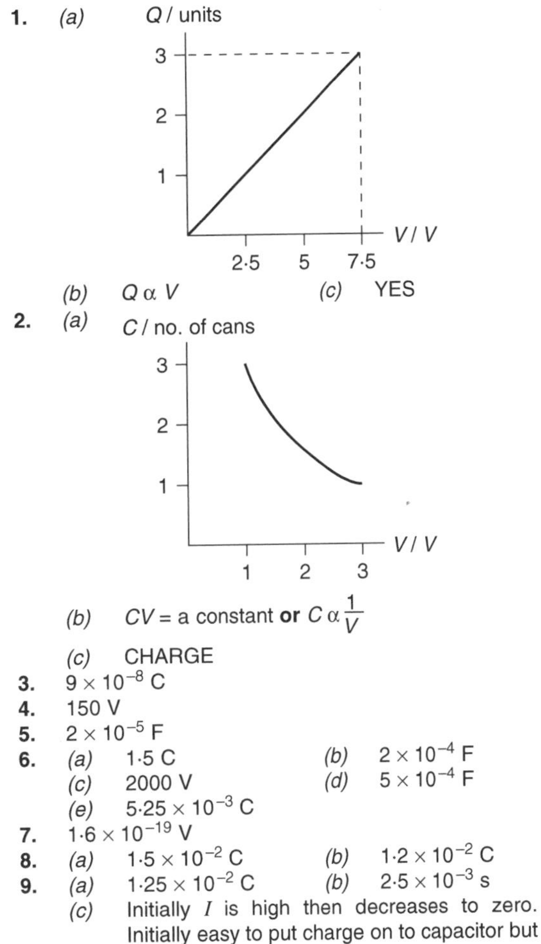

(b) $Q \propto V$ *(c)* YES

2. *(a)*

(b) CV = a constant **or** $C \propto \frac{1}{V}$

(c) CHARGE

3. 9×10^{-8} C
4. 150 V
5. 2×10^{-5} F
6. *(a)* 1·5 C *(b)* 2×10^{-4} F
 (c) 2000 V *(d)* 5×10^{-4} F
 (e) $5{\cdot}25 \times 10^{-3}$ C
7. $1{\cdot}6 \times 10^{-19}$ V
8. *(a)* $1{\cdot}5 \times 10^{-2}$ C *(b)* $1{\cdot}2 \times 10^{-2}$ C
9. *(a)* $1{\cdot}25 \times 10^{-2}$ C *(b)* $2{\cdot}5 \times 10^{-3}$ s
 (c) Initially I is high then decreases to zero. Initially easy to put charge on to capacitor but it gets harder when there is charge already on capacitor.
10. $3{\cdot}75 \times 10^{-6}$ s

Capacitance and Energy (page 85)

1.

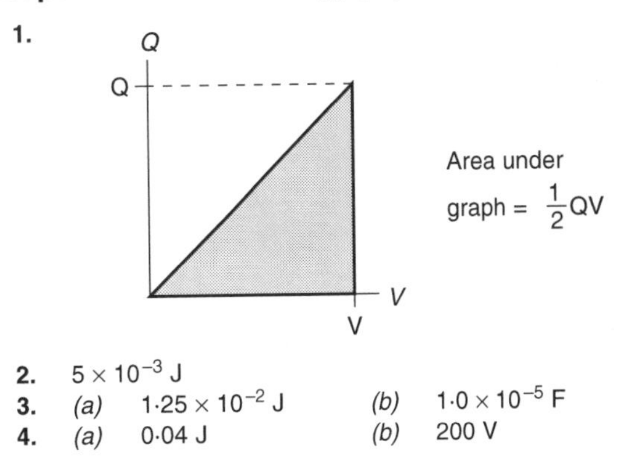

Area under graph = $\frac{1}{2}$QV

2. 5×10^{-3} J
3. *(a)* $1{\cdot}25 \times 10^{-2}$ J *(b)* $1{\cdot}0 \times 10^{-5}$ F
4. *(a)* 0·04 J *(b)* 200 V

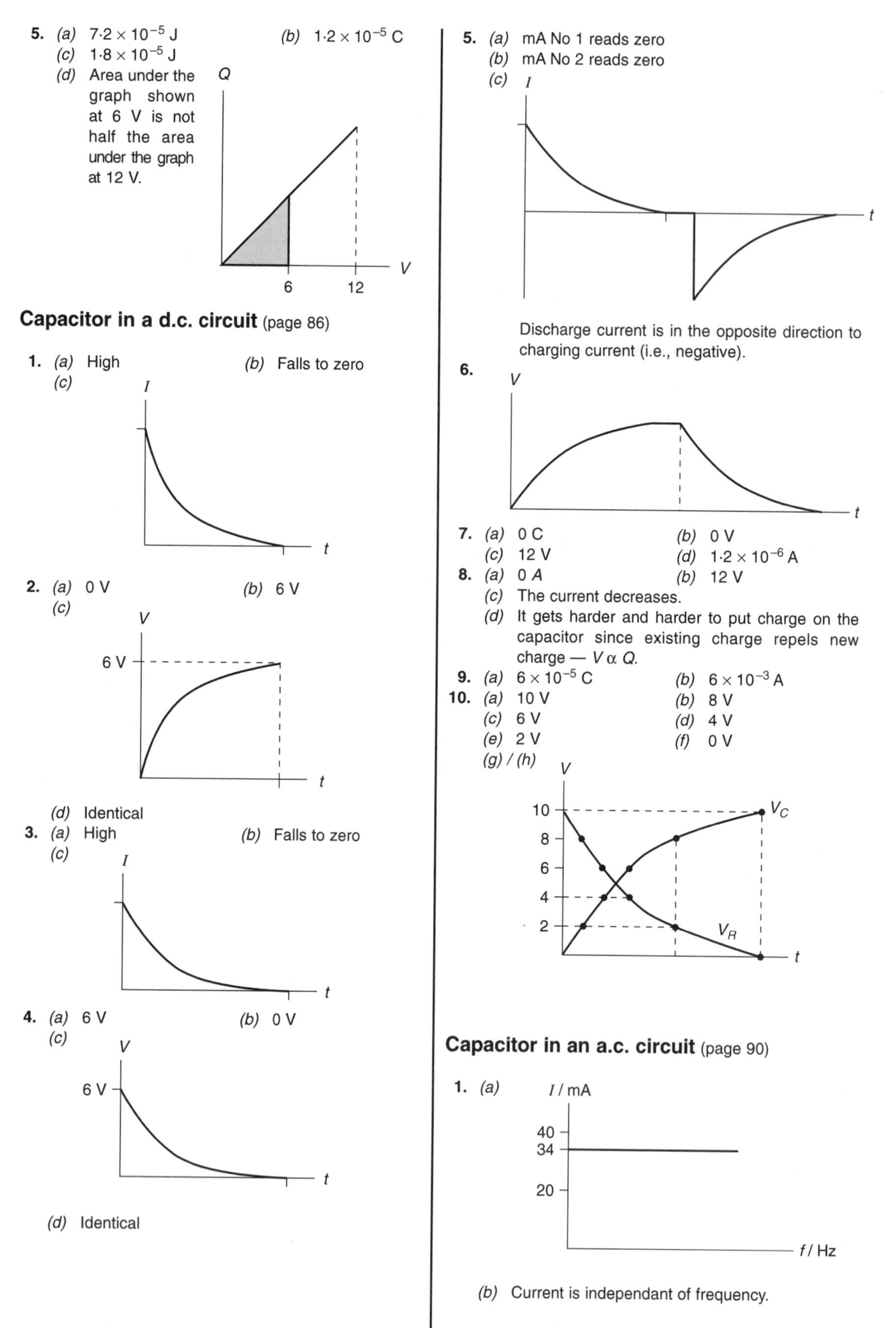

5. *(a)* $7{\cdot}2 \times 10^{-5}$ J *(b)* $1{\cdot}2 \times 10^{-5}$ C
   (c) $1{\cdot}8 \times 10^{-5}$ J
   (d) Area under the graph shown at 6 V is not half the area under the graph at 12 V.

Capacitor in a d.c. circuit (page 86)

1. *(a)* High *(b)* Falls to zero
   (c)

2. *(a)* 0 V *(b)* 6 V
   (c)

   (d) Identical
3. *(a)* High *(b)* Falls to zero
   (c)

4. *(a)* 6 V *(b)* 0 V
   (c)

   (d) Identical

5. *(a)* mA No 1 reads zero
   (b) mA No 2 reads zero
   (c)

   Discharge current is in the opposite direction to charging current (i.e., negative).
6.

7. *(a)* 0 C *(b)* 0 V
   (c) 12 V *(d)* $1{\cdot}2 \times 10^{-6}$ A
8. *(a)* 0 *A* *(b)* 12 V
   (c) The current decreases.
   (d) It gets harder and harder to put charge on the capacitor since existing charge repels new charge — $V \propto Q$.
9. *(a)* 6×10^{-5} C *(b)* 6×10^{-3} A
10. *(a)* 10 V *(b)* 8 V
    (c) 6 V *(d)* 4 V
    (e) 2 V *(f)* 0 V
    (g) / *(h)*

Capacitor in an a.c. circuit (page 90)

1. *(a)*

   (b) Current is independant of frequency.

2. *(a)*

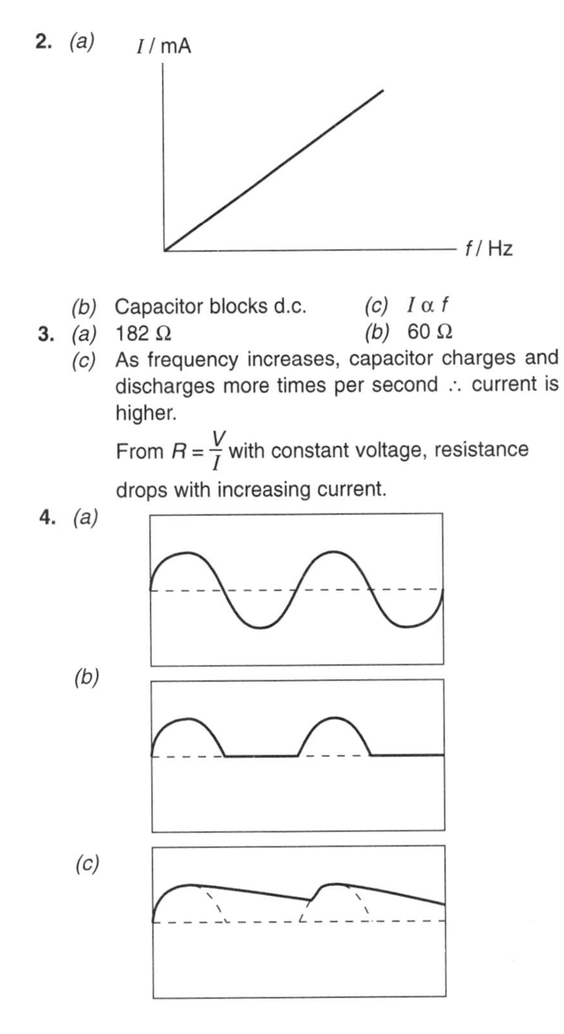

(b) Capacitor blocks d.c. *(c)* $I \propto f$

3. *(a)* 182 Ω *(b)* 60 Ω

(c) As frequency increases, capacitor charges and discharges more times per second ∴ current is higher.

From $R = \frac{V}{I}$ with constant voltage, resistance drops with increasing current.

4. *(a)* *(b)* *(c)*

5. *(a)* Gets brighter *(b)* Increases

CHAPTER 10

Voltage Division (page 92)

1. 2·5 V
2. 4 V
3. 2·4 V
4. 1·6 V
5. 2·25 V
6. 5 kΩ
7. 30 kΩ
8. 4 kΩ
9. 21 V
10. 0 → 8 V

Inverting Mode (page 96)

1. −2·5 V
2. *(a)* −5 V *(b)* −7·5 V *(c)* −11 V
3. *(a)* −0·5 V *(b)* −0·3 V *(c)* −2·5 mV
4. 100 kΩ
5. *(a)* −4 V *(b)* −0·48 V *(c)* −12·75 V approx. (saturation)
6. *(a)* 0·5 V *(b)* −5 V
7. *(a)* 0·4 V *(b)* −4 V
8. *(a)* 0·75 V *(b)* −6 V *(c)* −8
9. *(a)* 0·4 V *(b)* 7·5 kΩ *(c)* −10
10. Rf = 40 kΩ

$$\frac{R_X}{R_Y} = \frac{3}{5} \quad \text{e.g.,} \quad \begin{array}{l} R_X = 3\text{ k}\Omega \\ R_Y = 5\text{ k}\Omega \end{array}$$

Differential Mode (page 99)

1. 5 V
2. *(a)* 9 V *(b)* 2 V *(c)* 0·5 V
3. *(a)* 2 V *(b)* −2 V *(c)* −8 V
4. *(a)* 2 V *(b)* 7·2 V
5. 40 kΩ
6. *(a)* 1 V *(b)* 1·6 V
7. *(a)* 0·2 V *(b)* −0·3 V
8. *(a)* 1·2 V *(b)* 1·5 V *(c)* 2·4 V
9. *(a)* 1·0 V *(b)* 1·0 V *(c)* 12·5 kΩ *(d)* 1·54 V
10.

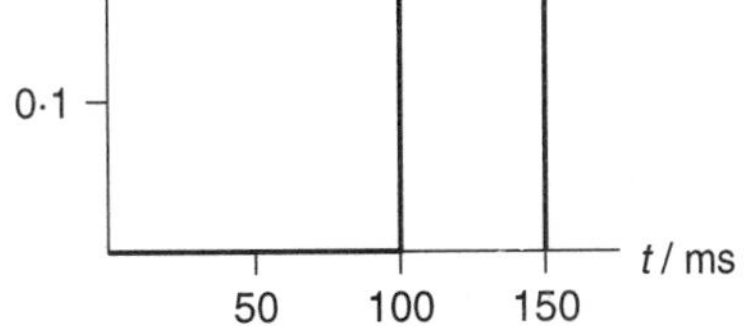

UNIT 3 — RADIATION AND MATTER

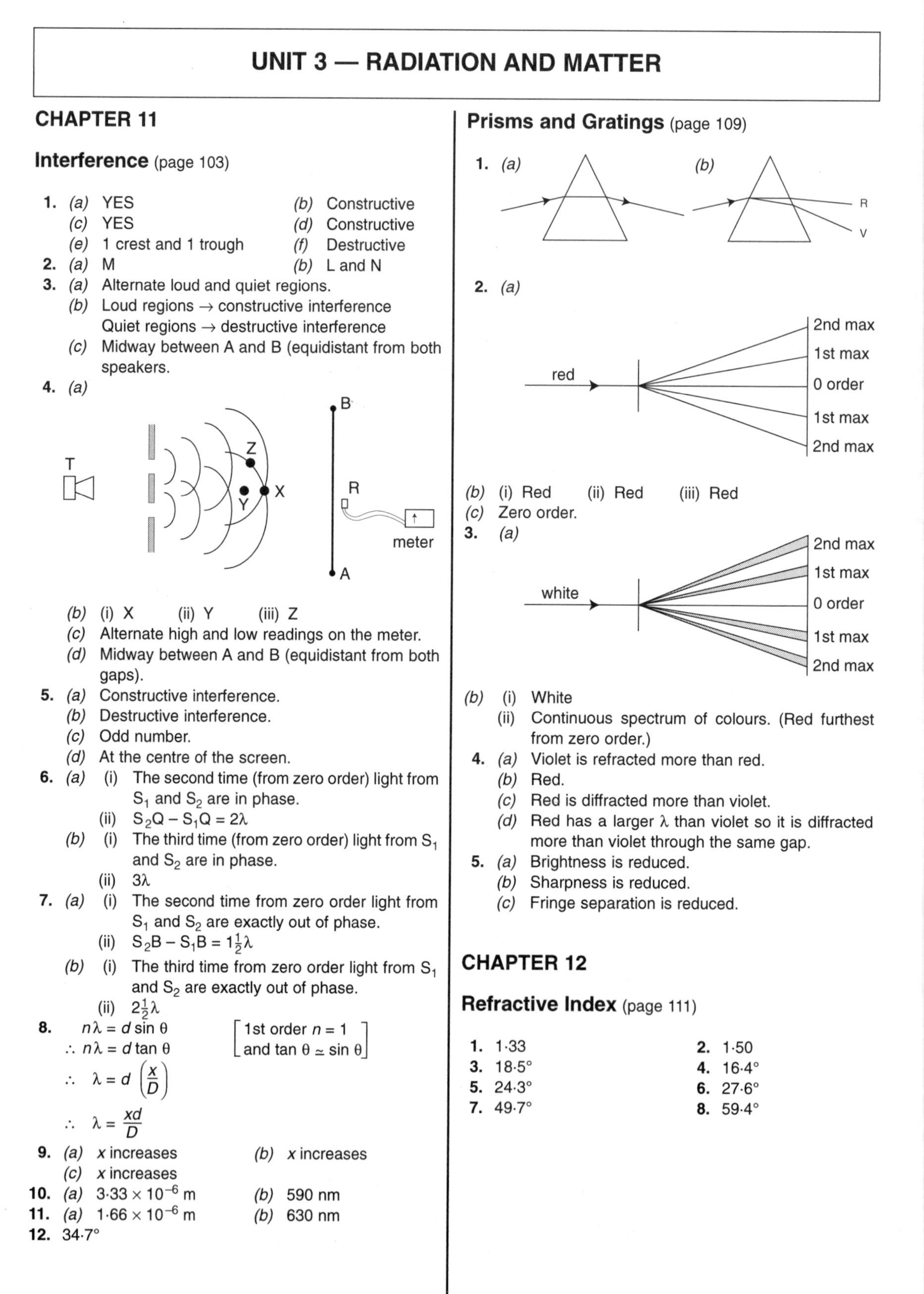

CHAPTER 11

Interference (page 103)

1. *(a)* YES *(b)* Constructive
(c) YES *(d)* Constructive
(e) 1 crest and 1 trough *(f)* Destructive

2. *(a)* M *(b)* L and N

3. *(a)* Alternate loud and quiet regions.
(b) Loud regions → constructive interference
Quiet regions → destructive interference
(c) Midway between A and B (equidistant from both speakers).

4. *(a)*

(b) (i) X (ii) Y (iii) Z
(c) Alternate high and low readings on the meter.
(d) Midway between A and B (equidistant from both gaps).

5. *(a)* Constructive interference.
(b) Destructive interference.
(c) Odd number.
(d) At the centre of the screen.

6. *(a)* (i) The second time (from zero order) light from S_1 and S_2 are in phase.
(ii) $S_2Q - S_1Q = 2\lambda$
(b) (i) The third time (from zero order) light from S_1 and S_2 are in phase.
(ii) 3λ

7. *(a)* (i) The second time from zero order light from S_1 and S_2 are exactly out of phase.
(ii) $S_2B - S_1B = 1\frac{1}{2}\lambda$
(b) (i) The third time from zero order light from S_1 and S_2 are exactly out of phase.
(ii) $2\frac{1}{2}\lambda$

8. $n\lambda = d\sin\theta$

$\therefore n\lambda = d\tan\theta$ $\left[\begin{array}{l}\text{1st order } n = 1\\ \text{and } \tan\theta \simeq \sin\theta\end{array}\right]$

$\therefore \lambda = d\left(\dfrac{x}{D}\right)$

$\therefore \lambda = \dfrac{xd}{D}$

9. *(a)* x increases *(b)* x increases
(c) x increases

10. *(a)* $3{\cdot}33 \times 10^{-6}$ m *(b)* 590 nm

11. *(a)* $1{\cdot}66 \times 10^{-6}$ m *(b)* 630 nm

12. 34·7°

Prisms and Gratings (page 109)

1. *(a)* *(b)*

2. *(a)*

(b) (i) Red (ii) Red (iii) Red
(c) Zero order.

3. *(a)*

(b) (i) White
(ii) Continuous spectrum of colours. (Red furthest from zero order.)

4. *(a)* Violet is refracted more than red.
(b) Red.
(c) Red is diffracted more than violet.
(d) Red has a larger λ than violet so it is diffracted more than violet through the same gap.

5. *(a)* Brightness is reduced.
(b) Sharpness is reduced.
(c) Fringe separation is reduced.

CHAPTER 12

Refractive Index (page 111)

1. 1·33 **2.** 1·50
3. 18·5° **4.** 16·4°
5. 24·3° **6.** 27·6°
7. 49·7° **8.** 59·4°

9. *(a)* 25·4° *(b)* 25·4° *(c)* 40°

10. *(a)*

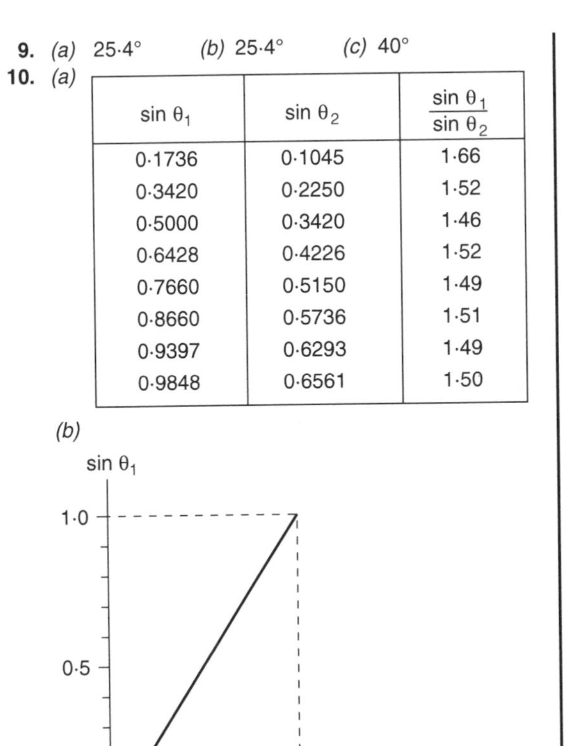

$\sin\theta_1$	$\sin\theta_2$	$\frac{\sin\theta_1}{\sin\theta_2}$
0·1736	0·1045	1·66
0·3420	0·2250	1·52
0·5000	0·3420	1·46
0·6428	0·4226	1·52
0·7660	0·5150	1·49
0·8660	0·5736	1·51
0·9397	0·6293	1·49
0·9848	0·6561	1·50

(b)

(c) $\frac{\sin\theta_1}{\sin\theta_2}$ = a constant

Refractive Index and Velocity (page 115)

1. *(a)* $2{\cdot}0 \times 10^8$ m s^{-1} *(b)* $2{\cdot}26 \times 10^8$ m s^{-1}
2. *(a)* $2{\cdot}04 \times 10^8$ m s^{-1} *(b)* $1{\cdot}24 \times 10^8$ m s^{-1}
3. True
4. *(a)* 1·37 *(b)* $2{\cdot}19 \times 10^8$ m s^{-1}
5. *(a)* 1·41 *(b)* $2{\cdot}13 \times 10^8$ m s^{-1}
6. 422 nm
7. *(a)* 375·9 nm *(b)* 333·3 nm
8. *(a)* 18·5° *(b)* 475·9 nm
9. *(a)* 387·1 nm *(b)* 363·6 nm
   (c) 5×10^{14} Hz *(d)* 5×10^{14} Hz
10. *(a)* $1{\cdot}99 \times 10^8$ m s^{-1} *(b)* $1{\cdot}96 \times 10^8$ m s^{-1}
   (c) θ_2 red = 25·19°
   θ_2 violet = 24·84°
   x (spread) = 0·35°

Critical Angle and T.I.R. (page 117)

1. 41·8° 2. 48·8° 3. 24·4°
4. *(a)* Critical angle = 41·8°
   Light strikes glass / air boundary at 45°, i.e., greater than critical angle, therefore total internal reflection occurs.
   (b) Binoculars.

5. *(a)*

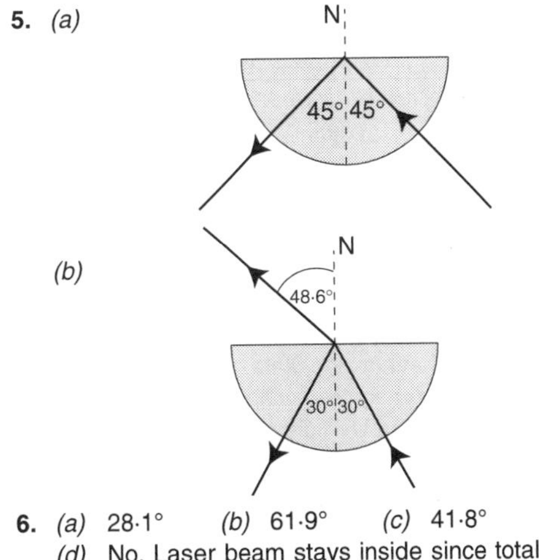

(b)

6. *(a)* 28·1° *(b)* 61·9° *(c)* 41·8°
   (d) No. Laser beam stays inside since total internal reflection occurs because angle x (61·9°) is greater than the critical angle (41·8°).

CHAPTER 13

Intensity of Light (page 120)

1. *(a)*

$\frac{1}{d^2}$ / m^{-2}
4
1
0·44
0·25
0·16
0·11

(b)

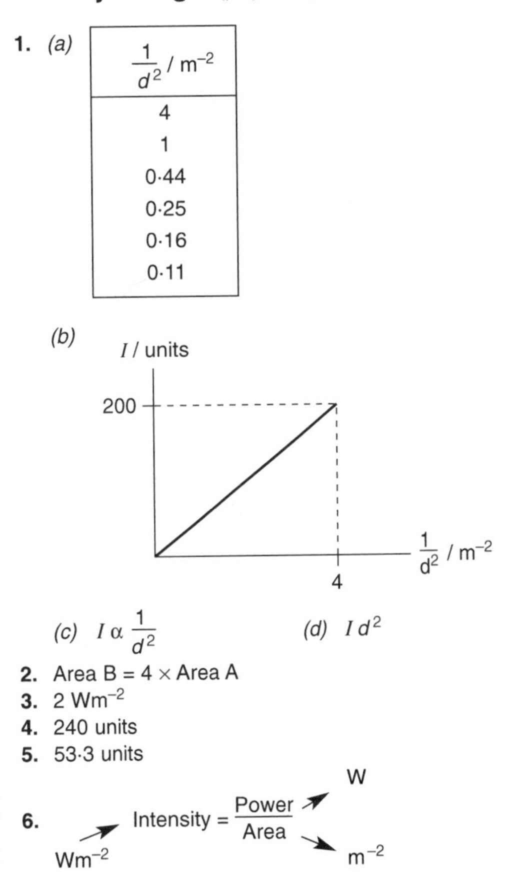

(c) $I \propto \frac{1}{d^2}$ *(d)* $I d^2$

2. Area B = 4 × Area A
3. 2 Wm^{-2}
4. 240 units
5. 53·3 units
6. Intensity = $\frac{\text{Power}}{\text{Area}}$ (Wm^{-2}; Power → W; Area → m^{-2})

The Photoelectric Effect (page 122)

1. *(a)*

Effect of UV light on leaf
No effect
No effect
No effect
Leaf collapses

(b) (i) Frequency(ies) of white light is lower.
(ii) Energy(ies) of white light is lower.

(c)
- Must have a zinc plate.
- Must be negatively charged.
- Must use a UV light source.

(d)
- Hold UV lamp closer **or**
- Use two UV lamps **or**
- Use UV lamp of higher power.

2. *(a)* Reading goes from zero to a constant value.
(b) Reading goes to zero.
(c) Electron gains enough energy to escape from the atom.

3. *(a)* Reading goes from zero to a constant value.
(b) Reading goes to zero.
(c) Electron absorbs UV photon and gains enough energy to escape from the atom.

4. *(a)* Threshold frequency f_0 means threshold energy hf_0.
Photons of frequency below f_0 have insufficient energy to free electrons.
(b) Photoelectric current increases when frequency increases provided frequency is above the threshold frequency.
(c) When frequenc increases, the energy of an individual photon increases ($E = hf$).
Photons with more energy will free more electrons (i.e., electrons in different shells).

5 *(a)* It increases.
(b)

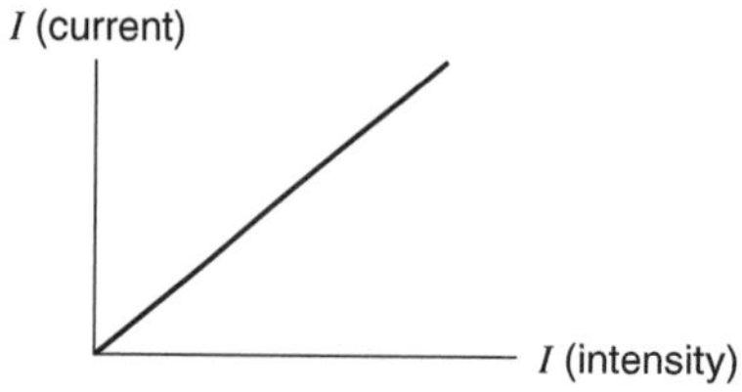

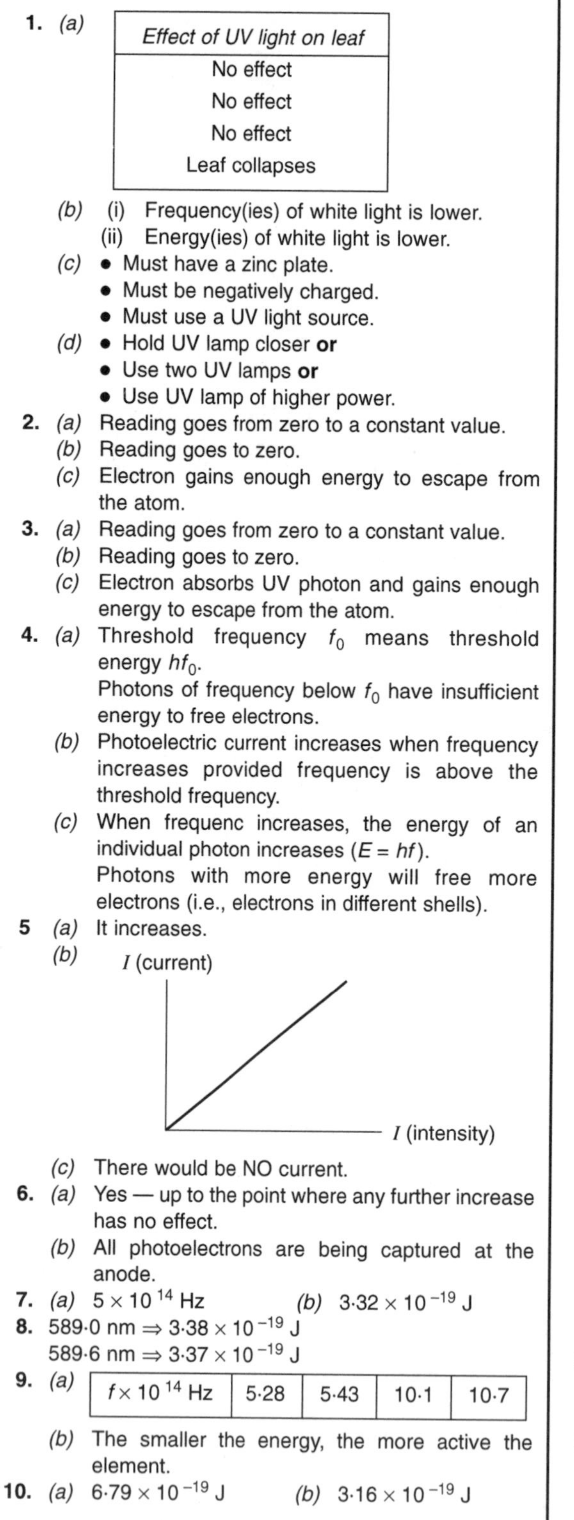

(c) There would be NO current.

6. *(a)* Yes — up to the point where any further increase has no effect.
(b) All photoelectrons are being captured at the anode.

7. *(a)* 5×10^{14} Hz *(b)* $3{\cdot}32 \times 10^{-19}$ J

8. 589·0 nm $\Rightarrow 3{\cdot}38 \times 10^{-19}$ J
589·6 nm $\Rightarrow 3{\cdot}37 \times 10^{-19}$ J

9. *(a)*

$f \times 10^{14}$ Hz	5·28	5·43	10·1	10·7

(b) The smaller the energy, the more active the element.

10. *(a)* $6{\cdot}79 \times 10^{-19}$ J *(b)* $3{\cdot}16 \times 10^{-19}$ J

Spectra (page 126)

1. *(a)*

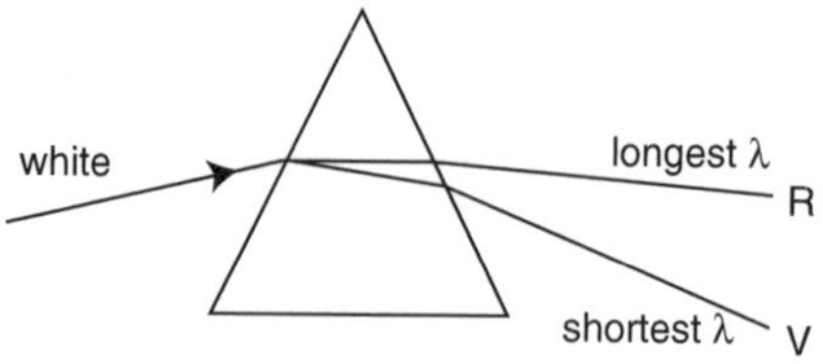

(b) Yes

2. *(a)*

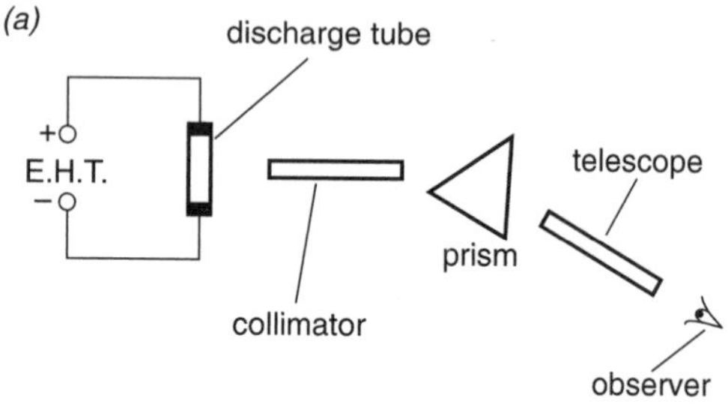

(b) Emission.
(c) Only certain wavelengths are present in a line spectrum.

3. *(a)* Electrons would lose energy, orbit at lower radius, eventually spiral into nucleus.
(b) A "jump" where an electron moves from one shell to another.

4. *(a)* (i) R
(ii) Q
(iii) R
(iv) Q
(v) Q
(vi) R

(b)

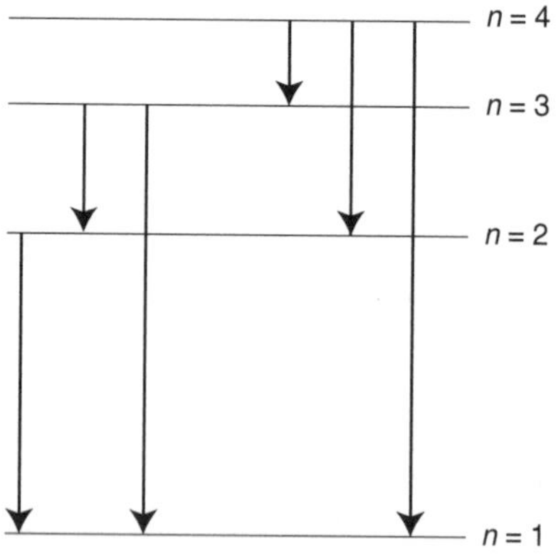

5. *(a)* Electron needs $21{\cdot}760 \times 10^{-19}$ J to escape from the atom (to be free).
(b) $16{\cdot}336 \times 10^{-19}$ J *(c)* $5{\cdot}424 \times 10^{-19}$ J

6. *(a)* $21{\cdot}760 \times 10^{-19}$ J *(b)* $3{\cdot}28 \times 10^{15}$ Hz
(c) Electron would escape as before but the "extra" energy supplied would give the electron kinetic energy.

7. *(a)* $1{\cdot}82 \times 10^{-22}$ kg m s^{-1} *(b)* $3{\cdot}64 \times 10^{-12}$ m

Lasers (page 128)

1. **L**ight **A**mplification by the **S**timulated **E**mission of **R**adiation.
2.

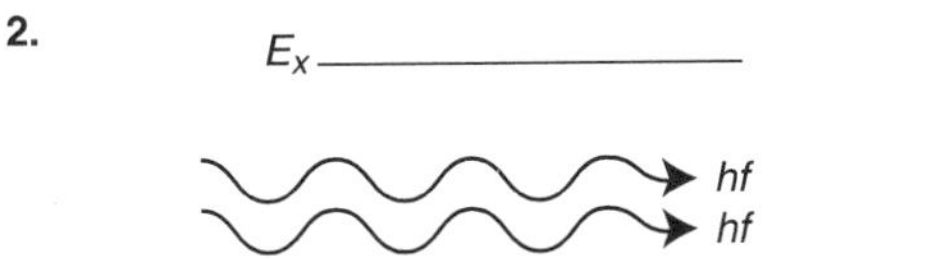

3. *(a)* True *(b)* True
   (c) True *(d)* True
4. *(a)* To trap the light between mirrors, reflecting the light back and forth to increase the stimulated emission of radiation.
   (b) M_1 is a fully reflecting mirror but M_2 is only a partially reflecting mirror.
5. 633 nm $\rightarrow 3{\cdot}14 \times 10^{-19}$ J
6. 127 Wm^{-2}
7. No, laser is more dangerous because the power is concentrated in a small area $\Rightarrow$ beam is more intense.

Semi-conductors (page 129)

1. *(a)* Copper, steel. *(b)* Paper, wood.
   (c) Silicon, germanium.
2. *(a)* Extra (5th) electron is free to move and conduction now takes place due to these free charge carriers.
   (b) *n*-type.
3. *(a)* Holes are created, i.e., spaces where electrons should be. Electrons move from neighbouring atoms to fill these holes. Hence conduction occurs.
   (b) *p*-type.
4. *(a)*

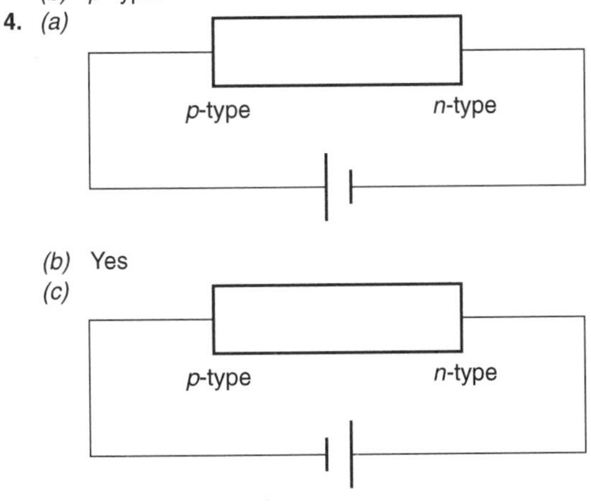

   (b) Yes
   (c)
   (d) No
5. *(a)* Forward biased
   (b) Electrons and holes recombine and emit energy in the form of light (photons).
6. $3{\cdot}06 \times 10^{-19}$ J
7. 190 Ω

8. *(a)* Photoconductive mode.
   (b) Increases. *(c)* Increases.
   (d) Photons of light free electrons (creating electron-hole pairs) which increases the number of free charge carriers / current increases / resistance drops.
9.

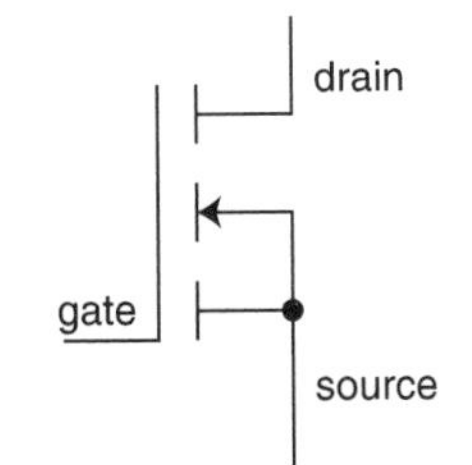

10. *(a)* 0 A
    (b) Now there is a current from the drain I_D.
    (c) I_D increases.
11. By increasing the drain voltage (source voltage 0 V).
12. Apply a voltage (greater than 2 V) to the gate. This switches on the MOSFET, allowing a drain current to flow and the bulb lights.

CHAPTER 14

The Nucleus (page 133)

1. *(a)*

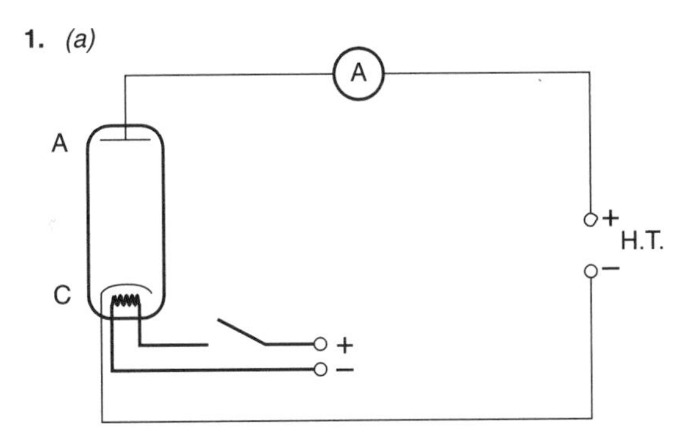

   (b) Thomson could get electrons to move but not protons. This suggested electrons being more mobile were lighter than protons.
2. *(a)*

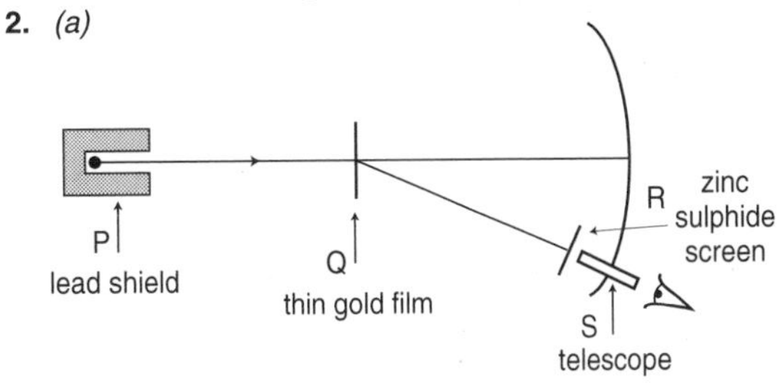

   (b) Yes.
   (c) Alpha particles were repelled by a very dense core of mass (nucleus) at the centre of the atom.
   (d) Most alpha particles went straight through.
   (e) At the edge of the atom, orbiting the nucleus.

3. *(a)* No

(b)

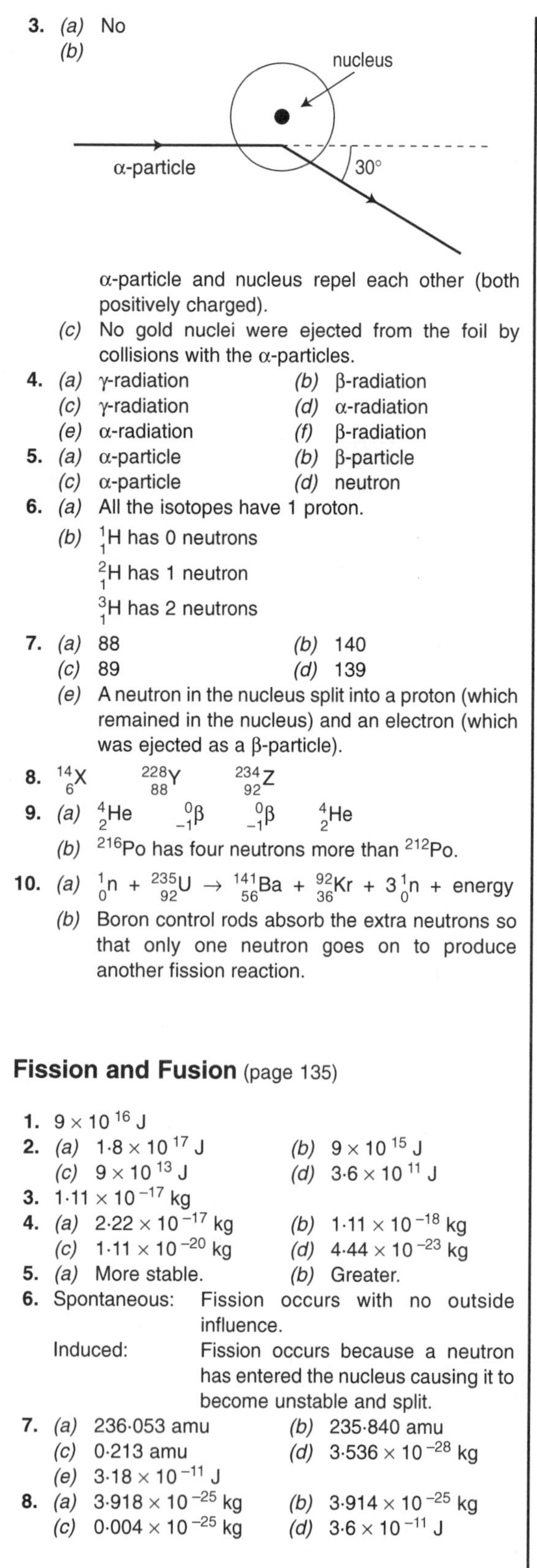

α-particle and nucleus repel each other (both positively charged).

(c) No gold nuclei were ejected from the foil by collisions with the α-particles.

4. *(a)* γ-radiation *(b)* β-radiation
(c) γ-radiation *(d)* α-radiation
(e) α-radiation *(f)* β-radiation

5. *(a)* α-particle *(b)* β-particle
(c) α-particle *(d)* neutron

6. *(a)* All the isotopes have 1 proton.
(b) $^{1}_{1}H$ has 0 neutrons
$^{2}_{1}H$ has 1 neutron
$^{3}_{1}H$ has 2 neutrons

7. *(a)* 88 *(b)* 140
(c) 89 *(d)* 139
(e) A neutron in the nucleus split into a proton (which remained in the nucleus) and an electron (which was ejected as a β-particle).

8. $^{14}_{6}X$ $^{228}_{88}Y$ $^{234}_{92}Z$

9. *(a)* $^{4}_{2}He$ $^{0}_{-1}\beta$ $^{0}_{-1}\beta$ $^{4}_{2}He$
(b) ^{216}Po has four neutrons more than ^{212}Po.

10. *(a)* $^{1}_{0}n + ^{235}_{92}U \rightarrow ^{141}_{56}Ba + ^{92}_{36}Kr + 3\,^{1}_{0}n$ + energy
(b) Boron control rods absorb the extra neutrons so that only one neutron goes on to produce another fission reaction.

Fission and Fusion (page 135)

1. 9×10^{16} J

2. *(a)* $1{\cdot}8 \times 10^{17}$ J *(b)* 9×10^{15} J
(c) 9×10^{13} J *(d)* $3{\cdot}6 \times 10^{11}$ J

3. $1{\cdot}11 \times 10^{-17}$ kg

4. *(a)* $2{\cdot}22 \times 10^{-17}$ kg *(b)* $1{\cdot}11 \times 10^{-18}$ kg
(c) $1{\cdot}11 \times 10^{-20}$ kg *(d)* $4{\cdot}44 \times 10^{-23}$ kg

5. *(a)* More stable. *(b)* Greater.

6. Spontaneous: Fission occurs with no outside influence.
Induced: Fission occurs because a neutron has entered the nucleus causing it to become unstable and split.

7. *(a)* 236·053 amu *(b)* 235·840 amu
(c) 0·213 amu *(d)* $3{\cdot}536 \times 10^{-28}$ kg
(e) $3{\cdot}18 \times 10^{-11}$ J

8. *(a)* $3{\cdot}918 \times 10^{-25}$ kg *(b)* $3{\cdot}914 \times 10^{-25}$ kg
(c) $0{\cdot}004 \times 10^{-25}$ kg *(d)* $3{\cdot}6 \times 10^{-11}$ J

9. *(a)* A chain reaction is one where the first reaction produces neutrons which cause the next reaction which produces neutrons which cause the next reaction in the chain.
(b) ^{235}U absorbs a neutron and becomes unstable and splits (usually into two fission fragments) and releases two or three neutrons. Each neutron can go on to create another reaction in the chain.
(c) Boron control rods absorb extra neutrons to control the rate of reaction.

10. *(a)* $6{\cdot}684 \times 10^{-27}$ kg *(b)* $6{\cdot}677 \times 10^{-27}$ kg
(c) $7{\cdot}0 \times 10^{-30}$ kg *(d)* $6{\cdot}3 \times 10^{-13}$ J

11. *(a)* $6{\cdot}0 \times 10^{-30}$ kg *(b)* $5{\cdot}4 \times 10^{-13}$ J

12. $2{\cdot}79 \times 10^{-12}$ J

CHAPTER 15

Dosimetry Equations (page 138)

1. 100 Bq **2.** 16·7 Bq
3. 0·5 Bq **4.** 6×10^{7} disintegrations
5. 0·05 Gy **6.** $2{\cdot}5 \times 10^{-3}$ Gy
7. $3{\cdot}33 \times 10^{-3}$ Gy
8. Fast neutrons have Q value of 10.
γ rays have Q value of 1.
The dose equivalent takes account of the Q value.
9. 500 μSv **10.** 100 μSv
11. 1260 μSv **12.** 1220 μSv
13. 0·23 μSv h^{-1} **14.** 36 μSv
15. It drops (but not to zero) because cosmic ray levels of radiation at high altitude are higher than close to the surface of the earth.
16. *(a)* 5·71 μSv h^{-1} *(b)* 12·5 mSv
17. Cosmic rays
Rocks / soil
Radon gas
18. 5 mSv per year **19.** 50 mSv per year
20. By increasing the distance from the source.

Half-life (page 140)

1. Approx. 3·25 days **2.** 144 c.p.m.
3. 20 minutes

Half-value Thickness (page 141)

1. The thickness of lead required to reduce the intensity of the beam of radiation by half.
2. *(a)* It takes 12 mm of lead to reduce the intensity of the beam of γ-rays by half.
(b) It takes 25 mm of concrete to reduce the intensity of the beam of γ-rays by half.

3. *(a)*

Corrected count rate / Bq
80
67
57
48
40
33
27
23
20

(b)

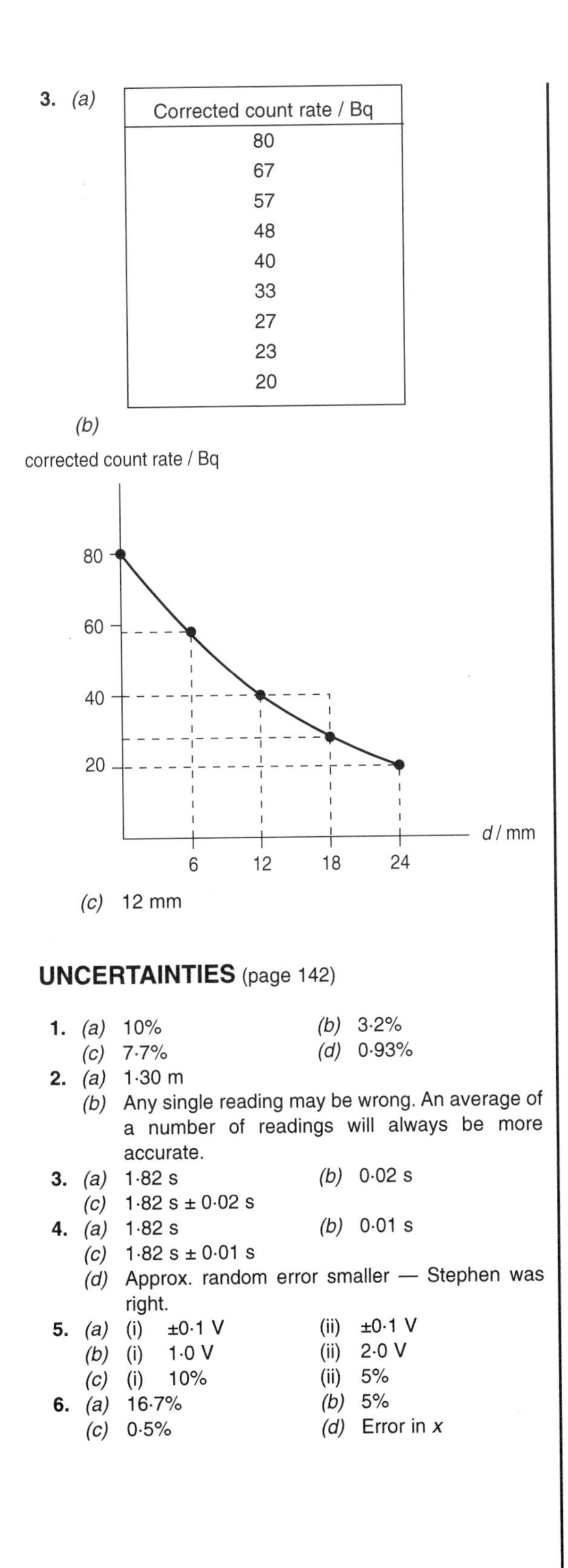

(c) 12 mm

UNCERTAINTIES (page 142)

1. *(a)* 10% *(b)* 3·2%
(c) 7·7% *(d)* 0·93%

2. *(a)* 1·30 m
(b) Any single reading may be wrong. An average of a number of readings will always be more accurate.

3. *(a)* 1·82 s *(b)* 0·02 s
(c) 1·82 s ± 0·02 s

4. *(a)* 1·82 s *(b)* 0·01 s
(c) 1·82 s ± 0·01 s
(d) Approx. random error smaller — Stephen was right.

5. *(a)* (i) ±0·1 V (ii) ±0·1 V
(b) (i) 1·0 V (ii) 2·0 V
(c) (i) 10% (ii) 5%

6. *(a)* 16·7% *(b)* 5%
(c) 0·5% *(d)* Error in *x*

NOTES

Printed by Bell & Bain Ltd., Glasgow, Scotland.